Cyber Terrorism and Information Warfare

IV. Research and Development Roadmaps

Yonah Alexander
and
Michael S. Swetnam

Eighth Volume, Second Series
Terrorism: Documents of International & Local Control

Yonah Alexander
Donald J. Musch
General Editors

Oceana Publications, Inc. / Dobbs Ferry, New York

You may order this or any other Oceana publications by visiting Oceana's website at http://www.oceanalaw.com

Terrorism: Documents of International and Local Control, Second Series

9780379214154
9780379214192

Library of Congress Catalog Card Number: 99-75945

Manufactured in the United States of America on acid-free paper.

TABLE OF CONTENTS

1. Preliminary Research and Development: Recommendations for Protecting and Assuring Critical National Infrastructures—Report of the President's Commission on Critical Infrastructure Protection, 1997 1

2. Preliminary Research and Development: Roadmap for Protecting and Assuring Critical National Infrastructures—Transition Office of the President's Commission on Critical Infrastructure Protection and the Critical Infrastructure Assurance Office, July 1998 33

3. Preliminary Research and Development: Roadmap for Protecting and Assuring the Banking and Finance Infrastructure 115

4. Preliminary Research and Development: Roadmap for Protecting and Assuring the Energy Infrastructure 159

5. Preliminary Research and Development: Roadmap for Protecting and Assuring the Information and Communications Infrastructure . . 265

6. Preliminary Research and Development: Roadmap for Protecting and Assuring the Transportation Infrastructure 307

7. Preliminary Research and Development: Roadmap for Protecting and Assuring the Vital Human Services Infrastructure 357

CHAPTER 1

RESEARCH AND DEVELOPMENT

RECOMMENDATIONS FOR PROTECTING AND ASSURING CRITICAL NATIONAL INFRASTRUCTURES

Report of the President's Commission on Critical Infrastructure Protection

1997

CONTENTS

ACKNOWLEDGEMENTS

EXECUTIVE SUMMARY

1. INTRODUCTION
   - 1.1 Purpose and Scope
   - 1.2 Research and Development Issue
   - 1.3 Report Organization

2. FOUNDATION FOR RECOMMENDATIONS
   - 2.1 External Information Sources
   - 2.2 PCCIP-Sponsored Studies

3. RESEARCH AREAS AND TOPICS
   - 3.1 Information Assurance
     - 3.1.1 System Level Security, Engineering, and Architectures
     - 3.1.2 Advanced Concepts and Theory
     - 3.1.3 Management of Information Protection
     - 3.1.4 Encryption Technologies
   - 3.2 Monitoring and Threat Detection
     - 3.2.1 Automated Monitoring and Detection
     - 3.2.2 Infrastructure Information System
   - 3.3 Vulnerability Assessment and Systems Analysis
     - 3.3.1 Vulnerability Assessment Tools
     - 3.3.2 Complex System Modeling
     - 3.3.3 Test Beds
     - 3.3.4 Verification Technologies
   - 3.4 Risk Management and Decision Support
     - 3.4.1 Risk Management
     - 3.4.2 Decision Support Systems
   - 3.5 Protection and Mitigation
     - 3.5.1 Real-Time Distributed System Control
     - 3.5.2 Infrastructure Hardening

3.5.3 Containment and Isolation

3.6 Incident Response and Recovery

3.6.1 Response Technologies

3.6.2 Recovery Technologies

4. RECOMMENDATIONS FOR ACTION

4.1 Strategy and Implementation Recommendations

4.2 Investment Requirements

5. REFERENCES

TABLES

3.1. R&D Areas and Topics

4.1. Recommended Government Infrastructure Assurance R&D Investments

FIGURES

1.1. Technology R&D in Support of Infrastructure Assurance Objectives

2.1. Key Sources of Information Used by the PCCIP in Developing Integrated R&D Recommendations

4.1. Infrastructure Assurance R&D Organizational Structure

ACKNOWLEDGMENTS

Many individuals at the Commission and within government, the Department of Energy national laboratory system, academia, and the private sector made important contributions to this report. In particular, the Commission gratefully acknowledges the assistance provided by Commissioners John Davis, David Jones and Merritt Adams; and James Peerenboom and Thomas Wolsko from Argonne National Laboratory, as well as the many valuable contributions made by the Commission's Laboratory Council and the research and development strategy teams from the Department of Energy's national laboratories. We also thank Blaine Burnham of the National Security Agency for characterizing information security research in the Department of Defense and Intelligence Community, William (Terry) Mayfield of the Institute for Defense Analyses for assessing commercial information assurance research and development, and Anita Jones of the University of Virginia for providing insightful review comments. Finally, we thank Carol Medill, Commission staff analyst, for providing valuable administrative assistance.

Members of the Commission's Laboratory Council

Terry Surles and Paula Scalingi, Argonne National Laboratory
Robert A. Bari, Brookhaven National Laboratory
David F. Cauffman, Idaho National Engineering Laboratory
Stewart Loken, Lawrence Berkeley National Laboratory
Ronald W. Cochran, Lawrence Livermore National Laboratory
Houston Terry Hawkins, Los Alamos National Laboratory
David E. Reichle, Oak Ridge National Laboratory
Landis D. Kannberg, Pacific Northwest National Laboratory
Samuel Varnado, Sandia National Laboratory

Leaders of the DOE National Laboratory R&D Strategy Teams

Ron Fisher and Dorland Edgar, Argonne National Laboratory (Oil & Gas)
James Peerenboom, Argonne National Laboratory (Interdependencies)
Tom Wolsko, Argonne National Laboratory (Electric Power Systems)
Trevor Pratt, Brookhaven National Laboratory (Interdependencies)
William Johnston, Lawrence Berkeley National Laboratory (Information & Communications)
Kathleen Bailey, Lawrence Livermore National Laboratory (Information & Communications)
Doug Mansur, Lawrence Livermore National Laboratory (Information & Communications)
Bill Hunteman, Los Alamos National Laboratory (Information & Communications)
Darryl Morgeson, Los Alamos National Laboratory (Transportation)
Mike Bronzini, Oak Ridge National Laboratory (Transportation)
John H. Sorensen, Oak Ridge National Laboratory (Emergency Services)
Bernie Saffell, Pacific Northwest National Laboratory (Oil & Gas)
Lance W. Vail, Pacific Northwest National Laboratory (Water)
Samuel Varnado, Sandia National Laboratory Albuquerque (Banking & Finance)

Executive Summary

RESEARCH AND DEVELOPMENT
Recommendations for Protecting and Assuring Critical National Infrastructures

This report summarizes research and development (R&D) recommendations for the President's Commission on Critical Infrastructure Protection (PCCIP). These recommendations address the eight critical infrastructures[1] identified in Executive Order 13010 as well as crosscutting, interdependency issues that affect more than one infrastructure.

The goal of the R&D recommendations is to provide a roadmap for the development of technologies that will counter threats and reduce vulnerabilities in those areas having the potential for causing "significant" national security, economic, and/or social impacts. Specific technologies considered are those that protect infrastructure and thereby reduce vulnerability; detect intrusions and provide warning; mitigate the effects of disruptions (incidents); assist in the response management of incidents; and facilitate recovery.

Basic research requiring long-term government investment is emphasized. This research must be accompanied by *technology development* within the private sector. Technology, broadly defined, includes processes, systems, models and simulations, hardware, and software. It is essential to have strong involvement from infrastructure owners and operators to ensure the development and acquisition of useful and usable products.

Summary of R&D Recommendations

1. *Conduct research and development in six areas:*

   * *Information assurance*

   * *Monitoring and threat detection*

   * *Vulnerability assessment and systems analysis*

   * *Risk management and decision support*

   * *Protection and mitigation*

   * *Incident response and recovery*

---

1 Information and communications (telecommunications), electric power systems, gas and oil delivery and storage systems, banking and finance, transportation, water supply systems, emergency services, and government services.

2. Increase the federal investment in infrastructure assurance research to $500 million in FY99 and incrementally increase the investment over a five-year period to $1 billion in FY04.

3. Establish a focal point for national infrastructure assurance R&D efforts and build a public/private-sector partnership to foster technology development and technology transfer.

The six recommended areas are:

- **Information Assurance.** Significant new investment and effort in R&D are required for effective protection of the communications infrastructure, and the information created, stored, processed, and transmitted on it. Assurance of vital information is increasingly a key component to the functioning of our interdependent infrastructures. The urgent need to develop new affordable means of protection is apparent, given the increasing rate of incidents, the expanding list of known vulnerabilities, and the inadequate set of solutions available. This sense of urgency is further compelled by the increasing rate of system integration and the resulting complexity of those infrastructure information systems whose behavior is becoming much less predictable.

- **Monitoring and Threat Detection.** Reliable automated monitoring and detection systems, timely and effective information collection technologies, and efficient data reduction and analysis tools are needed for identifying and characterizing localized or coordinated large-scale attacks against infrastructure (National Cyber Defense). Such technologies would support early threat warning to government organizations and private-sector infrastructure owners and operators, thereby preventing widespread infrastructure disruptions that have potentially serious consequences to our national security, economy, and quality of life.

- **Vulnerability Assessment and Systems Analysis.** Advanced methods and tools for vulnerability assessment and systems analysis are needed to identify critical nodes within infrastructures, to examine infrastructure interdependencies, and to help understand the behavior of complex systems. Such methods and tools would allow issues, such as physical and cyber security, to be addressed in an integrated fashion. Modeling and simulation tools and test beds for studying infrastructure-related problems also are important for experimentation that cannot be performed in realistic environments of any appreciable scale. In addition, techniques to verify and validate methodologies and tools are needed.

- **Risk Management and Decision Support.** Risk management and decision support system methodologies and tools are needed to help government and private-sector decision makers effectively prioritize the use of finite resources to reduce risk. These methodologies and tools would address risk from both familiar threats (e.g., natural disasters, physical attacks) and emerging and future threats (e.g., risk that arises from our increasing interdependence and reliance on cyber systems).

- **Protection and Mitigation.** Real-time system control, infrastructure hardening, and containment and isolation technologies are needed to protect infrastructure systems against the entire threat spectrum. Other advanced survivability, reliability, or assurance enhancement measures also need to be explored and/or developed.

- **Incident Response and Recovery.** A wide range of new technologies and tools are needed for effectively planning for, responding to, and recovering from incidents, such as natural disasters and physical and cyber-based attacks that affect local or national infrastructures.

We Recommend:

- A government investment on the order of $500 million in FY99, gradually increasing over a five-year period to about $1 billion in FY04, is needed to address these infrastructure assurance research needs. This increase, an approximate doubling of investment in FY99, is needed to "jump start" a focused, coordinated, and goal-oriented national research effort. In addition to this government investment, a similar or greater level of commitment and technology development investment is needed from the private sector. This increase in investment should occur as market demand for infrastructure assurance technology increases.

We Recommend:

- Close coordination and an innovative partnership among government, industry, and academia are essential for a successful research and technology development effort. To facilitate a joint effort and to ensure efficient use of limited R&D funds, a focal point (coordinating entity) for national infrastructure assurance R&D efforts is needed. Accordingly, the Commission has proposed that the National Infrastructure Assurance Office be established to stress partnership between government and the private sector, coordinate with established advisory and information exchange groups, and promote awareness and education. Its missions would include developing, coordinating, prioritizing, and overseeing the R&D agenda to meet critical national needs. It also would serve as a clearinghouse for disseminating such information.

Appropriate government agencies should manage federal infrastructure-specific R&D efforts.

We Recommend:

The National Research Council define more fully a national infrastructure assurance research program based on the information contained in this report. The Council should be designated to lead the effort, together with those departments and agencies of the federal government already engaged in R&D relevant to each infrastructure.

1. INTRODUCTION

> Our nation's infrastructures are undergoing a profound change. Networked information systems are becoming critical to the daily operation of increasingly large segments of government, industry, and commerce. Moreover, in responding to the needs of subscribers, critical infrastructures like the electric power utilities and public switched telephone network are increasing their dependence on computers and communications networks. But this growing dependence on networked computers is accompanied by increased risk. First, the infrastructure becomes vulnerable to new forms of attack–attacks that may not require physical penetration of a specific site or system by the perpetrator–and the number of targets is increased. Second, the use of extremely complex technologies always presents risks. For example, software systems today are rarely free of defects and are notoriously difficult to configure and operate. Finally, the interconnection of previously isolated infrastructures enables the propagation of attacks and failures from one to the other. In short, our nation's infrastructures could well evolve into an interdependent system of fragile and vulnerable subsystems. Understanding how to ensure that they will operate reliably is thus vital. [1]

Assuring reliable operation of critical national infrastructures requires a multifaceted, harmonized strategy. Such a strategy will include research and development (R&D), education and awareness, training, policies and standards, streamlined regulations, investment incentives, and other elements that involve both government and the private sector. This report focuses on R&D as one of these important elements.

1.1 PURPOSE AND SCOPE

This report summarizes the R&D recommendations of the President's Commission on Critical Infrastructure Protection (PCCIP) in support of its mission to develop an overall strategy for protecting and assuring the continued operation of the nation's critical infrastructures. The recommendations address the eight critical infrastructures identified in Executive Order 13010: information and communications (telecommunications), electric power systems, gas and oil delivery and storage systems, banking and finance, transportation, water supply systems, emergency services, and government services. They also address crosscutting, interdependency issues that affect more than one infrastructure. Near-term (5 year timeframe) R&D activities are emphasized, although long-term needs are addressed in selected areas.

The goal in making these recommendations is to support the development of technologies that will address the threats to, and vulnerabilities of, critical infrastructures that have potential for causing "significant" national security, economic, and/or social impacts. As illustrated in Figure 1.1, the technologies considered are those that:

- Protect infrastructure and detect intrusions,
- Mitigate the effects of disruptions (incidents),
- Assist in the management of incidents, or
- Facilitate recovery.

Basic research requiring long-term government investment is emphasized. This research must be accompanied by technology development within the private sector. Technology, broadly defined, includes processes, systems, models and simulations, hardware, and software. It is essential to have strong involvement from infrastructure owners and operators to ensure the development of useful and usable products.

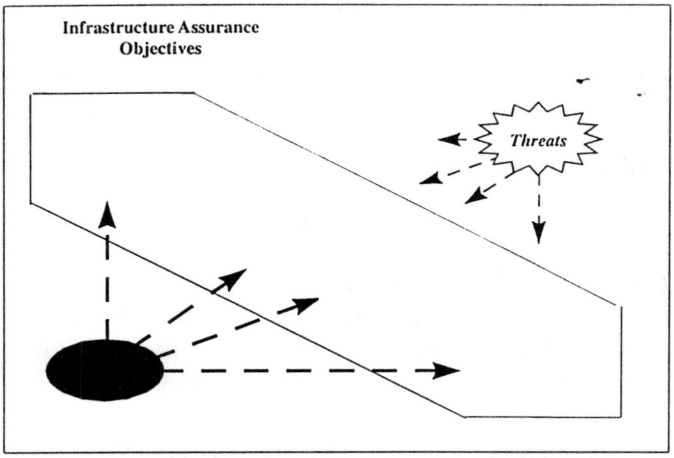

FIGURE 1.1 Technology R&D in Support of Infrastructure Assurance Objectives

Both physical and cyber threats must be considered. The former include threats to tangible property produced by accidents, sabotage, and natural hazards resulting from seismic, wind and water events. The latter include electronic, radio-frequency, or computer-based attacks on the information infrastructure or its components. Other threats arise from the complexity of automated systems and from increasing interdependencies among infrastructures and between physical and cyber systems.

1.2 RESEARCH AND DEVELOPMENT ISSUE

The fundamental R&D issue for critical infrastructure protection can be framed in terms of the following three interrelated questions:

- What R&D is needed to achieve the nation's infrastructure assurance objectives?
- What level of corresponding investment is required?
- Who should make this corresponding investment?

These questions must be answered within a partnership between government and the private sector. Both entities must recognize that: (1) infrastructure assurance risks cut across the public and private sectors; (2) the private sector holds much of the relevant technical and empirical data on infrastructure operations, interdependencies and vulnerabilities; and (3) the private sector develops technology only when it identifies a market for it. Successful implementation of technologies developed from government-funded research efforts will require close cooperation with private sector owners and operators of our nation's infrastructures.

The R&D recommendations presented here do not imply that government and the private sector are not investing in protection and detection, mitigation, incident response, and recovery. Current R&D investment is inadequate, and progress is too slow to deal effectively with current and future vulnerabilities. The scale and scope of R&D investments need to be expanded to address infrastructure assurance issues from a national perspective, with a long-term view of the health and welfare of the nation.

1.3 REPORT ORGANIZATION

The remainder of this report is organized as follows. Section 2 discusses the key information sources and PCCIP-sponsored studies that provided the foundation for developing integrated R&D recommendations. Section 3 summarizes specific R&D areas and topics. Finally, Section 4 focuses on recommendations for action, including strategy and implementation recommendations, as well as investment requirements.

2. FOUNDATION FOR RECOMMENDATIONS

In developing the R&D recommendations, the PCCIP (1) drew upon recent studies (external information sources) that address problems and technology R&D needs related to critical infrastructure assurance, and (2) sponsored a series of independent studies that focused on specific R&D issues. This approach helped the PCCIP to avoid duplication; gain valuable insights into infrastructure problems from the perspective of other task forces, committees, and study panels; and identify recurring themes. Figure 2.1 highlights key information sources and PCCIP-sponsored studies that provided the foundation for developing integrated R&D recommendations. The following sections briefly describe these sources and studies.

2.1 EXTERNAL INFORMATION SOURCES

Among the many relevant studies conducted recently, eight helped the PCCIP gain perspective and formulate R&D recommendations in the key critical infrastructure area of information assurance.

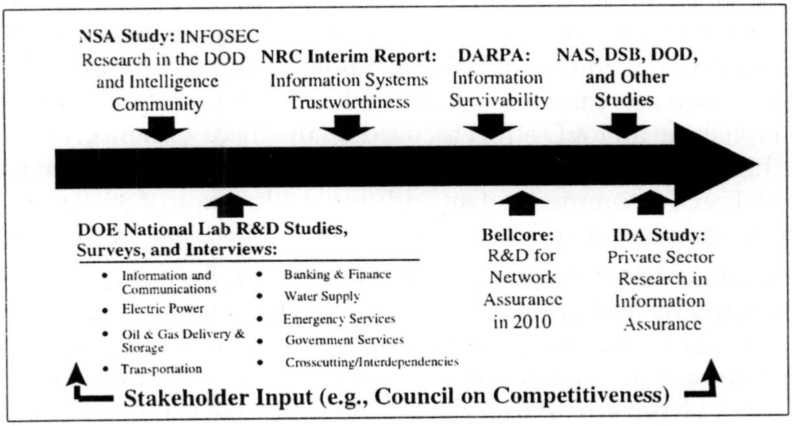

FIGURE 2.1 Key Sources of Information Used by the PCCIP in Developing Integrated R&D Recommendations

- ***National Research Council (NRC) Interim Report on Information Systems Trustworthiness [1].*** The motivation for the NRC report is summarized in the paragraph quoted on page 1 of this report. In particular, the NRC report elucidates a research agenda and program of technical activities for strengthening the reliability of information systems. The term "trustworthiness" encompasses all of the attributes a system must have so that society can *depend* on the system's operation of its critical infrastructures. Potential research areas for future exploration, such as mobile code, network infrastructure, and cryptography, are identified.

- ***Defense Science Board (DSB) Report on Information Warfare—Defense [2].*** This report documents the work of a DSB Task Force that focused on protection of information interests of national importance through the establishment and maintenance of a credible information warfare defensive (IW-D) capability. The Task Force found that: (1) current security products are not designed to protect large, distributed environments; (2) the Department of Defense (DOD) must evaluate carefully emerging commercial technologies and products (e.g., examine theft and fraud versus denial of service issues); and (3) academia, industry, and government must be part of the research effort. The Task Force recommended that the IW-D R&D program focus on several key areas: including robust survivable system architectures; techniques and tools for modeling, monitoring, and managing large-scale distributed/networked systems for automating detection and analysis of localized or coordinated large-scale attacks; tools for synthesizing and projecting the anticipated performance of survivable distributed systems; and test beds and simulation-based mechanisms for evaluating emerging IW-D technology and tactics. In addition, the Task Force recommended that the R&D community should consider establishing an R&D effort focused on the theory, science, and analysis of high-assurance, massively distributed systems. To get started, the Task Force recommended an additional allocation of $580 million over the next five years (FY97-FY01) to address R&D needs in IW-D.

- *Department of Defense Report on Improving Information Assurance [3].* Prepared by an Information Assurance (IA) Task Force established by the Assistant Secretary of Defense for Command, Control, Communications and Intelligence, this report is a general assessment of DOD's current IA posture. It describes a comprehensive approach for achieving an integrated IA program. The general assessment, while pointing to significant deficiencies within DOD's IA posture, acknowledges the benefit of ongoing IA initiatives among the Defense Components and emphasizes that the DOD must maintain and build on this momentum. The report sets forth a new three-point strategy for enhancing DOD information assurance posture: (1) risk management, (2) continuous improvement, and (3) sound investments (i.e., risk reduction return on investment). Two recommendations call for a comprehensive research and technology development program that:

  a. Leverages the collective capability of the Information Security (INFOSEC) research community, both public and private, and

  b. Ensures the availability of appropriate vulnerability countermeasures that are consistent with commercial product cycles.

- *National Security Agency Scientific Advisory Board INFOSEC Panel [4].* This Panel conducted a high-level examination of the INFOSEC program. In addition to advocating a stronger R&D program, the Panel made a number of recommendations, including:

  a. Significantly increasing the INFOSEC R&D budget to meet the myriad of challenges that must be addressed, and

b. Developing a world class understanding of information systems and technologies, with an emphasis on network security.

- ***Joint Security Commission Report on Redefining Security [5].*** The Commission found that information systems technology is evolving much faster than information systems security technology. Therefore, a carefully planned, well-managed R&D program is required. The Commission recommended that:

  a. R&D programs be given high priority in creating the secure products that DOD and the intelligence community need to protect their classified and unclassified information networks and systems, and

  b. The Secretary of Defense and the Director of Central Intelligence assign NSA as the executive agent for information systems security R&D for both classified and unclassified information for DOD and the intelligence community.

- ***Report of the Commission on Protecting and Reducing Government Secretary [6].*** The Commission noted that in the next century, the federal government and industry must work more closely to develop technologies that address the problems resulting from rapid proliferation of information systems within the government. In terms of R&D, the Commission advocated developing auditing and intrusion detection systems. Such systems must be combined with timely assessment and response capabilities to achieve effective systems security.

- ***DARPA Program on Information Survivability [7].*** The goal of this program is to provide affordable, verifiable, and scalable technologies to ensure a robust and secure defense infrastructure. The program is composed of four subareas: high-confidence computing systems, high-confidence networking, survivability of large-scale systems, and wrappers and composition. Its top three priorities are:

  a. Operating system security (influence future commercial operating system development; adaptive system paradigm),

  b. Intrusion detection (extremely high accuracy; detection capability for unknown intrusion types), and

  c. Assurance technologies (well integrated into system development tools).

- ***Stanford Workshop on Protecting and Assuring Critical National Infrastructure: Setting the Research and Policy Agenda [8].*** One session focused on technologies and tools for critical infrastructure protection. In addressing the issue of who should perform research, workshop participants recommended:

a. Forming private/public partnerships to redesign the infrastructure. Sponsoring research that results in demonstration projects.

b. Funding by the government of basic research to cast the architectural framework. Challenging companies to model specific infrastructures and focus on solving problems.

2.2 PCCIP-SPONSORED STUDIES

To supplement the sources cited above, the PCCIP sponsored four external studies and one internal R&D study.

- ***National Security Agency Study on INFOSEC in the DOD and Intelligence Community [9].*** This study estimated that the government investment (including personnel costs) in INFOSEC research is approximately *$150 million per year.* The investments are weighted heavily in two areas (1) damage avoidance, detection, and recovery; and (2) assurance. The emphasis in the former is on intrusion detection. The emphasis in assurance is on risk management. The study recommends that an additional $100–150 million per year is needed over the next three to five years to study critical INFOSEC problems.
- ***Institute for Defense Analyses (IDA) Study on Commercial Perspectives on IA R& D [10].*** The *IDA* conducted interviews with 21 computer and telecommunications technology providers to (1) assess commercial IA R&D funding and (2) determine where commercial technology providers are investing and where they think they should invest in the future.

  IDA was unable to obtain funding information from such interviews as such information is either proprietary or not uniquely captured and classified as IA research (i.e., it is integrated into product development). In the absence of such funding data, IDA independently developed a gross estimate of commercial IA R&D funding from publicly available industry data. This estimate indicates that commercial IA R&D ranges between $120 and $355 million per year. A framework for addressing IA technology R&D is provided in which the wide ranging views for IA R&D investment obtained through the interviews are organized. This framework segments the IA research needs into (1) Basic Research in IA Fundamentals, (2) System-level Security Engineering, and (3) Individual Component Development. System-level Security Engineering is the highest priority research need. The report contains the following findings:

  a. The U.S. commercial IA R&D activity is fairly robust in breadth, but is lacking in depth.

  b. Industry believes that it "owns" the commercial IA technology problem and should spend to solve it.

c. US commercial IA R&D investment is focused on satisfying customer demand primarily in electronic commerce.

d. All the companies interviewed indicated that their R&D investments in IA technology were increasing and that, for most companies, this trend should increase for the next few years.

e. There are important areas of IA research that either are not being pursued by commercial technology providers or require additional emphasis and funding.

f. Technology transfer remains a significant problem.

g. Export control policy is perceived to be the biggest barrier to further commercial IA investment, thereby reducing the capability to protect our critical infrastructures.

h. Government-funded research, leadership, and vision can make a difference.

- ***Department of Energy (DOE) National Laboratory R&D Studies, Survey, and Interviews [11–13]***

  a. Teams of subject-matter experts from the national laboratories were formed to develop technology R&D recommendations in the eight critical infrastructure areas and in the crosscutting, interdependency area. Each team examined threat and vulnerability issues, elicited stakeholder and user community inputs, analyzed trends (technology, regulatory, market, social) that impact infrastructure assurance, and reviewed commercial off-the-shelf (COTS) and government off-the-shelf (GOTS) technologies. The teams also looked at ongoing R&D efforts that could be used to meet the identified needs. The six topical R&D categories and many of the specific recommendations in this report were based on these studies.

  b. A survey of the DOE national laboratories and the private sector was conducted to identify technologies and capabilities applicable to the eight critical infrastructures. More than 1,600 combinations of technologies and capabilities were identified in the vulnerability/threat assessment, detection, response, mitigation, and recovery areas that could be used to meet infrastructure assurance needs.

  c. More than 40 interviews, primarily with representatives of the private sector, were conducted in the eight critical infrastructure areas. Vulnerabilities, threats (physical, cyber, conventional, and unconventional), technology needs, ongoing R&D efforts, and R&D gaps were discussed. Encryption devices and techniques, network and security management, intrusion detection, physical and cyber protection technologies, and modeling and simulation tools were among the specific areas identified for continued R&D efforts.

- ***Bellcore Study on R&D for Network Assurance in 2010 [14].*** This study presents Bellcore's view and characterization of the R&D areas that are critical for providing the desired levels of network assurance in the future public telecommunications infrastructure in the United States, including both the Internet and the Public Switched Telecommunications Network. Government R&D and industry-sponsored R&D are both needed. The key recommendations of this study are that the government should maintain its current level of R&D funding and promote R&D in critical areas that directly impact network assurance. These critical R&D areas include:

  a. Security (operating system security, software integrity, cryptography, intrusion detection, and firewalls);

  b. Distributed control;

  c. Network assurance measurement infrastructure (metrics, criteria, techniques, and tools);

  d. Interprovider policy routing/architectures;

  e. Advanced services (quality of service, multicast);

  f. Stability of dynamic Internet Protocol and Asynchronous Transfer Mode routing protocols; and

  g. New technologies, services, and applications.

  The study specifically notes that security R&D lags behind corresponding product releases and recommends continued support for critical government programs [such as the Next Generation Internet (NGI) project] that sponsor R&D in many areas that impact network assurance.

- ***Internal PCCIP Study [15].*** A detailed review of the R&D budgets of 13 major companies revealed that many R&D items that affect information security were not listed in the budgets as individual line items. The review clearly showed that many developments that would affect security were buried in other major development items. This study indicated that the private-sector R&D expenditures associated with information security range from $1 billion to $1.5 billion on an annual basis. Further, the study showed little research was being conducted in the private sector.

3. RESEARCH AREAS AND TOPICS

To address the range of physical, cyber, and other threats facing our nation's critical infrastructures, research is needed to:

- Secure information while it is stored, being processed, and in transit;
- Monitor and detect threat activity, and provide warning in real time;
- Assess the vulnerability of both components and entire infrastructures;
- Manage risk and support decision making;
- Protect infrastructures physically and mitigate damage; and
- Aid in rapid incident response and recovery.

Specific research areas and topics are identified in Table 3.1 and described in the following sections.

3.1 INFORMATION ASSURANCE

As national infrastructures increasingly depend on computers and networked information systems to improve efficiency and enhance economic competitiveness, they also become more vulnerable to potential cyber attacks. In addition, the basic technology is changing rapidly, and government policy is encouraging increased competition. These changes affect the individual critical infrastructures and national interdependent infrastructures, as well as increase infrastructure vulnerability as a whole.

Significant new investment in R&D is required to protect the communications infrastructure, and the information created, stored, processed, and transmitted on it. Security of vital information is a key component for functioning of interdependent infrastructures, such as electric power, emergency services, banking and finance, and transportation. The need to develop new means of protection is apparent, given the increasing rate of incidents, the expanding list of known vulnerabilities, and the inadequate set of solutions available. R&D recommendations for four topics in the information assurance area are discussed in the following sections.

TABLE 3.1 R&D Areas and Topics

R&D Areas	R&D Topics
Information Assurance	System Level Security Advanced Concepts and Theory (for Information Protection) Management of Information Protection Encryption Technologies
Monitoring and Threat Detection	Automated Monitoring and Detection Infrastructure Information System

R&D Areas	R&D Topics
Vulnerability Assessment and Systems Analysis	Vulnerability Assessment Tools Complex System Modeling Test Beds Verification Technologies
Risk Management and Decision Support	Risk Management Decision Support Systems
Protection and Mitigation	Real-Time Distributed System Control Infrastructure Hardening Containment and Isolation
Incident Response and Recovery	Response Technologies Recovery Technologies

3.1.1 System Level Security, Engineering, and Architectures

The current and anticipated future state of the information architectures that support our national infrastructures needs to be characterized. The very nature and behavior of the system of information being exchanged among information providers and processors on the one hand, and communications channel and support providers on the other, are not well understood. Such new forms as electronic signatures, electronic money, and the virtual enterprise create new reliability and security challenges as fast as they create new economic opportunities. Understanding the anatomy and dynamics of this new system, and developing appropriate security and assurance practices, requires R&D, with the coordinated effort of government and industry.

Security architectures can be used to organize individual security components and services into working systems that provide information and resource confidentiality, integrity, and availability. Architectures specify how protection protocols and data exchange interfaces allow the interoperation of security components. The role of architectures is becoming more important, as security services become distributed like the systems that they protect and as the software industry begins to provide individual security mechanisms as independent modules. R&D is required for addressing standards for: evaluating information protection when different tools and measures are combined in the infrastructure; characterizing architectures for robustness, scalability, and overall strength of security; streamlining performance of protective systems to reduce the costs of using them, especially in terms of time and ease of operation; and incorporating, where feasible, advanced information protection concepts, such as information that carries with it conditions for its use.

These security architectures require technologies that facilitate more efficient and effective interaction (communication) between computer-based systems and users. System complexity must be reduced, and ease of use must be enhanced without sacrificing security or increasing risk. For example, security and interactive problem-solving technologies (e.g., interactive agents), which are integral to system designs, must be developed to augment user strengths and compensate for user weaknesses.

3.1.2 Advanced Concepts and Theory (for Information Protection)

Considerable R&D is needed to provide a proper theoretical base for protecting the communications and information infrastructure and supporting different paradigms, models, and implementations. Fundamental research to generate new concepts is required on intrusion detection, malicious software, access control, authorization, authentication, interoperability, denial of service, and system complexity. Research also is needed in information protection policy development and use, reconstitution and recovery for all levels of the infrastructure, and distributed hardware and software approaches. It is assumed that research efforts associated with the NGI, which have direct implications on network assurance, will continue and provide a foundation for these research efforts. This fundamental research is critical to the establishment of a system security engineering discipline.

3.1.3 Management of Information Protection

Security management today is a major operational cost consideration. Affordable methods and techniques for the use and management of information protection methods, tools, and practices are needed to support the protection of information in the infrastructure. Improved methods are needed for remote and local configuration management of the infrastructure components. The new methods and techniques should be scaleable and must anticipate and support advanced infrastructure and networking concepts, such as active and adaptive networks.

3.1.4 Encryption Technologies

Encryption can improve information security by providing privacy and supporting data confidentiality, user identification and authentication, data integrity, and access control. Encryption also can be used for implementing message integrity, digital signatures, nonrepudiation, and advanced authentication techniques. The mathematical algorithms used to encrypt data must be highly resistant to attack and computationally secure. The keys used for encrypting and decrypting data must be distributed properly, protected, and managed. Promising new encryption technologies, such as elliptic curve, could improve both security and economy of operations. New concepts of key management infrastructure could emerge to provide a variety of alternatives that industry could develop into interoperable products.

3.2 MONITORING AND THREAT DETECTION

Reliable automated monitoring and detection systems, timely and effective information collection technologies (e.g., using intelligence, open source, and voluntarily contributed private-sector information), and efficient data reduction and analysis tools are needed for identifying and characterizing localized or coordinated large-scale attacks against critical infrastructures. A "civil defense" capability in the cyber environment (National Cyber Defense) is an appropriate consideration to provide a national perimeter defense resulting in "defense in depth" protection and attack sensing and warning. In addition to supporting protection of the individual elements of the critical infrastructure, such a concept could facilitate communication of threat situations between and among these elements. It could also facilitate the exchange of technical information and technologies needed to ensure adequate protection at the element level. Such technologies would support early threat warning to government organizations and private-sector infrastructure owners and operators, thereby preventing widespread infrastructure disruptions that have potentially serious consequences on our national security, economy, and quality of life. As described below, both hardware (monitoring and detection devices) and software R&D activities are needed.

3.2.1 Automated Monitoring and Detection

Technologies that automatically monitor infrastructure and detect intrusions are crucial for establishing a more proactive approach to infrastructure assurance. Research is needed for developing monitoring technologies for sensing system instabilities and voltage collapse in the electric power sector, highly sensitive biological and chemical agent detectors for real-time monitoring of public spaces and water supply systems, automated technologies for detecting electronic intrusions into infrastructure control systems (e.g., supervisory control and data acquisition [SCADA] systems), and advanced terminals and real-time vehicle and cargo monitoring technologies. Advanced infrastructure monitoring techniques also are needed to detect dangerously deteriorating conditions in structures (e.g., "smart" sensors and "smart" materials technology, such as ultrasonic or magnetic corrosion detection, embedded fiber optics for enhanced visual inspection, and shape-memory alloys). Monitoring stations, similar to those in use by the electric power industry, are needed for other infrastructures.

3.2.2 Infrastructure Information System

The ability to prevent, mitigate, respond to, and recover from an attack could be enhanced significantly by developing and using advanced geographic information systems (GISs). These systems use remote sensing and geographic positioning system (GPS) technologies. While information exists for some infrastructures (e.g., gas and oil pipelines), it is not comprehensive and integrated. The collection of intelligence and other information (e.g., monitoring data) is the critical first step in identifying and characterizing threats, supporting policy-making and investment decisions, and providing timely, effective indications and warning systems. Threat assessment, threat warning, attack alert, and attack assessment concepts, tools, systems, and processes—as well as mitigation, incident management, and recovery systems—all directly depend on the timeliness and accuracy of information. "One-call" centers for real-time information about the location of critical infrastructure components, which would speed responses to threats and disasters, are possible only if accurate "as built" plans are available and highly detailed GIS/GPS technologies are developed.

Technologies and a process are needed to pull together sharable, appropriately sanitized information from the intelligence community, the law enforcement community, and the private sector to understand the dimension of potential threats. The information conveying the balance of threats and vulnerabilities needs to be plausible to warrant the investment of limited resources in assurance. Classified and proprietary informational issues must be addressed so that information sharing between government and industry is improved without compromising competitive advantage or shaking the confidence of customers and investors.

On-line and automated data reduction and analysis tools are an integral part of an information system for early detection and characterization of threats (physical or cyber) to one or more infrastructures. Timely data reduction and analyses provide vital information for assessing the extent of damage and the necessary information to simulate potential propagation through the infrastructures. Such information could help to select efficient response and recovery strategies. Timely automated data analyses techniques (e.g., time series analyses, pattern recognition, regression) on large sets of data, including data from real-time monitoring and detection systems, require innovative R&D efforts because of their complexity.

3.3 VULNERABILITY ASSESSMENT AND SYSTEMS ANALYSIS

Advanced methods and tools for assessing vulnerability and analyzing systems are needed to identify critical nodes within infrastructures, to examine infrastructure interdependencies, and to help understand the behavior of complex systems. These methods and tools would help address physical and cyber security issues in an integrated fashion. Modeling and simulation tools and environments (e.g., test beds) for studying infrastructure-related problems also are important. The advantage of modeling is that it allows experimentation that cannot be performed in realistic environments of any appreciable scale. Techniques also are needed to verify and validate methodologies and tools used for designing and building new systems, and to assess existing systems.

3.3.1 Vulnerability Assessment Tools

Vulnerability assessment tools are needed to determine the specific exploitable weaknesses (vulnerabilities) of infrastructure systems and components to credible threats. An example is vulnerabilities in administrative controls for operating and managing computer systems. Tools are needed to: measure the relative risks in terms of probability of occurrence, likelihood of success, and the degree of impact on national security, economic competitiveness, quality of life, and other important attributes; and to identify critical nodes and components where propagation could exacerbate the impact. These tools are necessary: to support national and local planning, prioritization, decision making, and investment strategies; to enhance the ability of users to perform consequence assessment and risk analysis; and to develop effective risk management approaches and strategies. In addition, technology assessments are required so that the infrastructure protection community can develop a comprehensive awareness of: (1) the inherent susceptibilities of current and future technologies on which infrastructures and key components are or will be reliant; (2) technologies that potentially could be used maliciously to disrupt, damage, or destroy infrastructures or key components; and (3) technologies that could have protective applications and potential for safeguarding infrastructures and components.

3.3.2 Complex System Modeling

In-depth research on the complexities and interdependencies in the critical infrastructures is needed. While "complexity" research has continued at an abstract level, the complexity/interdependency problem, as it relates to practical infrastructure assurance, has not been studied in depth. This research would provide the empirical and theoretical foundation for developing a diverse vulnerability assessment, monitoring, predictive modeling, and consequence analysis technologies needed for addressing infrastructure assurance issues.

Robust infrastructure and nodal analysis techniques and tools need to be developed for modeling large-scale distributed/networked systems and interdependent infrastructures. Such tools would facilitate identifying critical infrastructure nodes and components, the interdependencies among infrastructures, and the consequences resulting from degradation or loss of infrastructure capabilities. Advanced tools and methods also are required to support the identification and mapping (physically and logically) of infrastructure systems, the location of critical nodes and components, and the identification and quantification of net consequences to users (government and the private sector) in the event of degradation or loss. Such tools and methods also are needed to help assess the required redundancy margins and firebreaks to preclude catastrophic failures.

3.3.3 Test Beds

National, regional, and virtual test beds are needed (1) to test the nation's infrastructure under actual working conditions and (2) to test analysis, assessment, advanced predictive modeling, and other modeling and simulation systems and tools. Test beds allow scientists to perform experiments on different infrastructures and components, investigate incidents, examine improvements to hardware and software, examine genetic diversity issues, and conduct other necessary experiments usually too expensive and/or disruptive to be performed otherwise. The Next Generation Internet (NGI) could be an appropriate vehicle for large-scale experimentation and development into a new highly assured Internet backbone.

3.3.4 Verification Technologies

Substantial research has gone into formal methods to design and develop systems that can be proven to meet their design requirements. However, hardware and software bugs continue to be introduced. There is an urgent need for research on total design and verification strategies that can be applied to subsystems and the composition of subsystem of the critical infrastructure. While the entire problem may not be tractable, there may be subsets that are. It is vital to understand what is possible and then to fund research that will lead to high reliability systems. Automated technologies need to be developed, for example, that can uncover hidden "logic bombs" in critical software systems and, with a high level of confidence, the veracity and validity of software systems. In addition, more work needs to be done on hardware verifications.

3.4 RISK MANAGEMENT AND DECISION SUPPORT

Risk management and decision support system methodologies and tools are needed to help government and private-sector decision makers to prioritize the use of limited resources to reduce risk. These methodologies and tools would address risk both from familiar threats (e.g., natural disasters, physical attack) and from emerging and future threats, such as risk from our increasing interdependence and reliance on cyber systems.

3.4.1 Risk Management

Methodologies, tools, and organization processes are needed to identify and minimize the impact of risks on infrastructure sectors and information. Research areas include developing methodologies: for formulating management decisions based on operational missions and information value; for dealing with uncertainties in, or incomplete knowledge of, threats, vulnerabilities, and protection measures; and for managing risks across the multiple components and organizations involved in the infrastructures.

It is essential to understand the consequences of disruptions to our infrastructures to make effective decisions. A set of comprehensive analytical tools is needed to facilitate predictive rapid and detailed "post-mortem" analyses of disruptions that affect single or multiple infrastructures. These tools would facilitate investigation and estimation of the consequences of the disruption at the national, regional, and local levels. The tools would address in a systematic and comprehensive way, for example, economic impacts (direct and indirect), health and safety impacts, environmental impacts, and socioeconomic impacts.

3.4.2 Decision Support Systems

Decision analysis (which encompasses cost-benefit analysis) tools are needed for prioritization, facility siting, and resource allocation decisions. For example, these tools help identify and prioritize critical assets for protection and restoration, compute return on investment in competing security technologies, and develop overall infrastructure investment strategies. Measurable criteria need to be established that address national security, economic competitiveness, quality of life, and other important attributes, such as capital, operation and maintenance, and life-cycle costs. In the information and communications sector, methodologies and tools are needed to assist information owners in determining what protection is appropriate for information and in understanding the value or costs of information. This knowledge will enable them to judge what, where, and how much protection is needed. Such methodologies would help determine what infrastructure assets are critical and thus aid in the priority use of resources in a degraded environment.

Formalized techniques/tools are needed for predicting, testing, and verifying complex system performance. These tools help predict the behavior and properties of large-scale, complex systems that involve one or more infrastructures and infrastructure dependencies. They also are needed to help support decisions on how these systems can be protected/isolated and degraded gracefully, if necessary, to prevent cascading impacts. Research on behavior properties, parameter estimation, advanced artificial intelligence, and other innovative techniques will be required.

Lessons learned systems need to be developed to provide planners and analysts with a quick reference to past disruptions/events, initiating causes, impacts and consequences, corrective/protective, legal, and legislative/regulatory actions taken, organizational roles and responsibilities, and other key information. Lessons learned can be supplemented through exercises and simulations. Such information would be invaluable in supporting both proactive and reactive decisions to disruptions. A comprehensive up-to-date interactive distributed knowledge base (encyclopedia) of protection technologies and countermeasure techniques also would be helpful in ensuring that planners and operators are aware of the full range of protection options. This encyclopedia could address associated factors, such as cost, practicality, effectiveness, operational penalties, and maturity, which normally are used in making decisions.

3.5 PROTECTION AND MITIGATION

Real-time system control, infrastructure hardening, and containment and isolation technologies also are needed to protect infrastructure systems against the entire threat spectrum. Other current and advanced survivability, reliability, or assurance enhancement measures need to be explored and developed. Three aggregated research topics are described in the following sections.

3.5.1 Real-Time Distributed System Control

Real-time distributed system control technologies are needed to help protect and improve the efficiency and effectiveness of existing infrastructures. These technologies would reduce the need to build costly new infrastructures that may pose environmental, regulatory, and other undesirable problems. For example, the advanced real-time control technologies for electric power systems would allow better use of transmission and distribution systems.

3.5.2 Infrastructure Hardening

R&D work needs to enhance the ability of various infrastructures to survive disruptions of larger magnitude than previously considered. Guidance can be provided by the efforts of industry and government to engineer greater seismic margins into buildings located in earthquake-prone zones. Both physical and cyber systems need to be considered.

3.5.3 Containment and Isolation

Impact containment and isolation technologies are needed that limit the amount of damage due to chemical or biological contamination, explosions, information system disruption or data contamination, and other acts of terrorism. For example, blast-resistant containers are needed to reduce the impacts of explosive devices placed in vehicles or cargo holding facilities. Technologies that contain and isolate chemical and biological contaminants released in air and water supplies are needed to minimize exposure to the population. Technologies also are needed to contain and isolate the impacts of information system disruptions so that neither the complete system or interdependent infrastructures are affected.

3.6 INCIDENT RESPONSE AND RECOVERY

A wide range of new technologies and tools are needed for planning for, responding to, and recovering from incidents, such as natural disasters and physical and cyber-based attacks, that affect local or national infrastructures. Advanced planning methods and tools supporting preparation for, mitigation of, response to, and recovery from infrastructure attacks or failures are desired. R&D needs are described below.

3.6.1 Response Technologies

Technologies are needed that can aid in responding to a disruption of infrastructure. Tools are needed: for quick assessment of the size and location of populations at risk (e.g., from a chemical or biological agent) and the location of structures under imminent threat of damage; for optimal selection, dispatch, and routing of medical, police, fire, and other responders; and for crisis and consequence management that identify the infrastructure owners and operators, and the roles, responsibilities, authorities, and capabilities of federal, state, and local response organizations. For example, technologies are needed to speed the delivery or re-establishment of transportation services for an affected area, and to improve protective equipment and communications capabilities for emergency responders.

3.6.2 Recovery Technologies

Technologies need to be developed to aid in the rapid recovery and restoration of infrastructure and infrastructure-related services. This broad R&D area ranges from emergency medical and decontamination technologies to respond to, and recover from, a chemical or biological agent attack involving contamination of a municipal water supply, a major metropolitan area, or a federal facility, to technologies to recover from a highly destructive cyber assault on the stock exchanges and banking systems. Advanced technologies are needed to support federal, state, and local response organizations.

4. RECOMMENDATIONS FOR ACTION

A joint R&D effort among government, industry, and academia is needed to produce a successful infrastructure assurance research and technology development effort. The strategy and implementation recommendations presented in this section are made assuming a joint effort, and recognizing that R&D is only one component of an overall national infrastructure assurance strategy.

4.1 STRATEGY AND IMPLEMENTATION RECOMMENDATIONS

- *A focal point (coordinating entity) for national infrastructure assurance R&D efforts should be established.* Figure 4.1 illustrates this concept. This entity, which may be a successor to the PCCIP, would stress partnership between government and the private sector, coordinate with established advisory and information exchange groups, and promote awareness and education. Its missions would include developing, coordinating, prioritizing, and overseeing the R&D agenda to meet critical national needs. It also would serve as a clearinghouse for disseminating such information.

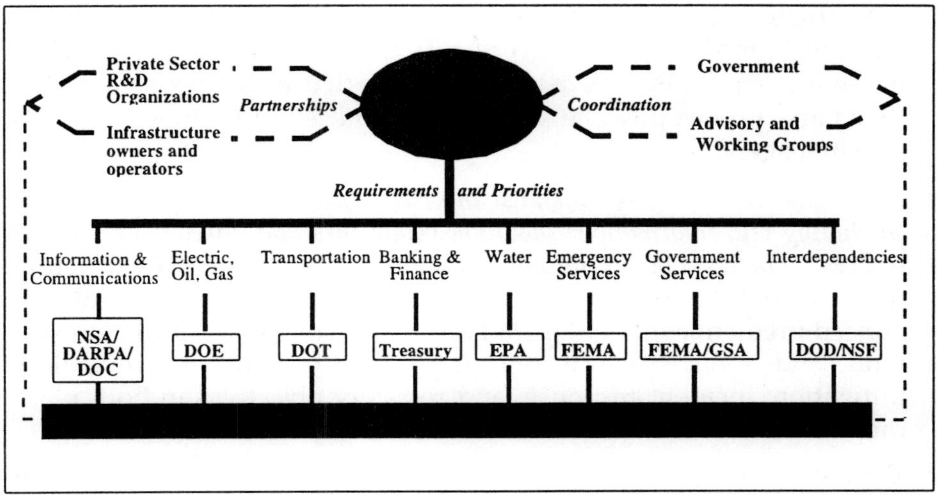

FIGURE 4.1 Infrastructure Assurance R&D Organizational Structure

- *Appropriate lead agencies should manage infrastructure-specific R&D efforts.* Close coordination with federal entities and with established advisory and information exchange groups is essential to ensure efficient use of limited funds. Partnerships must be established with private-sector R&D organizations and infrastructure owners and operators, and centers of excellence must be identified/established at universities, national laboratories, and private-sector R&D institutes. The responsible lead agencies should set their specific R&D agendas on the basis of established national objectives and guidance provided by a coordinating entity.
- *The National Research Council (NRC) should define more fully a national infrastructure assurance research program based on the information contained in this report.* The NRC should lead the effort, together with those departments and agencies of the federal government already engaged in R&D relevant to each infrastructure.
- *Promote the discipline of complex, interdependent systems engineering.* This discipline would provide the theoretical foundation for developing the diverse vulnerability assessment, monitoring, predictive modeling, and consequence analysis technologies needed for addressing

infrastructure assurance issues as they relate to the eight critical infrastructures. Concepts, such as system complexity, interaction, and coupling, would be examined. This new discipline is fundamental in providing large-scale system engineering and high confidence systems.

- *In-depth research on the complexities and interdependencies in the national infrastructures is needed.* While research is ongoing in many topical areas (e.g., modeling the power grid), the interdependency problem has not been studied in depth. Research that evaluates actual incidents and probes possible scenarios would lead to a more focused research agenda.
- *A national repository of validated infrastructure-related models and data (including GIS information) should be established and linked closely to the test beds.* The test beds would be used to test the nation's infrastructure under actual working conditions, and test analysis, assessment, advanced predictive modeling, and other modeling and simulation systems and tools. Such a repository would support prevention, mitigation, incident response, and recovery objectives in both planning and analysis and crisis situations.
- Various forums, such as conferences, workshops, and government and private-sector planning meetings, should be established. These forums would bring together researchers, private-sector infrastructure owners and operators, and government to discuss common problems and requirements, to establish research agenda, and to promote creative thinking on solutions to infrastructure problems.
- *Training, education, and awareness programs should be established.* First, these programs would develop a cadre of knowledgeable people ("infrastructure practitioners"). Second, they would ensure proper implementation and utilization of new technologies, methods, and tools.

4.2 INVESTMENT REQUIREMENTS

It is estimated that the government needs to invest approximately $500 million to $1 billion per year to address the infrastructure assurance R&D areas and topics identified in Table 3.1. A recommended investment profile for FY98 through FY04 is shown in Table 4.1. Information assurance is a separate item because it represents the largest single area needing R&D investment.

TABLE 4.1 Recommended Government Infrastructure Assurance R&D Investments

	Investment ($ Millions)						
R&D Investment Category	**FY98**	**FY99**	**FY00**	**FY01**	**FY02**	**FY03**	**FY04**
Information Assurance	150	300	360	420	480	540	600
Other Areas of Infrastructure Assurance	100	200	240	280	320	360	400
Total	250	500	600	700	800	900	1,000

To put these requirements into perspective, the recommended investment of $500 million in FY99 represents an approximate doubling of the current infrastructure assurance R&D funding level.[2] This increase in investment is needed to "jump start" a focused, coordinated, and goal-oriented national R&D effort. As shown in Table 4.1, the recommended level of investment would double again over the next five-year period (FY00–FY04), as the R&D program gains momentum and achieves critical mass in terms of researchers and innovative research ideas.

A similar or greater level of commitment and R&D investment is needed from the private sector. However, more comprehensive and detailed examinations are needed in the following areas: (1) specific R&D needs, (2) commercial off-the-shelf (COTS) and government off-the-shelf (GOTS) technologies that could be adapted to meet those needs, (3) ongoing R&D that could be leveraged, (4) legacy systems, (5) development timeframes, (6) development dependencies, and (7) potential implementation strategies (e.g., involving government laboratories, the private sector, and academia). Once these examinations have been completed, a final national technology R&D agenda and investment strategy for infrastructure assurance can be established.

---

2 As noted in Section 2.2, the current government investment in INFOSEC research (information assurance) is approximately $150 million per year. R&D investments in the other infrastructure assurance areas are more difficult to quantify because much of the relevant work is not identified explicitly or reported as being related to infrastructure assurance. Further, considerable value judgment must be applied in determining what specific R&D work should be so designated. Most research is likely to have been initiated for other purposes but is nevertheless applicable to infrastructure assurance needs. Overall, it is estimated that information assurance R&D needs constitute approximately 60% or more of the total infrastructure assurance R&D needs. This ratio is reflected in the recommended R&D investment profile shown in Table 4.1.

5. REFERENCES

1. *NRC, Information Systems Trustworthiness Interim Report,* prepared by National Research Council Computer Science and Telecommunications Board, published by National Academy Press, Washington, D.C. (1997).

2. DOD, *Information Warfare—Defense (IW-D),* U.S. Department of Defense, Office of the Undersecretary of Defense for Acquisition & Technology, Defense Science Board Task Force, Washington, D.C. (Nov. 1996).

3. DOD, *Improving Information Assurance (IA): A General Assessment and Comprehensive Approach to an Integrated IA Program for the Department of Defense,* U.S. Department of Defense, Assistant Secretary of Defense for Command, Control, Communications and Intelligence, Information Assurance Task Force, Washington, D.C. (Mar. 28, 1997).

4. National Security Agency, report prepared by the Scientific Advisory Board INFOSEC Panel (1997).

5. Joint Security Commission, *Redefining Security,* report to the Secretary of Defense and Director of Central Intelligence, Washington, D.C. (Feb. 28, 1994).

6. *Report of the Commission on Protecting and Reducing Government Secrecy,* U.S. Senate, Document 105-2, Washington, D.C. (1997).

7. Lunt, T., *DARPA Program on Information Survivability,* presentation (Aug. 1997).

8. Bambos, N., "Technologies & Tools for Critical Infrastructure Protection: Summary of Tools Session," presented at *Workshop on Protecting and Assuring Critical National Infrastructure: Setting the Research and Policy Agenda,* Stanford University, Calif. (July 21-22, 1997).

9. Burnham, B., INFOSEC *Research in the DOD and Intelligence Community,* Private Communications (July 1997).

10. Mayfield, W., and R. Ross, *Evolving a National Information Assurance Research Agenda: Issues and Opinions from Commercial Information Technology Providers,* report prepared for the President's Commission on Critical Infrastructure Protection by Institute for Defense Analyses, Alexandria, Va. (July 1997).

11. DOE, *Technology Research and Development Recommendations for Protecting and Assuring Critical National Infrastructures,* report prepared for the President's Commission on Critical Infrastructure Protection by U.S. Department of Energy National Laboratory R&D Teams (July 1997).

12. ANL, *National Laboratory and Private Sector Technologies and Capabilities for Protecting Critical Infrastructures,* report prepared for the President's Commission on Critical Infrastructure Protection by Argonne National Laboratory, Argonne, Ill. (July 1997).

13. ANL, *Summary Report on Critical Infrastructure Interviews,* report prepared for the President's Commission on Critical Infrastructure Protection by Argonne National Laboratory, Argonne, Ill. (July 1997).

14. Bellcore, *Research and Development for Network Assurance in 2010,* report prepared for the President's Commission on Critical Infrastructure Protection by Bellcore, Morristown, N.J. (July 25, 1997).

15. Adams, M., Private Communication (Sept. 1997).

CHAPTER 2

PRELIMINARY RESEARCH AND DEVELOPMENT

ROADMAP FOR PROTECTING AND ASSURING CRITICAL NATIONAL INFRASTRUCTURES

Transition Office of the President's Commission on Critical Infrastructure Protection and the Critical Infrastructure Assurance Office

July 1998

Contents

Preface

Study Team

Acknowledgments

Executive Summary

Section 1 Introduction

1.1 Purpose

1.2 Scope of the R&D Study

1.3 Sector Study Teams

1.4 Study Approach

1.5 Report Organization

Section 2 Sector R&D Topics and Roadmaps

2.1 Banking and Finance

2.1.1 Infrastructure Overview

2.1.2 Issues and Trends

2.1.3 Threats and Vulnerabilities

2.1.4 Summary of R&D Topics and Roadmaps

2.2 Energy

2.2.1 Infrastructure Overview

2.2.2 Issues and Trends

2.2.3 Threats and Vulnerabilities

2.2.4 Summary of R&D Topics and Roadmaps

2.3 Information and Communications

2.3.1 Infrastructure Overview

2.3.2 Issues and Trends

2.3.3 Threats and Vulnerabilities

2.3.4 Summary of R&D Topics and Roadmaps

2.4 Transportation

2.4.1 Infrastructure Overview

2.4.2 Issues and Trends

2.4.3 Threats and Vulnerabilities

2.4.4 Summary of R&D Topics and Roadmaps
2.5 Vital Human Services
2.5.1 Infrastructure Overview
2.5.2 Issues and Trends
2.5.3 Threats and Vulnerabilities
2.5.4 Summary of R&D Topics and Roadmaps
Section 3 Integrated R&D Topics and Roadmaps
3.1 Common R&D Themes
3.1.1 Information Assurance
3.1.2 Monitoring and Detection
3.1.3 Protection and Mitigation
3.1.4 Response and Recovery
3.1.5 Modeling and Simulation
3.1.6 Systems Analysis
3.1.7 Decision Support
3.1.8 Risk Management
3.1.9 Vulnerability Assessment
3.2 Crosscutting R&D
3.3 Interdependency and Complexity R&D
3.4 Integrated Roadmap
3.5 Resource Requirements
Section 4 Next Steps
4.1 Essential Elements of Information for Future Roadmapping
4.2 Portfolio Considerations
4.3 Policy Considerations
4.4 Technology Transfer Considerations
4.5 Interdependency and Complexity Considerations
4.6 Other Ingredients for a Successful R&D Program
Section 5 Subject-matter Experts and Reviewers

Tables

1.1 Research Categories

1.2 Roadmapping Information

2.1 Summary of Banking and Finance R&D Topics and Roadmaps

2.2 Summary of Energy R&D Topics and Roadmaps

2.3 Summary of Information and Communications R&D Topics and Roadmaps

2.4 Summary of Transportation R&D Topics and Roadmaps

2.5 Summary of Vital Human Services R&D Topics and Roadmaps

3.1 Common R&D Themes

3.2 Mapping among R&D Topics and Primary and Secondary Themes

3.3 Summary of Interdependency and Complexity R&D Topics and Roadmaps

3.4 Estimated Annual Infrastructure Assurance Resource Requirements for Recommended R&D Topics

Figures

1.1 Government and Private-sector Partnership for Meeting Infrastructure Assurance Objectives

1.2 Structure of the Sector Study Teams

3.1 Crosscutting R&D

3.2 Integrated R&D Roadmap

3.3 Near-term Resource Requirements by Theme

4.1 Essential Elements of Information for R&D Roadmapping

Preface

Developing a robust and harmonized national research and development plan that comprehensively addresses critical infrastructure assurance needs is a complex challenge. This report is intended to be a first step in helping to meet that challenge. The information presented was developed by study teams composed of individuals from government, the private sector, academia and research institutes, and the Department of Energy national laboratory system. The contributions by these individuals were voluntary, reflecting a strong commitment to this roadmapping activity and a recognition of its importance to the nation.

The study teams addressed five infrastructure sectors: banking and finance, energy (electric power, natural gas, oil), information and communications, transportation, and vital human services (water supply systems, emergency services, government services). This report highlights the results of the work in each of those sectors.

It should be noted that the majority of the work by the study teams was completed prior to the release of Presidential Decision Directive 63—Critical Infrastructure Protection—in May 1998 and the establishment by the Office of Science and Technology Policy of a Critical Infrastructure Protection Research and Development Interagency Working Group.

The study teams recognize that hard work remains to be done. The magnitude and complexity of the R&D question being considered make detailed planning and consensus difficult. It is the hope of the teams that the information presented is viewed in the positive spirit in which it is intended, and that it provides a basis for constructive debate and a foundation for the next steps in developing a viable infrastructure assurance R&D plan.

Study Team

Study Team Directors

John C. Davis, Commissioner *National Security Agency*

David A. Jones, Commissioner *Department of Energy*

Study Team Coordinator

Paula L. Scalingi *Argonne National Laboratory*

Sector Study Team Members

Baking and Finance

Kawika Daguio *American Bankers Association*
Peter H. Daly, Commissioner *Department of the Treasury*
Judy Moore *Sandia National Laboratories*
Anthony G. Oettinger *Harvard University*

Energy

Fernando L. Alvarado *University of Wisconsin–Madison*
William M. Burnett *Gas Research Institute*
Stephen Gehl *Electric Power Research Institute*
Jean-Michel Guldmann *Ohio State University*
David A. Jones, Commissioner *Department of Energy*
Landis D. Kannberg *Pacific Northwest National Laboratory*
Coordinators: William A. Buehring and Ronald E. Fisher *Argonne National Laboratory*

Information and Communications

Guy Copeland *Computer Science Corporation*
Douglas L. Mansur *Lawrence Livermore National Laboratory*
Terry Mayfield *Institute for Defense Analyses*
Irwin M. Pikus, Commissioner *Department of Commerce*
Coordinator: Craig Swietlik *Argonne National Laboratory*

Transportation

E. Fenton Carey *Department of Transportation*
Steven R. Ditmeyer *Federal Railroad Administration*
Bruce E. Peterson *Oak Ridge National Laboratory*
Joseph L. Schofer *Northwestern University*
Coordinator: Christopher L. Saricks *Argonne National Laboratory*

Vital Human Services

Stephen W. Clark *Environmental Protection Agency*
Joseph H. Keller *Idaho National Engineering and Environmental Laboratory*
Robert L. Sherwood *IIT Research Institute*
Richard A. Swanson *Computer Science Corporation*
Kevin Tonat *Department of Health and Human Services*
Coordinator: Jerry L. Gillette *Argonne National Laboratory*

Study Integrators

James P. Peerenboom *Argonne National Laboratory*
Thomas D. Wolsko *Argonne National Laboratory*

Acknowledgments

The study team gratefully acknowledges the encouragement and insight provided by Kerri-Ann Jones (Associate Director), Bruce MacDonald, and Steven Rinaldi of the National Security and International Affairs Division of the Office of Science and Technology Policy. We also thank the many subject-matter experts and reviewers listed in Section 5 for their substantive contributions to this report. Finally, we thank Argonne National Laboratory for coordinating the study effort and providing valuable administrative, editorial, and document preparation assistance.

Executive Summary

Introduction

This summary highlights the results of a four-month research and development (R&D) study conducted by the Transition Office of the President's Commission on Critical Infrastructure Protection. The study builds on work previously conducted by the Commission and provides a foundation for the next steps in developing a national infrastructure assurance R&D program. Preliminary R&D topics and associated roadmapping information are provided for eight critical national infrastructures: banking and finance, electric power, oil and gas production and storage, emergency services, government services, information and communications, transportation, and water supply.

The goal of this infrastructure assurance R&D is to support the development of technologies that will counter threats and reduce vulnerabilities in those areas having the potential for causing significant national security, economic, and/or social impacts. Physical and cyber threats—as well as new threats from the growing complexity of, and interdependencies among, infrastructures—are addressed. Specific technologies considered are those that protect infrastructure and thereby reduce vulnerability, detect intrusions and provide warnings, mitigate the effects of disruptions (incidents), assist in the management of incidents, and facilitate recovery.

Research requiring government investment is emphasized. This research must be accompanied by technology development within the private sector to ensure that useful products are developed. Although such private-sector development is outside the scope of this study, technology transfer activities that facilitate the integration of "research" and "development" are qualitatively considered.

Scope of Roadmapping Study

Study timeframe: FY2000 - FY2010.

Study focus: perceived technology shortfalls, or "gaps," between infrastructure assurance technology needs and available technologies

Categories of R&D included:

Basic—increases the fundamental knowledge necessary for developing infrastructure assurance technologies

Applied—investigates the feasibility and practicality of proposed technological solutions

Advanced technology development—includes efforts to develop technologies and test their feasibility, effectiveness, and interoperability

Proof of principle and validation—evaluates the effectiveness of technologies in an infrastructure environment; assesses the performance, cost-effectiveness, and practicality of the technology from the perspective of the infrastructure

Summary of Roadmapping Results

Over 70 R&D topics were identified to address infrastructure assurance needs across the eight infrastructures. The following themes describe the focus of these topics:

Vulnerability Assessment—assess the vulnerability of components, systems, and infrastructures.

Information Assurance—secure information while it is stored, being processed, and in transit.

Monitoring and Detection—monitor systems, detect threats and intrusions, and provide timely warning.

Protection and Mitigation—physically protect infrastructures and mitigate damage.

Response and Recovery— aid in rapid incident response and recovery.

Modeling and Simulation—develop models of components, systems, and infrastructures and examine the efficacy of alternative infrastructure assurance strategies and technologies.

Systems Analysis—analyze complex systems and identify and analyze infrastructure interdependencies.

Decision Support—support timely decision making with tools, methodologies, and information systems.

Risk Management—determine where best to allocate resources and how to manage risks.

Estimated resource requirements for the R&D topics total approximately $7 billion.

Investments beyond those associated with R&D in the critical infrastructures are needed to address interdependency and complexity.

Study Results

The study team identified more than 70 R&D topics. Roadmapping information R&D goals and challenges for three timeframes (near-term [before 2002], before 2005, before 2010), rationale, priority, and estimated resource requirements was developed for each topic. The team, consisting of representatives from government, industry, academia and research institutes, and the Department of Energy national laboratories, also solicited input from, and coordinated with, numerous experts and stakeholders from their respective areas of representation in developing the topics and roadmapping information.

The estimates of resource requirements reflect qualitative, order-of-magnitude judgments. They are intended to be representative of the resources needed for the R&D topics and are based on assumptions concerning the scope, the expected level of effort, and the pace of the research.

A number of common themes are evident within the R&D topics. Some of the themes directly correlate with the objectives of infrastructure assurance—to reduce critical vulnerabilities by protecting infrastructures, detecting intrusions, mitigating the effects of disruptions, assisting in the management of incidents, and facilitating recovery. Other themes focus on developing analytical or supporting technologies to help meet those objectives. Vulnerability assessment provides supporting baseline information for all of the other themes.

Estimated near-term (FY2000-FY2002) and mid-term (FY2003-FY2005) resource requirements total approximately $2 billion each, while long-term (FY2006-FY2010) resource requirements are estimated to be approximately $3 billion. A breakdown of near-term resource requirements by theme shows that information-assurance-related R&D requires approximately one-third of the total estimated resources. Monitoring and detection R&D represents about 15% of the portfolio, while vulnerability assessment and modeling and simulation each represent approximately 10%.

Included within each theme are elements that apply to, or crosscut, multiple infrastructures. With careful R&D planning and coordination, crosscutting elements could be combined into focused R&D areas to capitalize on synergies and reduce investment requirements.

R&D efforts need to focus on interdependencies and system complexity. The identification of interdependencies among national infrastructures and the characterization of how damage can propagate (cascade) across multiple infrastructures is a high priority.

Relevant ongoing and new R&D activities should be viewed as an integrated portfolio designed to meet strategic, technical, and programmatic infrastructure assurance objectives. Strategically, the portfolio should support the timely development of technologies to protect and assure critical infrastructures. Technically, the portfolio should include basic, applied, advanced technology development, and proof-of-principle and validation research. Programmatically, the portfolio should include R&D projects that, to the extent possible, comprehensively address requirements of the various infrastructures.

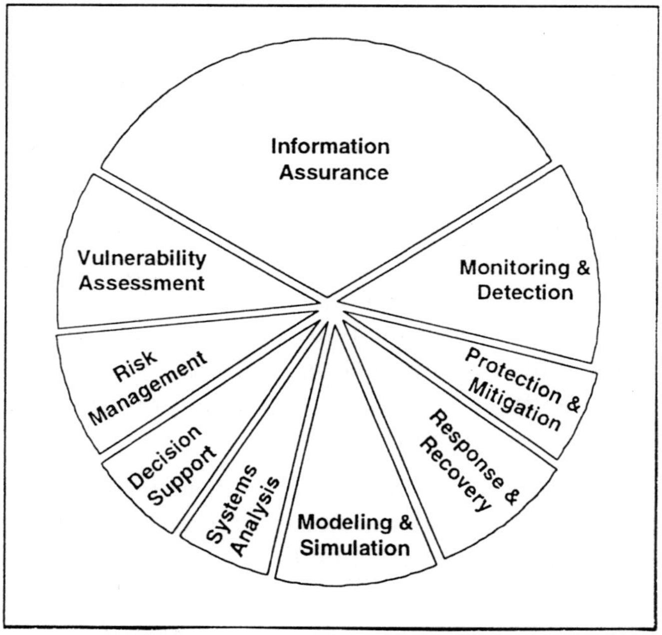

Successful implementation of technologies from government-funded R&D requires close cooperation with industry and the private-sector owners and operators of our nation's infrastructures. Technology transfer and embedding should be integral parts of the R&D process. A technology transfer plan should be prepared along with an R&D plan to elevate the awareness of the issues and accelerate the introduction of infrastructure assurance technologies.

R&D must be consistent with, and responsive to, national infrastructure assurance policy. Such policy provides a framework for establishing R&D objectives, setting R&D priorities, and shaping a multiyear, multifaceted R&D portfolio that is commensurate in scope and scale with the physical and cyber challenges of the twenty-first century. Moreover, it provides a framework for establishing education and awareness programs, building partnerships with industry, and developing legislative initiatives intended to reduce vulnerabilities.

Next Step Recommendations

Formally validated infrastructure assurance requirements (needs), a baseline inventory of ongoing infrastructure-assurance-related R&D activities, and an inventory of applicable commercial-off-the-shelf (COTS) and government-off-the-shelf (GOTS) technology should be developed. All of these elements are essential to ensure that:

- The R&D roadmap comprehensively addresses needs;
- Individual R&D topics are not addressed elsewhere, and
- New research efforts focus on critical R&D gaps.

Various forums, such as conferences, workshops, and joint planning meetings, should be established. These forums would bring together researchers, private-sector infrastructure owners and operators, and government agencies to discuss common problems and requirements, to establish research agenda, and to promote creative thinking to solve infrastructure problems.

Section 1
Introduction

> *Research and development are not presently adequate to support infrastructure protection. . . . [T]here is a need for additional technology with which to protect our essential systems.*
>
> Report of the President's Commission on Critical Infrastructure Protection, "Critical Foundations: Protecting America's Infrastructures," October 1997

1.1 Purpose

In July 1996, the President signed Executive Order 13010, which created a joint government and private-sector Commission—the President's Commission on Critical Infrastructure Protection. The Commission's goal was to develop a national strategy for protecting our critical infrastructures from a spectrum of threats and for assuring their continued operation. Eight critical infrastructures were identified: banking and finance; electric power; oil and gas production and storage; emergency services; government services; information and communications; transportation; and water supply.

After 15 months of evaluating these infrastructures, assessing their vulnerabilities, and deliberating assurance alternatives, the Commission submitted its report—*Critical Foundations: Protecting America's Infrastructures*—to the President. Among its findings, the Commission identified research and development (R&D) as a key element of a multifaceted infrastructure assurance strategy. This strategy incorporates R&D, information sharing, education and awareness, legal initiatives, and establishment of national structures to facilitate an effective partnership among the federal government, state and local governments, and infrastructure owners and operators. The Commission also recommended specific areas for research and initial levels of investment to provide the required technologies.

This report presents the results of a four-month R&D study conducted by the Commission's Transition Office. The purpose of this study was to define preliminary infrastructure assurance R&D areas, investment requirements, and associated roadmapping information. The study builds on work previously conducted by the Commission and provides a foundation for the next steps in developing a national infrastructure assurance R&D program. The goal of the R&D is to support the development of technologies that address the threats to, and vulnerabilities of, critical infrastructures that have the potential for causing significant impacts to our national security, economy, and/or social structure.

1.2 Scope of the R&D Study

The critical infrastructure sectors identified in Executive Order 13010 were addressed in this study. A timeframe of approximately 10 years, beginning in fiscal year (FY) 2000, was considered, although longer term needs were addressed in selected areas. The primary emphasis was on near-term R&D activities that would reduce critical vulnerabilities by protecting infrastructures, detecting intrusions, mitigating the effects of disruptions (incidents), assisting in the management of incidents, and facilitating recovery.

To the extent possible, this study focused on perceived technology shortfalls, or "gaps," between infrastructure assurance technology needs and available technologies. (Technology, broadly defined, includes processes, systems, models and simulations, hardware, and software.) However, given the breadth of R&D activities across the federal government and in the private sector, some of the recommended R&D may be addressed, at least in part, by other programs that may not focus specifically on infrastructure assurance. For example, portions of existing programs on force protection, information security and survivability, chemical and biological defense, and counterproliferation are likely to apply to infrastructure assurance as well. Additional efforts are needed to catalog such programs and establish a baseline of information to minimize duplication of effort, identify potential synergies among programs, and focus new research efforts on critical gaps not addressed elsewhere.

Table 1.1 defines the categories of research considered in this study. The emphasis was on research that requires government investment. However, as Figure 1.1 illustrates, this research must be accompanied by technology development within the private sector to meet infrastructure assurance objectives. Although such private-sector development was beyond the scope of this study, technology transfer activities that facilitate the integration of "research" and "development" were qualitatively considered.

Both physical and cyber threats were considered. The former include threats to tangible property, while the latter include electronic, radio-frequency, or computer-based attacks on the information infrastructure or its components. Threats from aging infrastructure and natural disasters were outside the scope of this effort, although some of the recommended research could address problems in these areas.

Table 1.1 Research Categories

Basic research—increases the fundamental knowledge necessary for developing infrastructure assurance technologies

Applied research—investigates the feasibility and practicality of proposed technological solutions, including studies and investigations of system-specific and non-system-specific technologies

Advanced technology development—includes efforts to develop technologies and test their feasibility, effectiveness, and interoperability

Proof of principle and validation—evaluates the effectiveness of technologies in an infrastructure environment (e.g., test beds); assesses the performance, cost-effectiveness, and practicality of the technology from the perspective of the infrastructure.

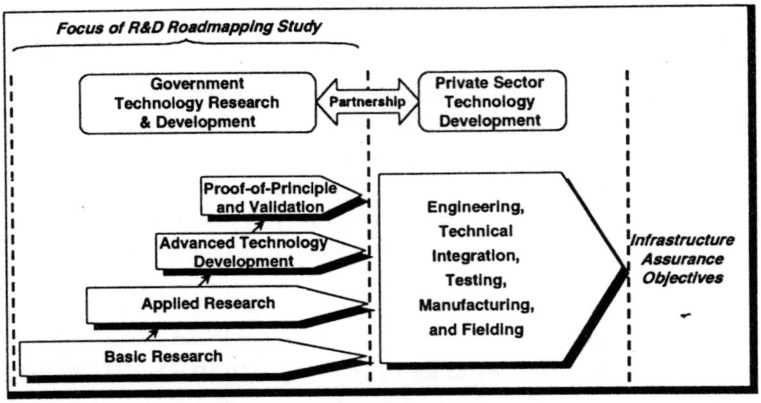

Figure 1.1 Government and Private-Sector Partnership for Meeting Infrastructure Assurance Objectives

Intrinsic threats from the growing complexity of, and interdependence among, infrastructures also were considered. Such threats increase the possibility that a rather minor, routine disturbance can cascade into a major problem that involves multiple infrastructures. These dependencies among infrastructures reflect multidimensional risk profiles and challenges that require comprehensive assurance planning based on innovative R&D.

1.3 Sector Study Teams

As depicted in Figure 1.2, five infrastructure sector study teams and an integration team were formed to develop roadmapping information for the eight critical infrastructures. This consolidation allowed the teams to study infrastructures with similar technology needs together. For example, the Energy Team addressed both the electric power and the oil and natural gas production and storage infrastructures, while the Vital Human Services Team addressed the water-supply system, emergency services, and government services infrastructures. The Integration Team coordinated the overall roadmapping activity, identified common research topics, examined interdependencies among the infrastructures, and integrated the sector roadmapping information.

To ensure a balanced R&D perspective, promote partnership, and facilitate outreach, each sector study team consisted of at least four members and a coordinator. The members represented government, industry, academia and research institutes, and the national laboratories (Figure 1.2). Team members solicited input from, and coordinated with, experts and stakeholders from their respective areas of representation.

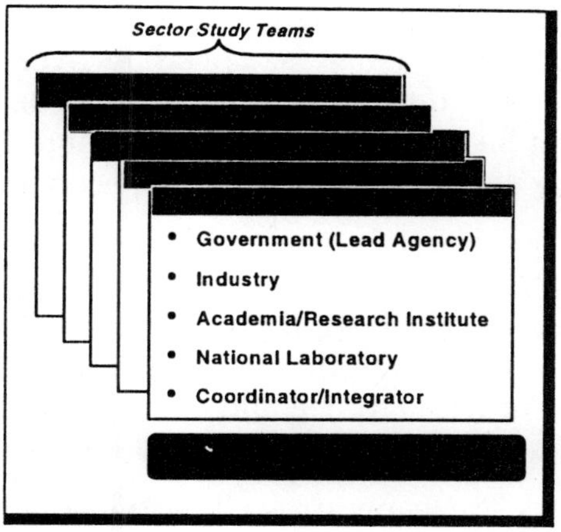

Figure 1.2 Structure of the Sector Study Teams

1.4 Study Approach

The substantial body of information previously developed by and for the Commission provided the foundation for this study. This information included the *Critical Foundations* report, a series of comprehensive sector reports, and several R&D reports that contained initial recommendations for protecting and assuring critical national infrastructures. The sector study teams also drew upon recent studies conducted by government organizations; advisory groups, committees, and task forces; industrial organizations; academic institutes; and national laboratories. This approach allowed the teams to identify related efforts, gain valuable insights and perspectives, and identify recurring topics.

In preparing its roadmap, each sector study team examined threats and vulnerabilities, identified key structural and regulatory issues, and formed assumptions about trends that could affect future infrastructure assurance. This effort required extensive interaction among team members, as well as with external subject-matter experts and stakeholders. In addition, each team held one or more meetings that included both team members and other experts from government, industry, academia and research institutes, and the national laboratories. These meetings provided a forum for discussing infrastructure assurance and technology transfer issues and for developing roadmapping information. Engaging external reviewers from the various areas of representation also ensured that the recommendations were comprehensive and meaningful.

Table 1.2 identifies the elements included in the sector roadmaps. Although all of the R&D recommendations were judged to be important, three priority categories were established (i.e., most important, very important, important). In prioritizing the R&D topics, the teams considered a number of interrelated factors, including the extent to which the research, if successful, would be expected to reduce vulnerabilities, lessen the effects of incidents, assist in managing incidents, or speed recovery activities after incidents. Other factors considered were the magnitude of the potential consequences that would be prevented or mitigated and the importance of the research for ensuring national security and the economy.

Estimates of resource requirements were prepared for each R&D topic. The estimates reflect qualitative, order-of-magnitude judgments. They are intended to be representative of the resources needed for the R&D topics and are based on assumptions concerning the scope, the expected level of effort, and the pace of the research. Detailed cost estimates must be prepared in concert with the development of detailed R&D plans.

In identifying R&D topics, the teams stressed partnership between government and the private sector. It was recognized explicitly that infrastructure risks affect both the public and private sectors. Also, the private sector holds much of the relevant technical and empirical data on infrastructure operations, interdependencies, and vulnerabilities. Further, the private sector generally develops technology only when it identifies a market for it. Therefore, successful implementation of technologies from government-funded research efforts requires close cooperation with industry and the private-sector owners and operators of our nation's infrastructures.

Table 1.2 Roadmapping Information

R&D topics—specific R&D that should be conducted and the expected product.

Goals and challenges—the performance goals for the R&D for three timeframes and the associated technical challenges.

Rationale—why the research is important (e.g., prevention, detection, mitigation, incident management, or recovery) and the risks of not having the technology available.

Priority—the relative priority of the R&D topic (most important, very important, or important).

Timeframe—the time needed to conduct the recommended R&D, including phases and sequencing.

Resource requirements—the estimated level of resources, as a function of time, needed to complete the research.

1.5 Report Organization

The remainder of this report is organized as follows. Section 2 summarizes R&D topics and preliminary roadmapping information for the five infrastructure sectors. Section 3 presents integrated roadmapping information, including estimated resource requirements. Section 4 presents recommendations for the next steps to take in future roadmapping and planning efforts. Finally, five attachments (tabs) provide detailed roadmapping information for the five infrastructure sectors. Tabs A-E provide R&D roadmapping information for the Banking and Finance, Energy, Information and Communications, Transportation, and Vital Human Services sectors, respectively.

Section 2
Sector R&D Topics and Roadmaps

Research and development topics and roadmapping information for the five infrastructure sectors are summarized below. To put this information into perspective, a brief description of each sector is provided along with an overview of the issues and trends that affect the infrastructure. A summary of the threats to, and vulnerabilities of, the infrastructure is also provided. (Detailed infrastructure sector reports are provided in Tabs A–E.)

2.1 Banking and Finance

2.1.1 Infrastructure Overview

The banking and finance infrastructure consists of institutions, agencies, and support systems (physical, procedural, and data) that facilitate lending, borrowing, issuing, trading in, or caring for money, credit, and other representations of value. This infrastructure includes banks and credit unions; insurance companies; lending and credit institutions of all kinds; securities and commodities dealers; state, federal, and international oversight and regulatory agencies; and the web of communications equipment and linkages that support transactions among those systems.

2.1.2 Issues and Trends

Several emerging trends threaten the safety and soundness of the banking and finance infrastructure. These trends include:

- Deregulation and increased competition, which can result in less marginal capability to absorb the costs of added security measures.
- Convergence of technologies in computing, communications, networking, and encryption, which increases the efficiency and flexibility of transaction support, but can add vulnerabilities.

- Internationalization of commerce, which gives new, nondomestic entities unprecedented access to U.S. systems and information.
- Changing definitions of value. For example, the *form* of money and the *way* that information about money are managed have become valuable assets.

The effect of these trends on the U.S. banking and finance infrastructure can be moderated by the way in which government and industry respond to four challenges:

- Making policy trade-offs to balance competing goals among open markets, regulatory management, national security, and free trade;
- Adapting to the technical revolution in two infrastructures: (1) information and communications and (2) banking and finance;
- Accommodating the internationalization of commerce and information; and
- Defining new assets that require protection.

2.1.3 Threats and Vulnerabilities

Potential threats to, and vulnerabilities of, the banking and finance infrastructure originate from the lack of a clear understanding of how alternative responses in each of four areas might affect the industry.

Regulation and Control

If the architecture and dynamics of the banking and finance infrastructure are not well understood, the regulatory regimes intended to maintain the safety and surety of that infrastructure would be rapidly overcome by changes in technology, markets, and practices in the industry. The nexus between the concerns of the banking and finance infrastructure and those of the information and communications infrastructure is becoming so complex that policies developed in one area can have serious, unintended consequences to the other.

New Technologies

As the banking and finance community adopts new technologies to streamline transactions, the systems that support those transactions become more complex and difficult to secure. The efficiency, flexibility, and adaptability that make the new technologies attractive to the industry also create subtle (and potentially catastrophic) weaknesses in the system. Innovative use of the new technologies makes it possible for each point of presence in the infrastructure network to create a customized interface to the industry. Without proper protection and management, each point of presence can become a point of entry for someone intending to do harm to, or through, the infrastructure.

Internationalization of Markets

As the banking and finance infrastructure becomes more open to world commerce, many nondomestic points of presence enter the networks. Domestic standards and practice may not be the norm for such entities. These differences may result in unforeseen vulnerabilities. In addition, the hardware and software that exemplify the new technologies may originate from nondomestic manufacturers and suppliers. The standards and practices by which these items are integrated into the infrastructure must take into account the potential vulnerabilities.

Financial Information

As individual entities and systems are integrated into the banking and finance infrastructure, the information collected, stored, and transmitted among various points of presence becomes more vulnerable to manipulation, disclosure, or destruction. Methods and techniques for securing both the system and the information it handles must keep pace with the points of presence and the sophistication of technologies available.

2.1.4 Summary of R&D Topics and Roadmaps

Table 2.1 summarizes the R&D topics and their corresponding roadmaps for the banking and finance infrastructure. The table provides brief descriptions of research topics grouped by priority (i.e., most important, very important, important); summaries of research activities for three timeframes (near-term [before 2002], before 2005, and before 2010); and *estimates* of the financial resources required to support the R&D activities for each timeframe. Table A contains more detailed descriptions of these research topics, supporting rationale, goals and challenges, threats and vulnerabilities addressed by the research, and research roadmap information.

Table 2.1 Summary of Banking and Finance R&D Topics and Roadmaps[a]

R&D Topic			
No.	**Title**	**Description (Type[b])**	**Research Roadmap (Resource Estimate[c])**
		Most Important R&D Topics	
1	Simulation Model Development	Development and maintenance of a simulation model of the banking and finance infrastructure and analysis of management alternatives and policies. (A, ATD, POP)	**Near-term:** Engage industry and design, develop, maintain, and elaborate a constructive strategic simulation model (CSSM). ($18 million) **~2005:** Develop the requirements, legal basis, policies, and techniques for protecting the sensitive, proprietary, and classified data required for the CSSM. Leverage existing work, models, mechanisms, etc. ($10 million) **~2010:** Prepare field operational model and life-cycle management plan. ($1 million
2	Information Security Analysis	Analysis and evaluation of current cryptographic and surety analysis technology applications. Transfer and development or adaptation of new technologies. (B, A, ATD, POP)	**Near-term:** Develop a legal and procedural basis for expediting access to government off-the-shelf cryptographic analysis and surety analysis technology. Analyze and evaluate the efficacy of implementations of cryptographic and surety technologies. Develop and validate security implementation standards for banking and finance information applications (scaleable, supporting variable security levels). ($32 million) **~2005:** Implement anonymity balance. Field scaleable key public management systems. ($6 million) **~2010:** Field entity authentication technologies. ($1 million)
		Very Important R&D Topics	
3	Intrusion Indication and Warning (I&W) Tools	Development of tools for detecting, discriminating, and managing intrusions and anomalies in information systems. (B, A, ATD, POP)	**Near-term:** Use insight from the development of the CSSM to determine where within the system I&W and sensitivity tools and techniques are applicable. Determine what data are required to implement those tools and techniques. ($29 million) **~2005:**Develop an initial suite of tools. ($7 million) **~2010:** Field operational tools. ($1 million)

No.	R&D Topic: Title	R&D Topic: Description (Type[b])	Research Roadmap (Resource Estimate[c])
4	Systems Reliability Enhancement	Development and transfer of high-reliability trusted systems, network security agents, self-healing systems, and dynamic configurable firewalls. (B, A, ATD, POP)	**Near-term:** Develop, publish, and begin to implement initial standards and specifications. Develop prototypes of network security agents. ($54 million) **~2005:** Complete implementation of standards and specifications, and prototypes of network security agents. ($15 million) **~2010:** Field prototypes of self-healing systems, configurable firewalls, and network defense agents. ($2 million)
		Important R&D Topics	
5	Information System Standardization	Development of an open architecture standard for the banking and finance infrastructure. (A)	**Near-term:** Publish initial standards for open architecture. ($6 million)
6	Electronic Commerce Security Enhancement	Development and implementation of networking equipment and standards for managing security of electronic commerce. (B, A, ATD, POP)	**Near-term:** Publish initial standards and specifications for equipment and support tools. ($9 million) **~2005:** Field standards. ($9 million) **~2010:** Field operational tools. ($3 million)

[a] The order of the R&D topics within a priority category (i.e., most important, very important, important) does not imply relative importance.

[b] B = basic; A = applied; ATD = advanced technology development; and POP = proof of principle and validation.

[c] Resource estimates reflect qualitative, order-of-magnitude judgments. They are intended to be representaative of the resources needed for the R&D topics and are based on assumptions concerning the scope, the expected level of effort, and the pace of the research. Detailed cost estimates must be prepared in concert with the development of detailed R&D plans.

2.2 Energy

2.2.1 Infrastructure Overview

The energy infrastructure includes electric power, oil, and natural gas. Each requires production, processing, and transportation to provide energy to customers, including residential, commercial, industrial, and government end users. Production consists of generation of electricity by power plants and well-head extraction of both oil and natural gas. Each requires large, complex transportation networks to deliver energy to end users. Each has transmission and distribution lines. Electric power requires substations and transformers; oil requires pumping stations and refineries; and natural gas requires compressor stations and gas processing centers. Storage is also a key component for oil and natural gas and is becoming a major component for electricity.

In addition to the physical components that comprise these three networks, each infrastructure uses Supervisory Control and Data Acquisition (SCADA) systems. SCADA systems help to monitor and operate the physical components and can increase efficiency and safety within the infrastructure. Also, each of these infrastructures depends on other infrastructures, including information and communications and transportation systems, for operation.

These energy infrastructures are highly interdependent. Many electrical generating plants consume natural gas and oil. Electricity is required to operate petroleum refineries and pumping stations as well as most natural gas appliances. Even motor gasoline cannot be pumped without electricity.

2.2.2 Issues and Trends

The energy infrastructures (electric power, oil, natural gas) are essential to the quality of life in our society. When one or more of these energy infrastructures fail, then, in addition to personal and economic losses, this failure generates significant negative attitudes about the quality of life in our society. Our society and economy depend heavily on reliable and sustainable energy sources, such as electricity to operate our computers, gasoline to fuel our vehicles, and natural gas to heat our homes. Some of the emerging issues and trends in the energy infrastructure include the following:

- Deregulation and rapid restructuring are occurring in both the electric power and the natural gas industries, which is designed to enhance the competitive environment.
- The emphasis on competition is reducing operating margins, thereby increasing the likelihood of system disturbances from small events.
- Marketing companies, mergers and acquisitions, and competitive markets are changing the way in which commodities are purchased, and they test the energy infrastructure in new ways.
- Reduced investments in new technology create the potential for less reliable operation and additional disruptions in supply.
- The age of critical energy components, combined with decreasing operating budgets, represents a potential concern.
- Downsizing of the energy industry creates the potential for disgruntled "insiders" and a significant loss of expertise.

- The "not-in-my-backyard" attitude severely limits the number of new rights-of-way, which are needed for electric transmission lines and natural gas and oil pipelines.
- Increased dependence on information systems based on open architectures, centralized operations, increased communication over public networks, and remote maintenance creates additional vulnerabilities.
- Our dependence on foreign supplies and vendors raises concerns about the reliability of our energy supplies.
- Reliance on automated systems increases vulnerability to technological failure and cyber attacks.

2.2.3 Threats and Vulnerabilities

Threats to the U.S. energy system arise from a number of sources, including hostile governments, terrorist groups, other organized groups, disgruntled employees, malicious intruders, natural disasters, accidents, system complexities, and dependence on other infrastructures. The U.S. Department of Energy has documented more than 1,000 incidents directed against the U.S. energy system over the past 15 years; some supply disruptions have caused significant damage.

Well-organized groups (perhaps working with insiders) can cause massive physical and cyber damage to our energy supply systems. These groups could damage the system so severely that major cities, or multistate regions, could suffer severe, long-term energy shortages.

Furthermore, cyber vulnerabilities are rapidly increasing, as the industry becomes more automated and interconnected. While there are relatively few documented cases of insider attacks on computers, the reality is that a knowledgeable insider has an almost unlimited ability to cause problems, from bypassing access authorization to subverting systems.

The electric power and oil and natural gas infrastructures face many vulnerabilities, including the following:

- Those created in the operating system because of the rapid introduction of information systems based on open architectures, centralized operations, and increased communications over public telecommunications networks.
- SCADA systems because they often use common commercial hardware and software, connect to other company networks, and rely on dial-back modems that can be bypassed.
- Increased availability of vulnerability information, much of which is mandated by regulatory bodies to facilitate competition, and the availability of tools to exploit those vulnerabilities.

- Rapid assimilation of advanced technologies with inherent complexities.
- Consolidation of infrastructure corridors (e.g., communications, electric transmission lines, pipelines).
- Complexity of the system so that a failure is possible, either from accidental events or a deliberate attack, when the system has minimum capacity reserves and energy transfers are large.

2.2.4 Summary of R&D Topics and Roadmaps

Table 2.2 summarizes R&D topics and their corresponding roadmaps for the energy infrastructure. The table provides brief descriptions of research topics grouped by priority (i.e., most important, very important, important); summaries of research activities for three timeframes (near-term [before 2002], before 2005, before 2010); and *estimates* of the financial resources required to support the R&D activities for each timeframe. Tab B contains more detailed descriptions of these research topics, supporting rationale, goals and challenges, threats and vulnerabilities addressed by the research, and research roadmap information.

Table 2.2 Summary of Energy R&D Topics and Roadmaps[a]

R&D Topic			
No.	**Title**	**Description (Type[b])**	**Research Roadmap (Resource Estimate[c])**
		Most Important R&D Topics	
1	Real-time Control Mechanisms	Integration of real-time control systems to support timely decisions involving electric grid operations. System includes instrumentation and monitoring, models and simulations, control methods, and decision support tools.	(See topics 1.1–1.4 for roadmapping information.)

R&D Topic			
No.	**Title**	**Description (Type[b])**	**Research Roadmap (Resource Estimate[c])**
1.1	Instrumentation and Monitoring for Distributed Control	Applied research and technology development to produce hardware and software systems designed to collect and manage large data streams for implementing real-time control systems. (A, ATD)	**Near-term:** Implement common data model and identify measurement requirements. ($5 million) **~2005:** Develop advanced sensors, measurement timing standards, and data compression tools. Establish high bandwidth communication channels. ($32 million) **~2010:** Establish wide area monitoring, data storage and retrieval, and adaptive monitoring methods. ($57 million)
1.2	Analysis and Computation for Large-scale Systems	Basic research, technology development, and proof-of-principle pilots to develop advanced simulation techniques, user-friendly interfaces, and expert systems for handling large volumes of information. (B, A, ATD, POP)	**Near-term:** Implement on-line security assessment tools. ($15 million) **~2005:** Establish stability indices. Develop measurement-based analysis tools and parameters for integrating measurement-and model-based tools. ($37 million) **~2010:** Establish uncertainty theory and implement integrated analytical approach. ($48 million)
1.3	Advanced Control Methods	Primarily basic research to develop a new control theory for large-scale systems. Theory will apply to other large-scale systems (e.g., space structures). (B, POP)	**Near-term:** Assess current state of robust control theory and decentralized control theory. ($8 million) **~2005:** Advance theoretical basis for robust and decentralized control. ($32 million) **~2010:** Develop proof of principle and validation on integrated large-scale system control theory. ($48 million)

R&D Topic			
No.	**Title**	**Description (Type[b])**	**Research Roadmap (Resource Estimate[c])**
1.4	Decision Support Tools	Basic research to technology development of hardware and software systems to support real-time decision making. (B, A, ATD, POP)	**Near-term:** Develop new visualization techniques and operator interfaces for increased data volume. ($6 million) **~2005:** Implement first-generation reasoning tools. Develop tools to assist operators in handling many transactions. ($10 million) **~2010:** Develop autonomous agents and implement multiconstraint optimization tools. ($33 million)
2	Analysis of Scale and Complexity	Development of a better understanding of the stability of large electric power systems; effects of uncertainties and changing conditions on the system; effects of complexity and scale on the behavior of people involved with the system; large network interactions, voltage collapse, and network security; techniques to reduce complexity; and countermeasures to avoid and control malicious acts aimed at the system. (B, A, ATD, POP)	**Near-term:** Study restructuring effects on complexity. Develop theoretical understanding of complex systems and applied understanding of the evolving complexity of the power grid. ($45 million) **~2005:** Develop an understanding of human interfaces and how humans handle scale and complexity. Understand effects of uncertainties on vulnerability and develop mitigation methods. ($30 million)
3	Vulnerability Assessment	Assessment of vulnerabilities to support decisions regarding research and capital investment for electric power system assurance. (B, A)	**Near-term:** Complete systematic and current estimates of vulnerabilities and threats. Estimate impacts of outages. Define modeling requirements. Characterize restructuring effects. ($9 million) **~2005:** Develop or enhance models. Analyze restructuring impacts. Evaluate infrastructure assurance options. ($9 million) **~2010:** Develop improved procedures and evaluate more options. ($14 million)

R&D Topic			
No.	**Title**	**Description (Type[b])**	**Research Roadmap (Resource Estimate[c])**
9	Critical Consequence Analysis	Development of models of the natural gas network to evaluate system vulnerability and response to incidents. (B, A)	**Near-term:** Complete and implement basic design of model. ($2 million) **~2005:** Develop incident/failure scenarios and consequence analysis, including curtailment impacts, by using the model. ($1 million)
10	Decision Support Systems	Development and implementation of risk management and decision support tools to allow natural gas and oil industry decision makers to prioritize resources, minimize risk, and respond to incidents. (B, A, ATD, POP)	**Near-term:** Assess data and tools. Assign decision analysis requirements with priorities. ($36 million) **~2005:** Develop expert system tools. Make models for highest priority items. Assess secondary priority items. ($36 million) **~2010:** Continue to develop high-priority items. Develop expert system tools and models for secondary priority items. ($48 million)
11	Physical Protection Assessment	Assessment of the physical assets of the natural gas and oil industry, vulnerable nodes, protection methods, and protection strategies. (B, A)	**Near-term:** Collect historic reports and data. Survey industry to determine highest vulnerabilities. Assess technology. Develop and implement strategies. ($5 million)
14	Cyber Protection Enhancement	Development of enhanced security measures for natural gas system SCADA control systems and electronic commerce. (B, A, ATD, POP)	**Near-term:** Identify encryption algorithms and standards. ($25 million) **~2005:** Complete technology review and selection. Manufacture chips. ($50 million) **~2010:** Implement enhanced protection system for SCADA and electronic commerce. Obtain acceptance of approved standards by industry. ($126 million)

R&D Topic			
No.	**Title**	**Description (Type[b])**	**Research Roadmap (Resource Estimate[c])**
16	Institutional Barriers	Investigation of the institutional issues that are potential impediments to the achievement of energy system infrastructure assurance objectives. (A)	**Near-term:** Develop partnerships. ($13 million) **~2005:** Develop tools and roles and establish priorities. ($15 million) **~2010:** Maintain support and networking needs, such as the FBI security center. ($45 million)
17	Infrastructure Interdependencies	Investigation of the interdependencies within the energy system (e.g., gas and electricity generation) and between the energy system and other infrastructures. (B, A, ATD)	**Near-term:** Relate technical complexities to business disruptions and economic losses. Complete in-depth analysis of technical impacts. Examine requirements for advanced computational modeling and simulation tools. ($6 million) **~2005:** Identify and analyze options to reduce interdependency impacts. Develop analysis tools. ($5 million) **~2010:** Obtain results of analyzing options to reduce interdependency-related vulnerabilities. ($11 million)
Very Important R&D Topics			
4	Information Assurance and Cyber Security	Development of cyber threat assessment and risk management tools for the electric power system. Understand complexity of large, dispersed information systems. Develop high-security SCADA network architectures. Develop efficient encryption techniques for the electric power system. Develop authentication/ authorization tools. Develop improved cyber intrusion detection techniques. Develop threat analysis of high frequency weapons on information systems.	(See topics 4.1–4.7 for roadmapping information.)

R&D Topic			
No.	Title	Description (Type[b])	Research Roadmap (Resource Estimate[c])
4.1	Threat Assessment and Risk Management	Applied and technology R&D to develop tools to help designers safely move the electric power industry into a more interconnected, market-based system. (A, ATD)	**Near-term:** Conduct systematic, industry-wide threat assessment and vulnerability mapping. Develop base risk management tools. ($15 million) **~2005:** Develop standardized, industry-wide threat model. Integrate risk management tools into design tools. Ensure consistent models are used to define threat environments and assess risk. Integrate models into design and validation tools. ($10 million)
4.2	Large Systems Analysis	Basic and applied research to develop and extend models to ensure the stability of the electric system in the face of faults, cyber attacks, and other assaults. (B, A, ATD, POP)	**Near-term:** Develop basic models and simulations and basic design tools. ($13 million) **~2005:** Develop integrated models and near real-time prediction, model-based control. ($14 million) **~2010:** Validate the entire power grid. Incorporate models into design. Develop simulation and validation tools. ($18 million)
4.3	High-security SCADA Systems	Applied research to develop high-security SCADA systems for electric power. Results include design guidelines, design tools, models, test and evaluation tools. (A)	**Near-term:** Develop a baseline understanding of existing systems and current industry practices. Develop design guidelines. ($24 million) **~2005:** Develop and validate proof of concept. Standardize efforts for deployment of new SCADA networks. ($24 million) **~2010:** Produce and adopt standard SCADA design guidelines. ($32 million)
4.4	Efficient, Adaptable Encryption	Basic and applied research to develop and implement encryption technologies that have minimal downside impacts on operations. (B, A)	**Near-term:** Develop a baseline understanding of requirements for major system areas. Evaluate encryption technologies. ($22 million) **~2005:** Deploy encryption technologies throughout the power industry. ($23 million) **~2010:** Deploy dynamic and high-bandwidth encryption. ($30 million)

R&D Topic			
No.	**Title**	**Description (Type[b])**	**Research Roadmap (Resource Estimate[c])**
4.5	Robust Authentication and Authorization	Basic and applied research is needed to develop and deploy strong authentication and authorization controls to both the SCADA and information networks in the electric power industry. (B, A, ATD)	**Near-term:** Map the requirements for authentication and authorization of existing systems. Define general-purpose, scaleable mechanisms. Begin working with standards. ($22 million) **~2005:** Work with the electric power industry and product manufactures to adopt standardized mechanisms. ($23 million) **~2010:** Implement standardized authentication and authorization models on all new systems added to the grid. ($30 million)
4.6	Intrusion Detection	Basic and applied research to detect probes, penetrations and attacks on information systems. Probes and attacks must be detected quickly to trigger a response. (B, A, ATD)	**Near-term:** Develop understanding of threats and current vulnerabilities. Deploy threat detection to both the communication and control infrastructure of the grid. ($22 million) **~2005:** Develop and deploy efficient, dynamic intrusion detection tools. ($23 million) **~2010:** Link intrusion detection into central threat center for grid-wide system monitoring. Deploy automated response capability. ($30 million)
4.7	Directed Energy Weapons Countermeasures	Basic and applied research to examine the vulnerability of the electric power grid to high-energy radio frequency weapons. Research needed to protect information systems and critical electric system components. (B, A)	**Near-term:** Develop understanding of the current state of high-energy weapons. Construct and test devices. Develop test bed. Prepare design guidelines for protection. ($18 million) **~2005:** Integrate information learned into overall design tools. ($18 million) **~2010:** Conduct further research into protecting against directed weapons. ($24 million)

R&D Topic			
No.	Title	Description (Type[b])	Research Roadmap (Resource Estimate[c])
5	Emergency Response and Recovery Information Technologies	Development of emergency response and recovery protocols and procedures for information technology systems within electric power grids. (B, A)	**Near-term:** Develop concept. Identify critical components and protection and mitigation strategies. Begin developing exercise process and computer simulation models. ($2 million) **~2005:** Conduct exercises on a periodic basis. Develop and apply lessons learned from exercises. Begin developing concept for oil and natural gas pipeline networks. ($3 million) **~2010:** Refine process as changes warrant. Begin conducting exercises for oil and gas pipeline networks. ($4 million)
6	Transmission and Distribution Technologies	Development of advanced technology to increase the security of electric power transmission and distribution. (ATD, POP)	**Near-term:** Examine specific infrastructure assurance contributions for several R&D topics. Improve siting and environmental impact process for new transmission lines. ($100 million) **~2005:** Develop hardware and software. Complete proof of principle for smart instrumentation and control systems. Make progress in advanced power electronics systems. ($100 million) **~2010:** Achieve significant progress in superconducting technologies. Implement advanced power electronics systems. ($166 million)
12	Multisensor and Warning Technologies	Development and implementation of a multisensor system that warns of attempted intrusions. (B, A, ATD, POP)	**Near-term:** Assess current technologies. Design needed technologies. Establish industry-government partnership. ($28 million) **~2005:** Roadmap national technologies. Develop software and hardware. ($31 million) **~2010:** Implement technology pilot program. Commercially develop technologies. Set up an oversight committee. ($101 million)

R&D Topic			
No.	**Title**	**Description (Type[b])**	**Research Roadmap (Resource Estimate[c])**
15	Evaluation of Policy Effects	Study of the cause-and-effect relationships among laws, directives, operating policies, standards, and vulnerability of the energy system. (B, A)	**Near-term:** Determine the effect of numerous proposed policies on vulnerability and security of energy systems. Explore grid operation implications. ($29 million) **~2005:** Establish college programs with technical and public policy aspects of infrastructure assurance. ($6 million)
Important R&D Topics			
7	On-line Security Assessment	Development of algorithms, models, and methods for on-line, near-real-time assessments of the safe operation of the electric power system. (B, A, ATD)	**Near-term:** Examine incremental algorithms for system perturbations. Obtain 1,000-fold increase in speed with subcycle state information. Develop database replication techniques. ($10 million) **~2005:** Reduce cost and running times. Develop accurate tools and models for the national grid. Develop tools for geographic decomposition in nonsymmetric complex cases. ($10 million) **~2010:** Develop and implement improved and new tools. Reduce cost and running times. ($16 million)
8	Dispersed Generation and Backup Infrastructures	Evaluation of the role of dispersed systems and backup systems in electric power generation; development of advanced technologies for these systems. (ATD, POP)	**Near-term:** Analyze infrastructure assurance benefits of dispersed generation. Prioritize options. ($20 million) **~2005:** Demonstrate and integrate distributed generation systems with storage. Demonstrate and control with custom power systems. Develop improved backup system. ($20 million) **~2010:** Continue reducing costs and improving reliability of technology options. Improve ability for systems to run unattended for long periods. ($33 million)

R&D Topic			
No.	Title	Description (Type[b])	Research Roadmap (Resource Estimate[c])
13	Emergency Response Capability Enhancement	Development of protocols and procedures for the gas and oil industry to respond to emergencies. (A)	**Near-term:** Develop industry-government partnership. Establish roles for government and industry. Identify technology gaps. ($22 million) **~2005:** Develop roles. Develop a national emergency plan. Begin technology implementations. ($30 million) **~2010:** Ensure that technologies and best practices are widely implemented in industry. ($100 million)

[a] The order of the R&D topics within a priority category (i.e., most important, very important, important) does not imply relative importance.

[b] B = basic; A = applied; ATD = advanced technology development; and POP = proof of principle and validation.

[c] Resource estimates reflect qualitative, order-of-magnitude judgments. They are intended to be representative of the resources needed for the R&D topics and are based on assumptions concerning the scope, the expected level of effort, and the pace of the research. Detailed cost estimates must be prepared in concert with the development of detailed R&D plans.

2.3 Information and Communications

2.3.1 Infrastructure Overview

The information and communications infrastructure has three components: an underlying "link" for moving data, a network and transport component, and computing systems. The underlying physical link moves data from point to point (e.g., satellites, copper wire, optic fibers, wireless transmissions). The network and transport component is hardware (e.g., circuit switches) and software (e.g., control systems) that deal with addressing, routing, and data transport services. The computing systems generate, manipulate, store, display, or control information.

The combination of these components provides the communication, computation, control, information, and human collaboration systems that are critical to the functioning of other infrastructures and society. This highly complex infrastructure depends on interconnected multiple carriers across the nation and integrated advanced system hardware and software components. This infrastructure also forms the backbone of the Internet and connects with computer networks and communication networks on an international level.

2.3.2 Issues and Trends

The explosive growth of the Internet and its incorporation into business through the World Wide Web—for advertising products and services, electronic mail communications, and electronic commerce—have imposed an expanding new communications medium over the infrastructure. In addition to traditional telephone services, this infrastructure is increasingly being required to support Internet communications and new services. The interconnection of computer networks at an international level facilitates communications across countries without the traditional protections and protocols imposed by geographic boundaries. Information can be disseminated around the world in seconds through the Internet.

The increasing use of sophisticated computer control systems for the information and communications (telecommunications) infrastructure has introduced new technologies through additional hardware and software components and communications protocols. Further, the interconnection of multiple carriers and equipment types adds a new dimension in complexity.

Developments in technology and new security products continue to increase. Much of this development and manufacturing work is being done at non-U.S. locations by wholly or partly foreign-owned companies. This trend has the potential to introduce unknown vulnerabilities into systems and networks. The rapid growth of wireless and satellite communications to supplement wire lines adds a new aspect to telecommunications, and with it, a host of specialized technologies with exploitable vulnerabilities.

The telecommunications industry recently experienced many consolidations and mergers. These trends affect the implementation of security through corporate downsizing, reduced competition, and the potential for less diversity in product security.

Furthermore, other infrastructures depend more on the information and communications infrastructure for their continued operation. These infrastructures use remote control equipment (e.g., SCADA systems) more frequently, which creates a strong and direct dependency.

As the Internet becomes a medium of commerce, various legal issues in regard to the security of electronic commerce and privacy have emerged. The development and enforcement of laws to protect the Internet and systems are increasingly important areas that have not been definitively addressed.

2.3.3 Threats and Vulnerabilities

Threats to the information and communications infrastructure can come from many sources, such as deliberate attacks (cyber or physical) by insiders or outsiders, natural disasters, simple accidents, and failure of poorly designed or configured equipment. The goal is to continuously improve the protection of our systems and networks from security threats and vulnerabilities.

Because computer networks over the Internet are interconnected, an attack can originate from anywhere in the world. The traditional protection afforded by country boundaries and checkpoints is no longer sufficient. Systems are vulnerable because many networks are interconnected, and they are only as secure as the weakest link. This interconnection also provides intruders with a level of anonymity and impedes the ability to trace the specific location of an attack. The computing power available to intruders is becoming increasingly sophisticated, and advanced attack tools are available on the World Wide Web. Further, the design of security products often lags behind the technological capability of intruders to penetrate systems.

New technologies and features are launched rapidly in the telecommunications industry, potentially introducing new vulnerabilities as a result of incompatible protocols and interfaces. Moreover, technology that lacks component-level and integrated environment testing is used with other existing technologies in the network. Increasingly sophisticated hardware and software components and system control technologies have the potential to introduce design flaws, especially when these components are integrated into large-scale legacy systems. Finally, the increased loads on existing communications infrastructures, which have resulted from the expanded use of the Internet, place additional burdens on these systems.

2.3.4 Summary of R&D Topics and Roadmaps

Table 2.3 summarizes R&D topics and their corresponding roadmaps for the information and communications infrastructure. The table provides brief descriptions of research topics grouped by priority (i.e., most important, very important, important); summaries of research activities for three timeframes (near-term [before 2002], before 2005, and before 2010); and *estimates* of the financial resources required to support the R&D activities for each timeframe. Tab C contains more detailed descriptions of these research topics, supporting rationale, goals and challenges, threats and vulnerabilities addressed by the research, and research roadmap information.

Table 2.3 Summary of Information and Communications R&D Topics and Roadmaps[a]

R&D Topic			
No.	**Title**	**Description (Type[b])**	**Research Roadmap (Resource Estimate[c])**
Most Important R&D Topics			
1	Vulnerability Detection and Analysis	Identification, collection, and dissemination of vulnerability information; development of threat and vulnerability lexicon; development of methodologies and technologies to avoid, reduce, or eliminate vulnerabilities. (B, A, ATD)	**Near-term:** Develop lexicon and procedures for collecting, analyzing, and disseminating vulnerability information. ($90 million) **~2005:** Develop database to identify vulnerability information about the infrastructure. Develop metrics and measures to gauge the effectiveness of tools to detect and analyze vulnerabilities, and automate tools to detect vulnerabilities. ($90 million) **~2010:** Develop coordinated and scaleable tools for vulnerability detection and data notification at the national level. Establish international cooperation for collecting and sharing information on vulnerabilities. ($150 million)
4	Characterization and Notification of Threats	Collection of data, analysis, and development of tools to address threats to the information and communications infrastructure. (B, A)	**Near-term:** Develop procedures for collecting, analyzing, and disseminating threat data. ($25 million) **~2005:** Implement national database of threat and response information. Profile potential attackers. ($30 million) **~2010:** Develop and distribute coordinated, national-level tools for threat notification. Establish international cooperation for collecting and sharing threat data. ($40 million)

R&D Topic			
No.	Title	Description (Type[b])	Research Roadmap (Resource Estimate[c])
5	Intrusion and Incident Detection and Warning	Development of efficient and cost-effective tools and methodologies for rapid incident detection and warning. (B, A, ATD)	**Near-term:** Develop manual tools and procedures to detect incidents and issue warnings. Establish metrics for assessing intrusion detection systems. ($90 million) **~2005:** Develop automated tools to detect incidents and issue warnings, strategy-based intrusion detection systems, automated trace-back tools, and scaleable detection systems. ($90 million) **~2010:** Develop scaleable tools at a national level to detect indications and warnings of an attack. Establish international cooperation and sharing of data on attacks. Create scaleable assessment tools to evaluate Internet threats. ($150 million)
6	Response, Recovery, and Reconstitution	Development of methods to contain, stop, or eject intruders; mitigate damage; and restore service. (B, A, ATD)	**Near-term:** Develop manual tools to detect, contain, and eject intruders, and to perform triage for recovery on attacked systems. ($95 million) **~2005:** Develop automated tools to detect, contain, and eject intruders, and perform triage for recovery on attacked systems. ($105 million) **~2010:** Continue development of automated tools to improve robustness, efficiency, and timely response in recovery. ($100 million)
7	Security Architectures	Development of new and improved security architectures. (B, A, ATD)	**Near-term:** Establish methodologies for automated distribution of security patches. Prepare security implementation policies. ($125 million) **~2005:** Develop advanced firewall technologies and active, dynamic network technologies. ($150 million) **~2010:** Develop scaleable, robust security architectures to integrate security components. ($250 million)

R&D Topic			
No.	**Title**	**Description (Type[b])**	**Research Roadmap (Resource Estimate[c])**
8	Assurance Technologies	Development of tools and methodologies to implement new and improved assurance technologies. (B, A, ATD)	**Near-term:** Establish standards and methods of incorporating assurance into system development and complete product evaluation policies. ($95 million) **~2005:** Develop tools for efficient product evaluation and system-level evaluations. ($105 million) **~2010:** Continuously develop and refine methodologies and techniques for incorporating assurance into system development. ($175 million)
10	Management of Information Protection	Development of tools and methodologies for effective management of information protection in information and communication systems. (B, A, ATD)	**Near-term:** Research and develop concepts and techniques for protecting data and performing configuration management in local and remote infrastructure components. Define performance metrics for evaluating information protection. ($30 million) **~2005:** Research information protection concepts that carry use conditions, or metadata, with the information. Establish economic metrics for evaluating information protection. ($30 million) **~2010:** Continuously develop and refine measurement concepts, tools, and technologies for managing the protection of data in diverse environments. ($50 million)
Very Important R&D Topics			
2	Valuation of Information	Development of tools and methodologies to assist information owners in determining the value of their information and choosing cost-effective protective measures. (B, A)	**Near-term:** Develop manual tools, techniques and procedures to assess the value of information. ($30 million) **~2005:** Develop automated tools to assist information owners in assessing the value of information and determining appropriate levels of protection. ($30 million) **~2010:** Develop and refine automated tools to assist information owners in assessing the value of information and protection, including information that can be aggregated from multiple sources. ($50 million)

R&D Topic			
No.	Title	Description (Type[b])	Research Roadmap (Resource Estimate[c])
9	Advanced Concepts and Theory	Development of tools and methodologies to design and implement cost-effective security measures. (B, A, ATD)	**Near-term:** Establish standards, techniques, and procedures for software development. ($30 million) **~2005:** Research and develop ways to use expert systems in network management and to adaptively secure systems. ($30 million) **~2010:** Develop self-describing secure systems. ($50 million)
11	Characterization of Minimum Infrastructure for Essential Services	Identification of the critical elements in the information and communication infrastructure required to provide essential national, governmental, and military services. (A, ATD)	**Near-term:** Define and characterize minimum essential government and military communications, operations and services, and the required infrastructure to support those services. ($15 million) **~2005:** Establish interagency contingency and coordination plans and address the introduction of redundant systems in critical applications. ($15 million) **~2010:** Develop plans and deploy additional technologies to ensure redundancy as new technologies emerge and the scope of government services evolves. ($25 million)
13	Modeling and Simulation Tools	Development of tools and methodologies for simulating complex information and communication systems and architectures and can analyze alternative security configurations. (B, A, ATD)	**Near-term:** Define requirements and initiate modeling and simulation on small network systems. ($135 million) **~2005:** Develop tools and models for modeling complex systems at the architectural level, and tools and techniques for modeling interdependencies and vulnerabilities in systems. ($150 million) **~2010:** Develop automated tools for detecting deviations from system specifications at the architectural level, and technologies and specifications for self-describing systems. ($250 million)

R&D Topic			
No.	Title	Description (Type[b])	Research Roadmap (Resource Estimate[c])
Important R&D Topics			
3	Risk Analysis	Development of automated tools for analyzing risks to information and information systems. (B, A)	**Near-term:** Develop semiautomated risk analysis tools and formulate techniques and metrics to assess risk. ($75 million) **~2005:** Develop automated risk analysis tools to dynamically assess risk on systems and networks as components change. ($75 million) **~2010:** Develop advanced and automated risk analysis tools to incorporate the emergence of new technologies and system components. ($50 million)
12	Encryption Technology	Development of cost-effective suite of hardware and software technology for encryption. (B, A, ATD)	**Near-term:** Establish national standards for security key management. ($125 million) **~2005:** Develop robust, high-performance, cost-effective, cryptographic technologies. ($150 million) **~2010:** Continually advance and refine robust encryption technologies given the significant increases in computing power available. ($250 million)

[a] The order of the R&D topics within a priority category (most important, very important, important) does not imply relative importance.

[b] B = basic; A = applied; ATD = advanced technology development; and POP = proof of principle and validation.

[c] Resource estimates reflect qulaitative, order-of-magnitude judgments. They are intended to be respresentative of the resources needed for the R&D topics and are based on assumptions concerning the scope, the expected level of effort, and the pace of the research. Detailed cost estimates must be prepared in concert with the development of detailed R&D plans.

2.4 Transportation

2.4.1 Infrastructure Overview

The transportation infrastructure is composed of all surface, air, and waterborne components of the U.S. transportation system but excludes pipelines, which are part of the energy infrastructure. These components include the following:

- Public and private airborne and groundside aviation activity,
- Railway and highway movement and trans-shipment of goods and people (including intercity passenger and mass transit services), and

- Inland waterborne commerce and maritime navigation and their associated port and terminal facilities.

2.4.2 Issues and Trends

Despite the increased freedom to enter the carrier market, which was a product of deregulation that began 20 years ago, the number of rail, bus, and barge companies in the U.S. has declined since 1990. Many new air carriers have tried unsuccessfully to enter the market. It is becoming more common to see privately held infrastructure concentrated in fewer hands, leading to an unprecedented degree of centralized command and control of essential functions. Although the Intermodal Surface Transportation Efficiency Act of 1991 enabled improvements to our primary and secondary highway system, these roads remain in an unsatisfactory condition in light of the demands placed upon them. The gap between highway needs and performance is the greatest it has been in decades, primarily as a result of deferred spending and reduced maintenance budgets. A recent trend—the public's unwillingness to pay for transportation infrastructure through tax-supported mechanisms—has resulted in private commercial interests and joint public-private ventures that provide more transportation capabilities. This shift transfers much of the responsibility for transportation security to organizations less experienced in, and thus potentially less capable of, handling such responsibility (e.g., tollway authorities).

The desire to reduce costs and increase efficiency has led to increased reliance on information technologies as substitutes for capital investments. Experienced human surveillance has been replaced by automated surveillance. Because so much of the fixed transportation infrastructure is relatively isolated, reliability and dependence on automated systems become critical issues. The degree to which reliability is compromised by the open architectures of many data handling systems is currently unknown.

2.4.3 Threats and Vulnerabilities

Many threats and vulnerabilities are direct consequences of emerging open architectures, which allow extensive information sharing and asset management, centralized control, and infrastructure isolation. The lack of a fully secure and equally reliable alternative to the space-based navigation system is also problematic. Moreover, concern has been expressed about the nature of actual security threats (physical and cyber) and management's understanding and ability to prepare for and deal with threats before they become catastrophic. Recent events have shown that terrorists are willing and able to unleash chemical and biological agents in mass transit facilities; moreover, it cannot be ruled out that they are equally willing and able to attack air terminals, undertake large-scale cyber invasions, or wreak concerted destruction on multiple road and rail "choke points."

2.4.4 Summary of R&D Topics and Roadmaps

Table 2.4 summarizes R&D topics and their corresponding roadmaps for the transportation infrastructure. The table provides brief descriptions of research topics grouped by priority (i.e., most important, very important, important); summaries of research activities for three timeframes (near-term [before 2002], before 2005, and before 2010); and *estimates* of financial resources required to support the R&D activities for each timeframe. Tab D contains more detailed descriptions of these research topics, supporting rationale, goals and challenges, threats and vulnerabilities addressed by the research, and research roadmap information.

Table 2.4 Summary of Transportation R&D Topics and Roadmaps

R&D Topic			
No.	**Title**	**Description (Type)**	**Research Roadmap (Resource Estimate)**
		Most Important R&D Topics	
1	Vulnerability Analysis of Existing Systems	Investigation of vulnerabilities of existing transportation systems within and between operating modes, with special emphasis on communication and architectures and on distributed and centralized command and control systems. (B, A, ATD)	**Near-term:** Conduct pilot studies of actual operations. ($9 million) **~2005:** Develop assessment tools. ($9 million) **~2010:** Complete assessments of transportation systems. ($6 million)
7	Real-time Hazard Threat and Detection Monitoring	Development of reduced cost (both unit and systemwide) detection devices for widespread use in transport systems. (B, A, ATD, POP)	**Near-term:** Ensure applied R&D is under contract. Develop detection devices. ($8 million) **~2005:** Complete prototype testing. ($12 million) **~2010:** Commercialize public-private ventures. ($12 million)

R&D Topic			
No.	**Title**	**Description (Type)**	**Research Roadmap (Resource Estimate)**
13	Intrusion Detection	Adaptation and development of customized intrusion detection systems for both physical and cyber assets of the transportation system. (ATD, POP)	**Near-term:** Define requirements and award contracts to customize intrusion detection systems. ($4 million) **~2005:** Complete design and testing of systems. Begin to implement multiple applications. ($6 million) **~2010:** Commercialize intrusion detection for physical and cyber assets. ($1 million)
15	Threat/Intelligence Database and Network	Creation of a fully integrated facility to provide intelligence regarding plots for destroying physical infrastructure and/or invading electronic control and data systems. (ATD, POP)	**Near-term:** Define requirements and award contracts for an integrated facility for providing intelligence concerning threats. ($1 million) **~2005:** Complete a fully functional facility. ($2 million)
16	Information Assurance	Identification and implementation of appropriate artificial-intelligence (AI)-based technologies for preventing acceptance of corrupted or erroneous material into information handling systems. (A, ATD)	**Near-term:** Define requirements and use existing tools to develop AI-based technologies. ($2 million) **~2005:** Complete design and testing of new tools. ($3 million) **~2010:** Implement and commercialize AI-based technologies. ($1 million)
17	Software Assurance	Identification and implementation of appropriate AI-based technologies for on-line fault checking and self-diagnosis in critical day-to-day information handling systems. (A, ATD)	**Near-term:** Identify requirements for on-line fault checking in information systems. ($4 million) **~2005:** Complete design and testing of new tools in critical information systems. ($6 million) **~2010:** Complete field implementation and commercialization. ($1 million)

R&D Topic			
No.	**Title**	**Description (Type)**	**Research Roadmap (Resource Estimate)**
18	Human Factors Analysis	Characterization and analysis of problems and limitations in event preparedness, prediction, and response specifically attributable to the human role in operating the transportation system. (A)	**Near-term:** Characterize problems and limitations inherent in preparedness, prediction, and response. Award contract. ($6 million) **~2005:** Fully identify and implement changes for preparedness/prediction. ($4 million)
21	Public/Private Infrastructure Security Responsibility	Analysis of jurisdictions and legal structures to clarify command and decision chains for incident mitigation and situation management involving both public and private elements of the transportation infrastructure. (POP)	**Near-term:** Conduct scoping conferences. Issue requests for proposals. Select project teams. ($2 million) **~2005:** Propose legislation (as needed).
		Very Important R&D Topics	
2	Simulation Tool Development	Creation of a suite of event prediction and management tools to be used in the evaluation of system disruptions for each mode of transport. (A)	**Near-term:** Identify and evaluate ways to create tools that can be used in event prediction and management. ($15 million) **~2005:** Develop and validate basic tools. ($15 million) **~2010:** Validate and deploy completed model suite. ($5 million)
3	Determination Risk Perception of Transport System Managers	Identification and formalization of quantitative measures of risk perception of transport system managers at all appropriate decision levels. (B, A)	**Near-term:** Conduct scoping. ($2 million) **~2005:** Complete analyses. ($1 million) **~2010:** Update as required.

R&D Topic			
No.	**Title**	**Description (Type)**	**Research Roadmap (Resource Estimate)**
4	Communication and Inculcation of Sound Risk Management Principles	Development of information and training packages on security risks for operating authorities in all transportation modes; incorporation of vulnerability management into daily operations. (A, ATD, POP)	**Near-term:** Develop training program. ($2 million) **~2005:** Complete analyses and have training actively occurring in all operating functions. ($2 million) **~2010:** Identify and implement fully secure emergency response communications.
6	Emergency Communications	Identification and implementation of fully secure emergency response communications to be employed in the event of transportation system disruptions (A)	**Near-term:** Identify and implement fully secure emergency response communications. ($6 million) **~2005:** Commercialize high-reliability, secure emergency response communications. ($2 million)
8	Robotics Development and Adaptation	Development and adaptation of robotic, remotely controlled modules for performing damage assessment by first responders. (B, A)	**Near-term:** Develop and adapt robotic, remotely controlled modules. ($5 million) **~2005:** Complete prototype testing. ($7 million) **~2010:** Commercialize public/private ventures.
9	Improvement of In use Performance and Replacement Functionality of Transportation Structures	Development and adaptation of materials to maximize modularity, portability, and/or durability of function of permanent and temporary physical structures and assets in the transportation system. (A, POP)	**Near-term:** Develop and adapt materials to maximize modularity, portability, and/or durability. ($5 million) **~2005:** Complete field testing in up to five applications. ($7 million) **~2010:** Commercialize structures.

R&D Topic			
No.	**Title**	**Description (Type)**	**Research Roadmap (Resource Estimate)**
10	Unified Vehicle/Guideway Systems Hardening	Development and adaptation of materials technologies to improve the durability and resistance to damage from physical and cyber attacks on transportation systems including vehicles and guideways. (A)	**Near-term:** Complete scoping studies of materials technologies. ($2 million) **~2005:** Develop prototypes to improve durability of transport systems. ($2 million) **~2010:** Perform field testing, and define and implement standards. ($2 million)
11	Asset Management	Development of reliable quantitative measures to make the most efficient use of physical and cyber resources in the transportation system. (A, ATD)	**Near-term:** Conduct scoping. ($1 million) **~2005:** Validate and peer-review prototype tools. ($2 million) **~2010:** Commercialize tools. ($1 million)
12	System Representation Improvement	Development of improved methods to manage large quantities of interconnected and dependent transportation system data into clearly comprehensible formats (e.g., visual displays). (ATD, POP)	**Near-term:** Develop contracts with at least two teams. Improve methods to manage transport system data in a clear format. ($20 million) **~2005:** Integrate database. Complete prototype tools. ($30 million) **~2010:** Implement multiple applications. ($20 million) (full U.S. coverage assumed)
20	Computer Emergency Response and Emergency Response and Recovery Assessment Capacity Building	Development of a body of knowledge and training materials to support the management of incidents and of functional recovery in real time when a significant emergency occurs. (B, A, POP)	**Near-term:** Define needs and procedures. Develop research contracts. ($3 million) **~2005:** Deploy trained teams to standby mode at strategic locations. ($5 million) **~2010:** Introduce active information exchange and revise procedures as needed. ($3 million)

R&D Topic			
No.	Title	Description (Type)	Research Roadmap (Resource Estimate)
		Important R&D Topics	
5	Capacity Margin Analysis	Development of reliable quantitative estimates of losses associated with the absence of surplus carrying capacity in each component of the transportation system. (A)	**Near-term:** Sign contract for analytical team(s). ($1 million) **~2005:** Complete analytical effort. ($1 million)
14	Cyber Vulnerability Data Warehouse	Provision of access to information on advanced cyber security practices to owners of data repositories and networks in the transportation sector. (ATD, POP)	**Near-term:** Define requirements and award contracts. ($1 million) **~2005:** Complete and verify database. Warehouse access protocol. ($2 million)
19	Recovery Training	Development of training packages that maximize communication to and endorsement of the essential components of response and recovery by all transport system operating authorities. (A)	**Near-term:** Contract for training program development. ($1 million) **~2005:** Implement training program. ($2 million) **~2010:** Continue training program. ($1 million)

[a] The order of the R&D topics within a priority category (i.e., most important, very important, important) does not imply relative importance.

[b] B = basic; A = applied; ATD = advanced technology development; and POP=proof of principle and validation.

[c] Resource estimates reflect qualitative, order-of-magnitude judgments. They are intended to be representative of the resources needed for the R&D topics and are based on assumptions concerning the scope, the expected level of effort, and the pace of the research. Detailed cost estimates must be prepared in concert with the development of detailed R&D plans.

2.5 Vital Human Services

2.5.1 Infrastructure Overview

The vital human services infrastructure encompasses three infrastructures: water-supply systems, emergency services, and government services. The water-supply system infrastructure includes sources of water; reservoirs and holding facilities; aqueducts and other water transport systems; filtration, cleaning, and treatment systems; distribution pipelines and other delivery mechanisms; cooling systems; and water systems that deal with water runoff, wastewater, and fire-fighting needs. The emergency services infrastructure includes medical, police, fire, rescue systems, and personnel that plan for and respond to emergencies. The government services infrastructure includes the capability of federal, state, and local governments to provide essential services to the public during and after emergencies.

2.5.2 Issues and Trends

Vital human services are very intra- and interdependent infrastructures. For example, fire fighting is critically intradependent on a reliable water-supply system and heavily interdependent on the other critical infrastructures identified by the Commission. For example, emergency response functions could be hampered if part of the transportation infrastructure were out of order. In this era of reduced taxation and shrinking government services, it is difficult to maintain these infrastructures and manage the risk of future threats.

2.5.3 Threats and Vulnerabilities

Water-supply Systems

The vulnerability of community water-supply systems to contamination from biological agents, chemical agents, or toxins is of considerable concern. There are several specific instances of terrorist threats to contaminate water supplies with biological or chemical agents. However, most water-supply systems are fairly safe from such attacks because hazardous agents do not mix well or survive in water. These agents do, however, pose a threat if they are inserted at critical points in the system. In addition, water-supply systems are vulnerable to physical and cyber attacks. Pumping systems are quite vulnerable and, if destroyed, could shut down a water-supply system for months. Water-supply systems increasingly depend on computer systems, which are vulnerable to cyber attacks.

Emergency Services

First responders are the most vulnerable entity within the emergency services infrastructure. These personnel are trained to deal with a variety of materials, but they are not trained, nor do they have adequate equipment, to deal with weapons of mass destruction, such as biological or chemical warfare agents. First responders and the emergency services infrastructure are vulnerable because detection equipment and training to handle such emergencies in a timely fashion are not available.

Government Services

The primary vulnerability of the government services infrastructure is its evolving complexity and increasing dependency on all infrastructures to provide services. The information and communications, electric power, banking and finance, and transportation infrastructures are all critical components in providing government services.

2.5.4 Summary of R&D Topics and Roadmaps

Vital human services R&D topics and their corresponding roadmaps are summarized in Table 2.5. The table provides brief descriptions of research topics grouped by priority (i.e., most important, very important, or important); summaries of research activities for three timeframes (near-term [before 2002], before 2005, and before 2010); and estimates of the financial resources required to support the R&D activities for each timeframe. Tab E contains more detailed descriptions of these research topics, supporting rationale, goals and challenges, threats and vulnerabilities addressed by the research, and research roadmap information.

Table 2.5 Summary of Vital Human Services R&D Topics and Roadmaps[a]

R&D Topic			
No.	**Title**	**Description (Type[b])**	**Research Roadmap (Resource Estimate[c])**
		Most Important R&D Topics	
1	Identification and Characterization of Biological and Chemical Agents	Characterization of the behavior of chemical and biological agents in water, the effect of water treatment chemicals on these agents, and the actual risks posed by these agents in the water supply system. (B, A)	**Near-term:** Characterize known agents. ($14 million) **~2005:** Identify unknown agents and characterize their physical and chemical parameters and behavior in different environments. Develop and implement database and information exchange mechanisms. ($15 million) **~2010:** Continue to identify and characterize unknown agents. ($25 million)
2	Biological and Chemical Agent Detectors	Development of detectors that provide real-time analysis of water samples to detect the presence of biological and chemical agents in quantities that pose risks to the population. (B, A)	**Near-term:** Adapt current slate of detectors for applications to the water-supply system. ($30 million) **~2005:** Improve sensitivity of current detectors, enhance capability for real-time measurements, and extend detector capabilities to other agents. ($45 million) **~2010:** Develop new generation of detectors to meet more stringent requirements associated with additional, newer agents. ($55 million)

R&D Topic			
No.	Title	Description (Type[b])	Research Roadmap (Resource Estimate[c])
3	Supervisory Control and Data Acquisition (SCADA) Systems	Application of information assurance techniques to water-supply SCADAs; development of appropriate, cost-effective protocols. (A)	**Near-term:** Develop vulnerability assessment criteria and techniques for SCADA systems. ($15 million) **~2005:** Develop techniques to rectify security problems and preliminary protocols for design and operation of secure systems. Conduct pilot tests of improved systems. ($15 million) **~2010:** Conduct additional pilot tests and develop a final set of design and operational protocols. ($25 million)
4	Vulnerability Assessment of Water-supply Systems	Identification and development of methods, tools, and information to assess and cost-effectively reduce the vulnerabilities of water-supply systems. (A)	**Near-term:** Develop criteria for evaluating vulnerability-reduction options. Characterize options. ($9 million) **~2005:** Develop and pilot test evaluation methods and tools. ($12 million) **~2010:** Apply lessons learned to methods and tools, enhance information base, improve methods and tools, and perform additional validations. ($16 million)
5	Center of Excellence for Risk Assessment of Water-supply Systems	Establishment of a center of excellence to support communities in conducting vulnerability and risk assessments of water-supply systems and in making decisions regarding water-supply assurance. (B, A)	**Near-term:** Establish requirements for development and operation of center. Start up center. ($8 million) **~2005:** Develop/test tools, models, and communication methods. ($9 million) **~2010:** Continue research activities from earlier phases. Reevaluate the role of the center and adjust accordingly. ($11 million)

R&D Topic			
No.	Title	Description (Type[b])	Research Roadmap (Resource Estimate[c])
6	Detectors and Detection Systems for Emergency Services	Development of inexpensive, sensitive, rugged, easy to operate, and portable contaminant detectors and detection systems for use by first responders to an emergency. (B, A)	**Near-term:** Identify requirements for known contaminants. Adapt robotic technologies for this use. Initiate basic research into the science of new detectors. ($30 million) **~2005:** Produce detectors with first generation requirements. Continue basic and applied research into new detectors and robotics. ($45 million) **~2010:** Develop/test a new slate of detectors and robotics for emergency services. ($55 million)
8	Multihazard, Real-time Simulation and Modeling	Upgrading of simulation models of hazards and protective actions to incorporate real-time data for emergency managers and decision makers. (A)	**Near-term:** Define requirements for such a system and initiate development. ($17 million) **~2005:** Develop and pilot test a prototype system. Integrate lessons learned into next version of system. ($21 million) **~2010:** Conduct additional pilot tests. Develop, test, and distribute a final set of models constituting the system. ($23 million)
10	Decontamination Technologies	Identification, characterization, development, and adaptation of decontamination technologies to be used in chemical/biological incidents. (A)	**Near-term:** Identify and characterize appropriate existing technologies. Develop decision needs for evaluating and selecting decontamination options. ($55 million) **~2005:** Focus on developing new decontamination technologies. Finalize evaluation and selection criteria for deciding what technologies are most appropriate for any given application. ($75 million) **~2010:** Complete development and demonstration activities on the technologies examined in the previous timeframe. Initiate research on another set of technologies. ($105 million)

R&D Topic			
No.	Title	Description (Type[b])	Research Roadmap (Resource Estimate[c])
11	Systems Analysis of Public Health Emergency Response Systems	Comprehensive analysis of the public health response system to characterize threats and vulnerabilities, determine critical elements and linkages, and identify technology needs. (A)	**Near-term:** Conduct surveys on treatment capabilities and initiate development of analysis tools. ($13 million) **~2005:** Develop and pilot test analytical models. Develop a preliminary set of alternative treatment practices and conduct emergency preparedness exercises. ($15 million) **~2010:** Complete analysis tools. Develop/distribute information on alternative treatment practices and emergency preparedness practices. Conduct additional emergency preparedness exercises. ($17 million)
Very Important R&D Topics			
7	Integrated Emergency Management System	Development of an integrated emergency management support system to assist in effective response by emergency services personnel. (A)	**Near-term:** Specify system requirements and work on the development of a prototype system. ($13 million) **~2005:** Develop and test the prototype. Develop and test a full, integrated system. ($15 million) **~2010:** Complete research and deploy system. ($5 million)
12	Support Systems for Reconfiguring Government	Development of software support systems that aid governments in reconfiguring services during emergencies. (A)	**Near-term:** Define basic requirements for such a system and develop a limited prototype. ($10 million) **~2005:** Develop and pilot test more enhanced prototypes. ($12 million) **~2010:** Complete development of the system. Test, validate, and deploy full-scale system. ($16 million)

R&D Topic			
No.	Title	Description (Type[b])	Research Roadmap (Resource Estimate[c])
Important R&D Topics			
9	Behavioral/Psychological Studies of Reactions to Incidents	Determination of public and emergency responder reactions to chemical/biological incidents; preparation of training and communication techniques. (A)	**Near-term:** Establish a baseline of required and anticipated responses. ($6 million) **~2005:** Develop and conduct training courses. Develop and pilot test enhanced communication techniques. ($6 million) **~2010:** Distribute study results and recommendations to emergency services organizations. ($2 million)

[a] The order of the R&D topics within a priority category (i.e, most important, very important, important) does not imply relative importance.

[b] B = basic; A = applied; ATD = advanced technology development; and POP = proof of principle validation.

[c] Resource estimates reflect qualitative, order-of-magnitude judgments. They are intended to be representative of the resources needed for the R&D topics and are based on assumptions concerning the scope, the expected level of effort, and the pace of the research. Detailed cost estimates must be prepared in concert with the development of detailed R&D plans.

Section 3
Integrated R&D Topics and Roadmaps

Common R&D themes are described, and crosscutting issues, as well as interdependency and complexity R&D needs and topics, are discussed. An integrated R&D roadmap and estimate of resource requirements are presented.

3.1 Common R&D Themes

A number of common themes underlie the R&D topics presented in Section 2. Some of these themes directly correlate with the objectives of infrastructure assurance to reduce critical vulnerabilities by protecting infrastructures, detecting intrusions, mitigating the effects of disruptions, assisting in the management of incidents, and facilitating recovery. Other themes focus on developing analytical or supporting technologies that are needed to help meet these objectives.

Table 3.1 highlights the common infrastructure assurance R&D themes. The first four themes—information assurance, monitoring and detection, protection and mitigation, and response and recovery—correspond to the aforementioned objectives. The analytical themes include modeling and simulation, systems analysis, decision support, and risk management. The final theme, vulnerability assessment, provides supporting baseline information for all of the other themes.

Table 3.1 Common R&D Themes

Information Assurance—secure information while it is stored, being processed, and in transit

Monitoring and Detection—monitor systems, detect threats and intrusions, and provide timely warning

Protection and Mitigation—protect infrastructures physically and mitigate damage

Response and Recovery—aid in rapid incident response and recovery

Modeling and Simulation—develop models of components, systems, and infrastructures and examine the efficacy of alternative infrastructure assurance strategies and technologies

Systems Analysis—analyze complex systems and identify and analyze infrastructure interdependencies

Decision Support—support timely decision making with tools, methodologies, and information systems

Risk Management—determine where best to allocate resources and how to manage risks

Vulnerability Assessment—assess the vulnerability of components, systems, and infrastructures

The sector R&D topics in Tables 2.1–2.5 can involve research element that correspond to one or more of the themes. For example, monitoring and detection, modeling and simulation, and decision support are all elements of energy R&D Topic No. 1 (Real-time Control Mechanisms). Because this topic involves integrating real-time control systems to support timely decisions, decision support is designated as the primary theme. The other themes are secondary.

Each of the themes is discussed below. Table 3.2 provides a mapping among R&D topics and themes. Primary and secondary themes are shown.

3.1.1 Information Assurance

As national infrastructures increasingly depend on computers and networked information systems to improve efficiency and enhance economic competitiveness, they also become more vulnerable to potential cyber attacks. In addition, the basic technology is changing rapidly, open architectures are being pursued, and government policy is encouraging increased competition. These changes affect both the individual critical infrastructures and the national interdependent infrastructures, and as well as increase infrastructure vulnerability as a whole. Significant new investments in R&D are required to protect the communications infrastructure, and the information created, stored, processed, and transmitted on it.

3.1.2 Monitoring and Detection

Reliable automated monitoring and detection systems, timely and effective information collection technologies, and efficient data reduction and analysis tools are needed to identify and characterize localized or structured attacks against infrastructure. Technologies are also needed to allow highly toxic chemical and biological agents to be detected, identified, measured, and subsequently treated. A protection and attack sensing and warning capability is needed to provide early threat warning to government organizations and private-sector infrastructure owners and operators, thereby preventing widespread infrastructure disruptions that have potentially serious consequences on our national security, economy, and quality of life.

3.1.3 Protection and Mitigation

Real-time system control, infrastructure hardening, and containment technologies are needed to protect infrastructure systems against threats and mitigate the impacts of disruptions. Advanced survivability, reliability, and assurance enhancement measures need to be explored and developed. Technologies also are needed to contain and isolate the impacts of information system disruptions so that the complete system or dependent infrastructures are not affected.

3.1.4 Response and Recovery

A wide range of new technologies and tools are needed for planning for, responding to, and recovering from incidents, such as physical- and cyber-based attacks that affect local or national infrastructures. This includes crisis and consequence management systems, personal protective equipment, and emergency medical and decontamination technologies.

Table 3.2 Mapping among R&D Topics and Primary and Secondary Themes[1]

R&D Topic										
No.	Title	Information Assurance	Monitoring and Detection	Protection and Mitigation	Response and Recovery	Modeling and Simulation	System Analysis	Decision Support	Risk Management	Vulnerability Assessment
Banking and Finance										
1	Simulation Model Development					P				
2	Information Security Analysis	P								
3	Intrusion Indication and Warning Tools		P				S			
4	Systems Reliability Enhancement			P					S	S
5	Information System Standardization						P	S		
6	Electronic Commerce Security Enhancement						P	S		S
Energy										
1	Real-time Control Mechanisms		S			S		P		
2	Analysis of Scale and Complexity			S			P			
3	Vulnerability Assessment									P
4	Information Assurance and Cyber Security	P	S						S	
5	Emergency Response and Recovery Information Technologies				P					
6	Transmission and Distribution Technologies			P						

1 P = primary theme; S = secondary theme.

R&D Topic										
No.	Title	Information Assurance	Monitoring and Detection	Protection and Mitigation	Response and Recovery	Modeling and Simulation	System Analysis	Decision Support	Risk Management	Vulnerability Assessment
7	On-line Security Assessment					P				
8	Dispersed Generation and Backup Infrastructures			P						
9	Critical Consequence Analysis				P	S				
10	Decision Support Systems							P	S	
11	Physical Protection Assessment									P
12	Multisensor and Warning Technologies		P							
13	Emergency Response Capability Enhancement				P					
14	Cyber Protection Enhancement	P								
15	Evaluation of Policy Effects						P			
16	Institutional Barriers						P			
17	Infrastructure Interdependencies						P			
	Information and Communications									
1	Vulnerability Detection and Analysis		S							P
2	Valuation of Information								P	
3	Risk Analysis								P	
4	Characterization and Notification of Threats		P							

R&D Topic										
No.	Title	Information Assurance	Monitoring and Detection	Protection and Mitigation	Response and Recovery	Modeling and Simulation	System Analysis	Decision Support	Risk Management	Vulnerability Assessment
5	Intrusion and Incident Detection and Warning		P							
6	Response, Recovery, and Reconstitution				P					
7	Security Architectures	P								
8	Assurance Technologies	P								
9	Advanced Concepts and Theory	P								
10	Management of Information Protection	P								
11	Characterization of Minimum Infrastructure for Essential Services	P								
12	Encryption Technology	P								
13	Modeling and Simulation Tools					P				
Transportation										
1	Vulnerability Analysis of Existing Systems					S				P
2	Simulation Tool Development					P				S
3	Determination of Risk Perception of Transport System Managers								P	
4	Communication and Inculcation of Sound Risk Management Principles								P	
5	Capacity Margin Analysis			P						

R&D Topic										
No.	Title	Information Assurance	Monitoring and Detection	Protection and Mitigation	Response and Recovery	Modeling and Simulation	System Analysis	Decision Support	Risk Management	Vulnerability Assessment
6	Emergency Communications			S	P					
7	Real-time Hazard Threat and Detection Monitoring		P							
8	Robotics Development and Adaptation				P					
9	Improvement of In-use Performance and Replacement Functionality of Transportation Structures				P					
10	Unified Vehicle/Guideway Systems Hardening			P						
11	Asset Management							P		
12	System Representation Improvement							P		
13	Intrusion Detection		P							
14	Cyber Vulnerability Data Warehouse		P							
15	Threat/Intelligence Database and Network		P	S						
16	Information Assurance	P								
17	Software Assurance	P	S							
18	Human Factors Analysis						P			
19	Recovery Training				P					

R&D Topic										
No.	Title	Information Assurance	Monitoring and Detection	Protection and Mitigation	Response and Recovery	Modeling and Simulation	System Analysis	Decision Support	Risk Management	Vulnerability Assessment
20	Computer Emergency Response and Emergency Response and Recovery Assessment Capacity Building				P					
21	Public/Private Infrastructure Security Responsibility						P			
	Vital Human Services									
1	Identification and Characterization of Biological and Chemical Agents		S	P						
2	Biological and Chemical Agent Detectors		P							
3	Supervisory Control and Data Acquisition Systems	P								
4	Vulnerability Assessment of Water-supply Systems									P
5	Center of Excellence for Risk Assessment of Water-supply Systems							P		
6	Detectors and Detection Systems for Emergency Services		P							

R&D Topic										
No.	Title	Information Assurance	Monitoring and Detection	Protection and Mitigation	Response and Recovery	Modeling and Simulation	System Analysis	Decision Support	Risk Management	Vulnerability Assessment
7	Integrated Emergency Management System							P		
8	Multihazard, Real-time Simulation and Modeling					S		P		
9	Behavioral/ Psychological Studies of Reactions to Incidents						P	S		
10	Decontamination Technologies				P					
11	Systems Analysis of Public Health Emergency Response Systems						P			S
12	Support Systems for Reconfiguring Government							P		

[a] P = primary theme; S = secondary theme.

3.1.5 Modeling and Simulation

Modeling and simulation tools and environments (e.g., test beds) need to be developed for studying infrastructure-related problems and dynamic response mechanisms under varying conditions. Such tools allow experimentation that cannot be performed in realistic environments of any appreciable scale. For example, robust infrastructure and nodal analysis techniques and tools need to be developed for modeling large-scale distributed/networked systems and interdependent infrastructures. Such tools would support systems analysis and decision making.

3.1.6 Systems Analysis

Systems analysis needs to be performed to identify critical nodes and components within infrastructures, to examine infrastructure coupling and interdependencies, and to help understand the behavior of complex systems. Such analysis also is needed to help support decisions on how systems can be protected from physical and cyber threats and degraded gracefully, if necessary, to prevent cascading impacts within and across infrastructures. That is, comprehensive systems analysis techniques are needed for addressing physical and cyber security issues in an integrated fashion. Modeling and simulation tools and vulnerability assessment information support such analyses.

3.1.7 Decision Support

Decision support methodologies, tools, and information systems are needed to help identify and prioritize critical assets for protection, mitigation, incident management, and recovery; compute return on investment in competing security technologies; and develop overall infrastructure assurance investment strategies. Measurable criteria also need to be established that address national security, economic competitiveness, quality of life, and other important attributes. Such methodologies, tools, and information systems would help determine what infrastructure assets are critical, and thus aid in the priority use of resources in a degraded environment.

3.1.8 Risk Management

Methodologies and tools are needed to identify and manage risks to infrastructures and information, and to determine where best to allocate limited resources. Research areas include developing methodologies for measuring the relative risks and the degree of impact of infrastructure assurance investment strategies; for enhancing the ability of users to perform consequence assessment and risk analysis; for developing effective risk management approaches and strategies; for dealing with uncertainties in, or incomplete knowledge of, threats, vulnerabilities, and protection measures; and for managing risks across the multiple components and organizations involved in the infrastructures. Methods also are needed to more effectively characterize risks and communicate risk information.

3.1.9 Vulnerability Assessment

The specific weaknesses (vulnerabilities) of infrastructure components and systems to credible threats need to be identified and analyzed. A comprehensive awareness also needs to be developed of the inherent susceptibilities of technologies on which infrastructures and key components are or will be reliant; technologies that potentially could be used maliciously to disrupt, damage, or destroy infrastructures or key components; and technologies that could have protective applications and potentially be used to safeguard infrastructures and components. This baseline information provides a frame of reference for risk management and investment decisions.

3.2 Crosscutting R&D

Included among the many topics within each theme are elements that apply to, or crosscut, multiple infrastructure sectors (Figure 3.1). These elements primarily involve basic and applied research aimed at increasing the fundamental knowledge necessary for developing infrastructure assurance technologies and investigating the feasibility and practicality of proposed technological solutions. With careful R&D planning and coordination, crosscutting elements could be combined into focused R&D areas to capitalize on synergies and reduce resource requirements. Combining these elements also would promote integration of the R&D efforts and reduce the number of "stovepipe" activities (i.e., narrow, sector-specific activities that are not effectively coordinated across program boundaries).

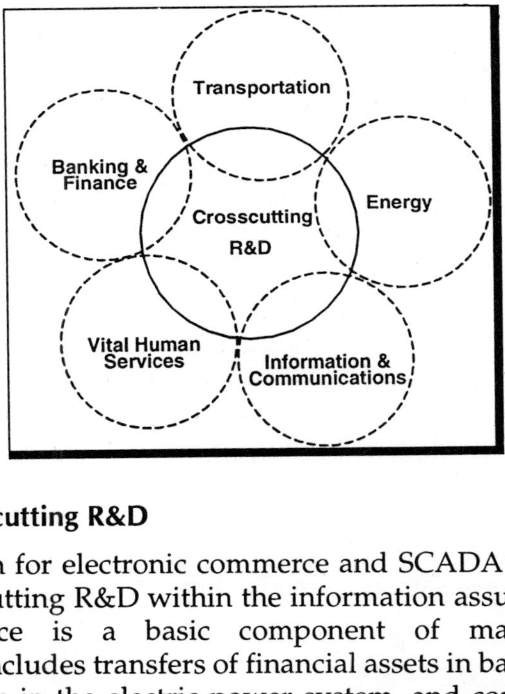

Figure 3.1 Crosscutting R&D

Cyber protection for electronic commerce and SCADA systems is one example of crosscutting R&D within the information assurance theme. Electronic commerce is a basic component of many infrastructure operations—it includes transfers of financial assets in banking and finance, power purchases in the electric power system, and confidential information sharing in government services. Similarly, transferring operational instructions to system control devices via SCADA systems is emerging as a primary operating method for many infrastructures (e.g., electric power system control of transmission; control of oil, gas, and water pipelines; and control of switching systems in transportation). These trends, coupled with the increased use of open and standardized information and communication architectures, have increased the vulnerability of both electronic commerce and SCADA systems to cyber attacks. New cyber protection technologies are needed to improve the security of these information transfer systems and protect the critical infrastructures they support.

Many basic and applied research topics identified in Table 3.2 (under Information Assurance theme) support the development and application of cyber protection technologies. For example, the basic research topic, Advanced Concepts and Theory, would provide fundamental knowledge for developing advanced information and communications systems and networks. Similarly, Security Architectures would include the design of new and improved security architectures composed of components (i.e., firewalls, switches, encryption technology) and services that ensure confidentiality, integrity, and availability for information and communications systems. While Encryption Technology would develop efficient and cost-effective technologies, Management of Information Protection is both a basic and applied research topic expected to provide methods, tools and techniques, and standards that support information protection in information and communications systems. Finally, Assurance Technologies would include both basic and applied research to develop tools and techniques that test and verify that the hardware and software components, and their integration into systems, meet information and communications system requirements. These research topics contribute to the development of cyber protection technologies for electronic commerce and SCADA systems that would benefit all infrastructures.

Another example of crosscutting R&D involves comprehensive and detailed vulnerability assessments, which are fundamental for making effective decisions about protecting infrastructures. The R&D topics shown in Table 3.2 (under Vulnerability Assessment theme) describe rigorous vulnerability assessments that would require new methods, tools, and techniques not currently available. It is important that vulnerability assessments are performed consistently across all sectors so that consistent infrastructure assurance strategies can be developed to protect critical infrastructures. Such assessments are also important to support interdependency analyses.

The development of large-scale models also would require significant basic and applied research (under Modeling and Simulation theme in Table 3.2). Advanced computational algorithms, advanced simulation architectures, approaches for dealing with complexity, and massive data storage and fast retrieval are some of the basic research elements that support large-scale modeling. Advanced visualization techniques, user-friendly machine interfaces, and expert systems for information handling are some of the applied research topics that support large-scale modeling and simulation. These basic and applied research elements would support the large-scale modeling and simulation topics included in the banking and finance, energy, and information and communications R&D roadmaps.

The detection and effective manaèons (cyber and physical) is another example of crosscutting R&D. The current infrastructure trend is to reduce labor costs and rely on automated systems. This trend places greater expectations on the capabilities of these automated systems to provide reliable and timely information.

As Table 3.2 shows, all sector R&D roadmaps identified topics that focus on monitoring and detecting intrusions. For example, the energy roadmap identified topics that address both cyber intrusions (e.g., Information Assurance and Cyber Security) and physical intrusions (e.g., Multisensor and Warning Technologies). Cyber intrusion topics were identified in the banking and finance (e.g., Intrusion Indication and Warning Tools) as well as in the information and communications (e.g., Incident Detection and Warning) roadmaps. R&D topics for water-supply systems focused on detecting chemical or biological agents (e.g., Identification and Characterization of Biological and Chemical Agents). Finally, transportation R&D topics were concerned with both cyber and physical intrusion detection (e.g., Intrusion Detection).

Although each infrastructure has specific needs for detecting and managing intrusions, significant synergy is present in the type of research being proposed. Cyber intrusion detection and management systems require basic and applied research to develop (1) authentication/authorization tools, (2) authentication management systems, (3) intrusion detection algorithms and technologies, (4) trace-back systems, and (5) intrusion warning systems. Physical intrusion and management primarily depend on the accuracy of detectors as well as on cyber components. Key factors in developing effective detectors are unit cost, reliability, durability, and maintainability, all of which have crosscutting dimensions.

Similar examples of crosscutting R&D can be found in each theme. As detailed programs are developed for the R&D topics, particular attention should be given to identifying such crosscutting R&D elements.

3.3 Interdependency and Complexity R&D

In addition to the crosscutting R&D areas that could reduce investment requirements, some R&D needs transcend the more narrowly focused R&D defined in the individual infrastructures. Such research requires investments beyond those associated with the individual sector topics. Perhaps the most compelling need involves interdependency and complexity.

This topic, which is not addressed adequately in the individual topics, focuses on the interdependence between physical and cyber infrastructure components both within and among the eight critical infrastructures. The complexity and interconnected nature of our infrastructures are due largely to an increased reliance on telecommunications and computer processing for their management. The power and sophistication of cyber technologies and their widespread integration in the infrastructures increase the likelihood of unforeseen vulnerabilities and unintended consequences. As a result, not all aspects of one infrastructure's dependence on another are documented or understood. Further, hidden interdependencies are a strong possibility because of complex, and heretofore, not understood linkages.

The most obvious dependencies between the elements of one or more infrastructures are those that are linked physically. For example, consider a substation in an electrical distribution system that provides electric power to a telecommunications center. Failure or loss of power in the substation would directly affect the telecommunications center (subject to backup power supplies). The telecommunications center, in turn, may control the SCADA systems for gas pipelines and water-supply systems. The gas pipelines may fuel critical gas-fired generators in the electric system, and so forth. Such dependencies, sometimes called system interactions, must be fully identified and evaluated.

Other dependencies are not physically linked but are coupled because of location and exposed environment. For example, a common utility corridor that contains overhead electric power transmission lines, buried gas pipelines, and telecommunications cables, dramatizes such dependencies. Collocating infrastructures makes them more susceptible to such physical hazards as explosion, fire, flood, and seismic events, as well as sabotage.

Subtle interactions are another type of dependency that can exist in complex systems and occur without a direct link. The failure of a substation, for example, could cause topological reconfiguration of the electric network, which, in turn, could overload a similar substation within the system if the demand at that time exceeds the substation capacity. Here, the direct link does not normally exist, and the failure could occur only if certain conditions were imposed (e.g., peak load).

Direct system interactions, indirect coupling as a result of collocation, and subtle interactions usually occur shortly after an incident. However, another type of interaction can occur over an extended time, that is, time for the effect to propagate through elements of the infrastructures. Understanding this time delay is important in designing appropriate detection and mitigation technologies. Infrastructures, such as the water-supply system and gas and oil storage, which are limited resources subject to depletion, are candidates for these interactions. Also, the effect of threats (e.g., cyber threats to the banking and finance infrastructure) requires time to propagate, and, therefore, early detection and recovery are important factors in controlling their effects.

Natural hazards, such as seismic events or extreme weather, clearly illustrate how threats can affect multiple infrastructures simultaneously. Such threats also reveal interdependencies that can complicate or delay mitigation or recovery of a particular infrastructure from an incident. A major earthquake, for example, can disrupt many infrastructures. At the same time, transportation structures, such as bridges and elevated highways, could collapse, making it difficult to provide vital emergency services.

Consequences of multiple disruptions to our infrastructure range from loss of human life and property to prolonged loss of shelter, food, and water, and disruption of financial services. Recovery of particular infrastructures from an incident can be delayed significantly or thwarted by the simultaneous unavailability of another infrastructure. Controlling or reducing the effect of interdependencies is a function of the type of incident, the area of occurrence, and the technology. Further studies should aim to improve our understanding of vulnerabilities that result from disruption to multiple infrastructures.

A well-organized, coordinated sabotage event could cause a wide area disruption of one or more infrastructures. A series of incidents, each planned and timed to reinforce the effects of the others, could interact (cascade) across critical infrastructures to degrade the services upon which all depend. The finely tuned, just-in-time interdependence of infrastructure systems gives potential attackers the capability to leverage localized damage into widespread system failure. A smaller scope sabotage could also propagate across several infrastructures because of embedded dependencies that exist within the architectures of our infrastructures. The complexity of automated systems induces additional risk. Table 3.3 summarizes several broad R&D topics and roadmaps needed to address interdependency and complexity issues.

3.4 Integrated Roadmap

Figure 3.2 provides integrated R&D roadmapping information for the three timeframes. Individual R&D topics are aggregated by theme. Interdependency and complexity R&D is also shown. The heavy bars indicate peak R&D activity. However, as indicated by the dashed lines, ongoing R&D is required at a reduced level throughout the study period.

Vulnerability assessment is an immediate need that will provide a baseline for focusing all of the other R&D activities. Such assessments must continue over time to capture the dynamics of the evolving threats and changes in the infrastructures (e.g., as a result of restructuring, market response mechanisms, or implemented infrastructure assurance technologies).

The four analytical themes—systems analysis, modeling and simulation, decision support, and risk management—focus on near- to mid-term R&D. However, some R&D efforts, particularly those involving modeling and simulation, are expected to extend through the long-term. Risk management R&D peaks after initial vulnerability assessments are completed. Applications of the developed tools and methodologies will likely motivate the need for continuing enhancement and development.

Table 3.3 Summary of Interdependency and Complexity R&D Topics and Roadmaps[a]

R&D Topic			
No.	Title	Description (Type[b])	Research Roadmap (Resource Estimate[c])
		Most Important R&D Topics	
1	Identification and Characterization of Dependencies	Identification of dependencies (direct and indirect) among national infrastructures, including space systems (e.g., Global Positioning System), and characterization of how damage can propagate across multiple infrastructures. (A)	**Near-term:** Identify and characterize infrastructure components, first-order dependencies, and degree of coupling among infrastructures. ($9 million) **~2005:** Identify and characterize higher order dependencies. Investigate coupling issues and resultant infrastructure vulnerabilities. ($9 million) **~2010:** Identify opportunities for decoupling infrastructures to reduce vulnerabilities and the potential for propagation of damage across infrastructures. ($10 million)
2	Analysis of Scale, Complexity, and Trends	Characterization of industry trends (e.g., restructuring) in terms of interdependence and effects of scale and complexity (e.g., due to cyber dependence) on system behavior. (A)	**Near-term:** Improve understanding of scale and complexity in terms of national interdependent infrastructures. Characterize industry trends that affect scale and complexity. ($6 million) **~2005:** Develop "science" of large-scale, complex, interdependent infrastructures. ($15 million) **~2010:** Develop strategies for mitigating effects of scale and complexity. ($15 million)

R&D Topic			
No.	Title	**Description (Type [b])**	**Research Roadmap (Resource Estimate[c])**
		Very Important R&D Topics	
3	Systems Analysis and Simulation Tools	Development of systems analysis methods and simulation tools (e.g., nodal analysis tools) for assessing potential interdependence-related vulnerabilities due to physical and cyber threats. (B, A, ATD, POP)	**Near-term:** Develop architectures and robust nodal analysis techniques and simulation tools to analyze infrastructure sector vulnerabilities. ($15 million). **~2005:** Develop integrated tools to simulate interdependent infrastructure operation, dynamic feedback mechanisms, and overall system response to threats. ($25 million)
4	Consequence Analysis and Risk Management Methodologies and Tools	Development of methods and tools for assessing potential consequences (e.g., national security, economic, social) of interdependence-related disruptions and for managing risks. (A, ATD)	**Near-term:** Examine historical data (e.g., large natural disasters and widespread power outages) to develop a baseline of consequence information. Develop basic risk management and consequence analysis methods and tools. ($15 million). **~2005:** Develop integrated risk management and consequence analysis tools for all infrastructure sectors and consequence dimensions. ($21 million).
		Important R&D Topics	
5	Protection and Mitigation	Development of protective measures (including infrastructure hardening) making the interdependent infrastructures able to resist a wider range of potential threats; system redundancy to improve reliability and reduce the chances of cascading impacts; and infrastructure survivability across a larger set of challenges. (B, A, ATD, POP)	**Near-term:** Identify existing protection and mitigation measures and technologies, including backup systems, workarounds, substitutes, and contingency plans, and characterize roles from an interdependence perspective. Initiate development of protection and mitigation technologies. ($27 million) **~2005:** Develop and pilot test protection and mitigation technologies. ($40 million) **~2010:** Demonstrate and validate effectiveness of protection and mitigation technologies. ($50 million)

R&D Topic			
No.	Title	Description (Type [b])	Research Roadmap (Resource Estimate[c])
6	Response and Recovery	Development of planning tools for identifying and evaluating response and recovery strategies. (B, A, ATD, POP)	**Near-term:** Develop tools for identifying and evaluating response and recovery mechanisms for multiple infrastructure disruptions. ($13 million) **~2005:** Develop and pilot test response and recovery tools and mechanisms. ($25 million) **~2010:** Demonstrate and validate effectiveness of response and recovery tools and mechanisms. ($25 million)

[a] The order of the R&D topics within a priority category (i.e., most important, very important, important) does not imply relative importance.

[b] B = basic; A = applied; ATD = advanced technology development; and POP = proof of principle and validation.

[c] Resource estimates reflect qualitative, order-of-magnitude judgments. They are intended to be representative of the resources needed for the R&D topics and are based on assumptions concerning the scope, the expected level of effort, and the pace of the research. Detailed cost estimates must be prepared in concert with the development of detailed R&D plans.

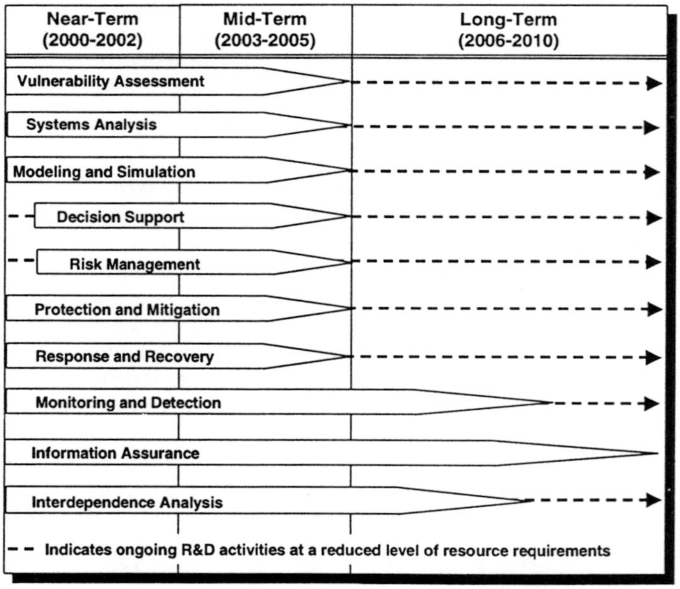

Figure 3.2 Integrated R&D Roadmap

Information assurance and monitoring and detection are both multifaceted, long-term R&D activities. As discussed previously, information assurance is critical for accomplishing the other R&D activities. That is, the rapid proliferation and integration of telecommunications and computer systems in virtually all aspects of infrastructure operation have made information assurance a critical activity. Research in the protection and mitigation and response and recovery themes varies significantly among the infrastructures, with a focus on near- and mid-term activities. As the dashed lines in Figure 3.2 indicate, long-term R&D activities are also likely to be required.

3.5 Resource Requirements

Tables 2.1–2.5 provide estimated resource requirements for the recommended R&D topics. The estimates are aggregated by sector into three timeframes: near-term (FY2000–2002), mid-term (FY2003–2005), and long-term (FY2006–2010). In preparing these estimates, each sector team made assumptions about the expected scope, the level of effort, and the pace of the research. They also made assumptions about government and private-sector responsibilities and the availability of ongoing R&D that could be leveraged. They emphasized near-term activities. The results of such activities will help to shape subsequent R&D effort in the mid- and long-term.

Table 3.4 summarizes the estimated annual resource requirements for the five infrastructure sectors. A sixth area—Interdependency and Complexity—is also shown. As described in Section 3.3, this area includes R&D that transcends the more narrowly focused R&D in the individual infrastructure sectors.

As Table 3.4 shows, the information and communications sector has the largest R&D portfolio—requiring approximately one-half of the total estimated near-term resources. More than one-fourth of the near-term resources focus on R&D for the energy infrastructure. Research and development for the other sectors range from approximately 5% to 10% of the total portfolio. Interdependency and complexity R&D requires about 5% of the total portfolio.

Table 3.4 Estimated Annual (Fiscal Year) Infrastructure Assurance Resource Requirements for Recommended R&D Topics

	Resource Requirements ($Millions/Fiscal Year)						
	Near-Term			Mid-Term			Long-Term
Infrastructure Sector	**2000**	**2001**	**2002**	**2003**	**2004**	**2005**	**2006–2010**
Banking and Finance	55	50	45	25	15	10	5
Energy	160	180	180	200	200	200	200
Information and Communications	260	350	350	350	350	350	320
Transportation	10	40	40	40	40	40	10
Vital Human Services	50	80	95	95	95	95	70
Interdependency and Complexity	20	30	35	50	45	35	20
Total	555	730	745	760	745	730	625

Overall, estimated near- and mid-term resource requirements total approximately $2 billion each, while long-term requirements are estimated to be approximately $3 billion. Total estimated resource requirements are approximately $7 billion.

Figure 3.3 displays a breakdown of near-term resource requirements by theme. As shown, information-assurance-related R&D requires approximately one-third of the total estimated resources. Monitoring and detection R&D represents about 15% of the portfolio, while vulnerability assessment and modeling and simulation each represent approximately 10%.

As discussed in Section 3.2, elements of some of the recommended R&D topics potentially could be combined to capitalize on synergies and to reduce investment requirements. Identifying such elements and estimating associated cost reductions need to be priorities of future roadmapping efforts. The common R&D themes discussed in Section 3.1 provide a starting point for identifying such elements and opportunities for synergy.

The sector investment profiles generally show that resource requirements increase during the near term, as the R&D programs gain momentum and achieve critical mass in terms of researchers and innovative research ideas. Critical requirements-definition and information-collection activities are typical front-end, critical path activities for most R&D topics.

The investment requirements shown in Table 3.4 are generally of the same order-of-magnitude as those recommended in the Commission's *Critical*

Foundations report. They show that a significant increase in investment is needed to "jump start" a focused, coordinated, and goal-oriented national infrastructure assurance R&D effort. The timeframes associated with national goals, when established, will determine the scope, priority, and pace of the R&D activities. Annual investment levels must be adjusted accordingly.

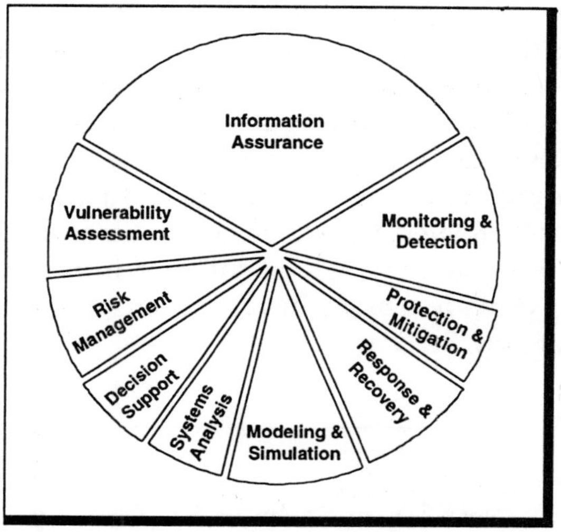

Figure 3.3 Near-term Resource Requirements by Theme

Section 4
Next Steps

The "next steps" observations and recommendations presented in this section focus on the roadmapping process and preliminary roadmapping results. Organizational issues relative to how the U.S. government should implement and structure a public-private R&D partnership to reduce the vulnerability of our infrastructures are not addressed. Rather, these issues are the focus of interagency deliberations and high-level policy directives. Clearly, however, extensive coordination, cooperation, education and awareness training, and information sharing are required. Establishing and coordinating R&D agendas and programs to encourage the introduction of increasingly capable methods for protecting our infrastructure will be especially challenging.

4.1 Essential Elements of Information for Future Roadmapping

The preliminary roadmapping information was developed over a four-month period without the benefit of formally validated requirements (needs), a baseline inventory of ongoing infrastructure-assurance-related R&D activities, or full knowledge of applicable commercial-off-the-shelf

(COTS) and government-off-the-shelf (GOTS) technology. All of these elements are essential to ensure that:

- The R&D roadmap comprehensively validated requirements;
- Individual R&D topics are not addressed elsewhere; and
- New research efforts focus on critical R&D gaps.

Figure 4.1 depicts the essential elements of information needed for developing a comprehensive and defensible R&D roadmap. The threats to, and the vulnerabilities of, our interdependent infrastructures drive the need for technology. Research and development gaps, or shortfalls, are determined by comparing needs with ongoing R&D activities, which may be directly or indirectly related to infrastructure assurance, and applicable COTS and GOTS technology. Clear national infrastructure assurance goals and policies provide a basis for prioritizing, sequencing, and determining the pace of new R&D activities.

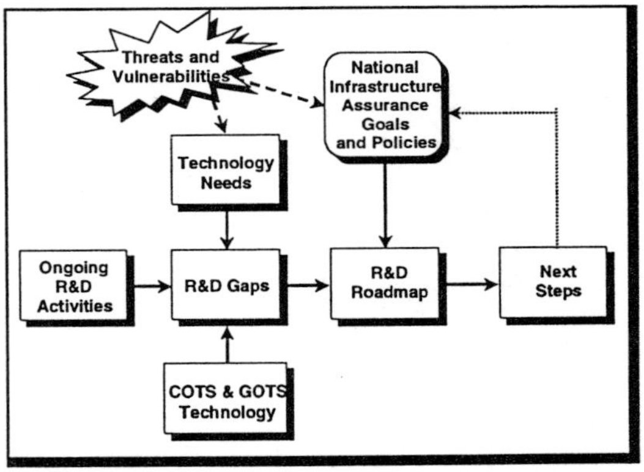

Figure 4.1 Essential Elements of Information for R&D Roadmapping

The study team recommends that all of the essential elements of information shown in Figure 4.1 should be assembled so that the preliminary roadmapping information can be critically reviewed and revised, as needed, to develop an R&D plan to meet national infrastructure assurance goals. To accomplish this recommendation may necessitate a formal requirements analysis process along with a survey to identify ongoing R&D activities within the various departments and agencies. Existing program plans and databases may contain some of these data. Although the study team members used their considerable knowledge, insight, and judgment concerning these elements of information, further study in this area is warranted so that defensible decisions can be made regarding resource allocation and scheduling.

4.2 Portfolio Considerations

From a national perspective, the relevant ongoing and new R&D activities should be viewed as an integrated portfolio designed to meet specified infrastructure assurance goals. As such, this portfolio should meet supporting strategic, technical, and programmatic objectives. Strategically, it should support the timely development of technologies that address the threats to, and vulnerabilities of, critical national infrastructures. Development of such technologies requires working effectively with the private sector (Figure 1.1). Technically, this portfolio should include basic, applied, advanced technology development, and proof-of-principle and validation research. This research should balance funding and development timeframes with degrees of technical risk. Programmatically, the portfolio should include diverse R&D projects that, to the extent possible, comprehensively address the requirements of the various infrastructures. These portfolio considerations should be debated at the interagency level.

4.3 Policy Considerations

As depicted in Figure 4.1, R&D must be consistent with, and responsive to, national infrastructure assurance policy (e.g., as promulgated through Presidential Decision Directives), which is intended to assure the continuity and viability of our nation's critical infrastructures. Such policy provides a framework for establishing R&D objectives, setting R&D priorities, and shaping a multiyear, multifaceted R&D portfolio that is commensurate in scope and scale with the physical and cyber challenges of the twenty-first century. It also provides a framework for establishing education and awareness programs, building partnerships with industry, and developing legislative initiatives intended to reduce vulnerabilities. It is essential, therefore, that R&D be viewed in a policy context as one element of an integrated national strategy, and that the effects of policies on private-sector actions (e.g., the commercialization of technologies to reduce vulnerabilities) be understood more fully and considered in developing an R&D plan.

4.4 Technology Transfer Considerations

Technology transfer and embedding should be an integral part of the R&D process. The spectrum of R&D identified in this roadmap—basic, applied, advanced technology development, and proof-of-principle and validation—must be accompanied by technology development within the private sector to ensure that useful, usable, and used products are developed. The R&D activities must be linked with commercialization activities, including engineering and manufacturing development, technical integration, testing, and fielding (Figure 1.1). Such linkages require effective partnerships with the private sector, sensitivity to economic and other barriers faced by industry in commercializing technologies, and the involvement of infrastructure owners and operators. A technology transfer plan should be prepared along with an R&D plan to elevate awareness of the issues and accelerate the introduction of infrastructure assurance technologies.

4.5 Interdependency and Complexity Considerations

A new "science" of interdependent, complex systems should be developed. This science would provide the theoretical foundation for developing the diverse vulnerability assessment, monitoring, predictive modeling, and consequence analysis technologies needed for addressing infrastructure assurance issues as they relate to the critical national infrastructures. Concepts, such as system complexity, interaction, and coupling, should be examined.

In-depth research on the complexities and interdependencies in the national infrastructure is needed. Each of our national infrastructures depends to varying degrees on the other infrastructures. Some dependencies are readily apparent, such as the strong reliance of the infrastructures on information and communications systems and electric power. Other dependencies are second or third order and appear only after long time periods or under extreme conditions. Researchers should identify and characterize such interdependencies and the associated dynamic feedback and response mechanisms. Research that evaluates historical incidents and probes possible scenarios would lead to a more focused research agenda.

A national repository of validated infrastructure-related models and data (including GIS information) should be established and linked closely to test beds. The test beds would be used to test the nation's infrastructure under actual working conditions, and test analysis, assessment, advanced predictive modeling, and other modeling and simulation systems and tools. Such a repository would support prevention, mitigation, incident response, and recovery objectives in both planning and analysis and crisis situations.

4.6 Other Ingredients for a Successful R&D Program

Various forums, such as conferences, workshops, and joint planning meetings, should be established. These forums would bring together researchers, private-sector infrastructure owners and operators, and government agencies to discuss common problems and requirements, to establish research agenda, and to promote creative thinking on solutions to infrastructure problems.

R&D-related training, education, and awareness programs should be established. These programs would enhance our "intellectual" infrastructure by helping to build a cadre of knowledgeable people ("infrastructure practitioners") within the federal government and the private sector. Also, they would ensure that the new technologies, methods, and tools that result from R&D efforts are implemented and used properly.

Section 5
Subject-matter Experts and Reviewers

The individuals listed below assisted the study team by helping to identify R&D topics and technical and programmatic issues; by providing background materials and studies for review; by facilitating coordination and outreach activities; and by providing insight into the value of R&D for protecting and assuring our critical national infrastructures. Many also provided valuable review comments on earlier drafts of this report.

Banking and Finance

Dennis Dutterer—*BOT Clearing Corporation*
Bill Finnamore—*INTEGRION*
Don Hawkins—*TCF Bank Holding Company*
Don Karmzian—*Chicago Board of Trade*
Joe Kubat—*Security Information Automation Corporation*
Edward Kufeldt—*Defense Finance and Accounting Service*
Bruce W. Moulton—*Fidelity Investments*
Kit Nedham—*Banking Information Technology Secretariat*
John Petersen—*LaSalle National Bank*
Dan Schutzer—*Citibank*
John Shelton—*On-Line Banking Association*
Tom Vartanian—*Fried, Frank, Harris, Shriver & Jacobson*

Energy

John Bartenhagen—*Defense Energy Support Center, Defense Logistics Agency*
Don Bennett—*Department of Defense*
Dennis S. Berry—*Sandia National Laboratories*
Stanley S. Borys—*Institute of Gas Technology*
David Cauffman—*Idaho National Engineering and Environmental Laboratory*
Michael Delurey—*Booz-Allen & Hamilton, Inc.*
David Diehl—*Joint Program Office for Special Technology Countermeasures*
Jerry Hadder—*Oak Ridge National Laboratory*
Mark Hanson—*Energy Center of Wisconsin*
Terry Hawkins—*Los Alamos National Laboratory*
William D. Ingle—*Gas Research Institute*

Maurice Katz—*Department of Energy*
James Mackey—*National Infrastructure Protection Center/Dept. of Energy*
Frank Olken—*Lawrence Berkeley National Laboratory*
Carl Piechowski—*Department of Energy*
Leslie Poch—*Argonne National Laboratory*
David Reichle—*Oak Ridge National Laboratory*
Fred Roach—*Los Alamos National Laboratory*
Ron Skelton—*Private consultant*
Jared R. Smith—*Institute of Gas Technology*
Robert Thomas—*Cornell University*
Jim VanCoevering—*Oak Ridge National Laboratory*
Gregory V. Welch—*Commonwealth Edison*
Sonny White—*Department of Defense*

Information and Communications

Michael Ackerman—*National Library of Medicine/National Institutes of Health*
Kathleen Bailey—*Lawrence Livermore National Laboratory*
Matt Bishop—*University of California—Davis*
Larry Brandt—*National Science Foundation*
Wayne Bryant—*NASA Langley Research Center*
Tom Burke—*General Services Administration*
Blaine Burnham—*National Security Agency*
Mel Ciment—*National Science Foundation*
Harry DeMaio—*Deloitte and Touche Security Services*
Virgil D. Gligor—*University of Maryland*
John Grimes—*Raytheon*
Bill Hunteman—*Los Alamos National Laboratory*
Bijan Jabbari—*George Mason University*
William E. Johnston—*Lawrence Berkeley National Laboratory*
Butler Lampson—*Microsoft Corporation*
Karl Levitt—*University of California—Davis*
Teresa Lunt—*Defense Advanced Research Projects Agency*
John McLean—*Naval Research Laboratory*
Robert Meushaw—*National Security Agency*
Larry Nelson—*AT&T*
Deborah Phillips—*Defense Information Systems Agency*
Mel Sobotka—*Booz-Allen & Hamilton, Inc.*
Stephen L. Squires—*Defense Advanced Research Projects Agency*
Dennis D. Steinauer—*National Institute of Standards and Technology*
David Tennenhouse—*Defense Advanced Research Projects Agency*
Fred Wentland—*Department of Commerce*

Transportation

Roy Allen—*Transportation Technology Center, Inc.*
Douglas Anson—*Los Alamos National Laboratory*
Allison Conway-Smith—*Amtrak*
Mark S. Daskin—*Northwestern University*
Richard Davis—*Oak Ridge National Laboratory*
Jerry Edwards—*U.S. Army Physical Security Equipment Management Office*
Thomas Falvey—*Department of Transportation*
Dan Foth—*American Public Transit Association*
Kevin Harnett—*Volpe National Transportation Systems Center*
Susan Hower—*Science and Engineering Associates*
Bill Hubbard—*National Institute for Environmental Renewal*
Paul Johnson—*Oak Ridge National Laboratory*
Pat Maier—*Boyd Maier and Associates*
Michael Maston—*Oak Ridge National Laboratory*
Howard Moody—*Association of American Railroads*
Gary Murphy—*Microsensors, Inc.*
Anita Parker—*Computer Sciences Corporation*
Rin Saunders—*Computer Sciences Corporation*
David Schulz—*Northwestern University*
LeRon Smith—*Los Alamos National Laboratory*
John Sorenson—*Oak Ridge National Laboratory*
Frank Southworth—*Oak Ridge National Laboratory*
Maurice Stewart—*Department of Defense*
Pat Student—*Union Pacific Railroad*
Richard A. Swanson—*Computer Science Corporation*
William C. Thompson—*Union Pacific Railroad*
Joyce Wegner—*Battelle Pacific Northwest Laboratory*
Athanasios Ziliaskopoulos—*Northwestern University*

Vital Human Services

Philip H. Burgi—*U.S. Bureau of Reclamation*
Paul E. Davies—*Boston Police Department*
Richard W. Hutchinson—*Chemical and Biological Defense Command*
William G. Nagle—*New York City/Mayor's Office of Emergency Management*
Donald E. Newsom—*Argonne National Laboratory*
Irwin M. Pikus, Commissioner—*Department of Commerce*
Stanley Ponce—*U.S. Bureau of Reclamation*
Geary W. Sikich—*Logistical Management Systems Corporation*

Elaine M. Sudanowicz—*Boston Emergency Management Agency*
David Tomasko—*Argonne National Laboratory*

Summary Report

Anita Jones—*University of Virginia*
Doug Sergent—*Joint Program Office for Special Technology Countermeasures*
Larry Schwartz—*University of California*
(Many of the subject-matter experts listed above also reviewed the summary report.)

Coordination Support

Don Bennett—*Department of Defense*
Maureen Clapper—*Department of Energy, New Brunswick Laboratory*

Chapter 3

PRELIMINARY RESEARCH AND DEVELOPMENT

ROADMAP FOR PROTECTING AND ASSURING THE BANKING AND FINANCE INFRASTRUCTURE[1]

---

1 This document is one component of a longer report entitled *Preliminary Research and Development Roadmap for Protecting and Assuring Critical National Infrastructures* (Transition Office of the President's Commission on Critical Infrastructure Protection and the Critical Infrastructure Assurance Office. Washington, D.C. July 1998)

Contents

Section 1 Introduction

1.1 Scope of the Infrastructure

1.2 Characterization of the Infrastructure

1.2.1 Sophisticated and Robust Systems

1.2.2 Emerging Trends

1.2.3 Planning for Potential Responses

1.3 Issues and Trends

1.3.1 Policy Trade-offs

1.3.2 New Technologies

1.3.3 Internationalization of Information and Trade

1.3.4 New Definitions of Value

Section 2 Threats and Vulnerabilities

2.1 Effects of Regulation and Control

2.2 Effects of New Technologies

2.3 Effects of Protecting Monetary Information

2.4 Effects of the International Marketplace

Section 3 R&D Topics and Activities

3.1 R&D Objectives

3.2 Technological Needs

3.2.1 Simulation Model Development

3.2.2 Information Security Analysis

3.2.3 Intrusion Indication and Warning Tools

3.2.4 Systems Reliability Enhancement

3.2.5 Information System Standardization

3.2.6 Information Security Support for Electronic Commerce

3.3 Technology R&D Shortfalls

3.3.1 Modeling and Simulation

3.3.2 Key Management Systems

3.3.3 Authentication Technologies

3.3.4 Intrusion and Anomaly Detection Tools

3.3.5 Computer and Network Security

3.3.6 Physical and Electronic Protection Technologies

3.3.7 Electronic Payment Systems

3.3.8 Network Security Management Systems

3.4 R&D Topics and Roadmaps

Section 4 R&D Topic Roadmaps

Section 5 References

Tables

A.1 Summary of Banking and Finance R&D Topics

A.2 Summary of the Banking and Finance Infrastructure R&D Roadmap

Section 1
Introduction

This report examines the potential threats and vulnerabilities to the banking and finance infrastructure. In particular, various entities and systems are examined that enable the transfer of funds and monetary instruments throughout the United States and into international commerce. The purpose of this report is to present a clear and useful analysis of threats to the stability, reliability, and security of the banking and finance infrastructure. This report also prioritizes and recommends research and development (R&D) activities needed to address potential vulnerabilities.

Research and development for the banking and finance infrastructure must not only support adequate functioning of the infrastructure, but also preserve the confidence of the American public that these services are functioning. Researchers need to develop technical solutions to strengthen the overall security of our nation's financial entities and their supporting systems.

1.1 Scope of the Infrastructure

The banking and finance infrastructure consists of institutions, agencies, and support systems (physical, procedural, and data) that facilitate lending, borrowing, issuing, trading in, or caring for money, credit, and other representations of value. Included in this infrastructure are banks and credit unions; insurance companies; lending and credit institutions of all kinds; securities and commodities dealers; state, federal, and international oversight and regulatory agencies; and the web of communications equipment and linkages that support transactions among those systems. The principal stakeholders in this infrastructure are listed below:

- Federal and state governments in their roles as
  - guardians of consumer rights, protections, and responsibilities
  - issuers of legal tender and managers of the money supply
  - guarantors of national defense
  - law enforcement agencies that investigate financial crimes and illegal uses of money
  - trading partners
- Banking
- Brokerage and financial institutions
- Retail and merchant industries
- Consumers and investors

- International governments that depend on the value of the U.S. dollar
- Technology and service providers that support infrastructure security

Because of changes in the technology of, and the practices by which, the banking and finance infrastructure conducts business, it has become inexorably intertwined with the information and communications infrastructure. The primary focus of this report, however, is to look at the technical issues that affect banking and financial services. When issues are important to both infrastructures, this fact is noted, but not discussed in depth.

1.2 Characterization of the Infrastructure

1.2.1 Sophisticated and Robust Systems

The U.S. banking and finance infrastructure is the most advanced and robust system of its kind in the world. It was established to preserve the safety and stability of our financial institutions and has served our nation well. The President's Commission on Critical Infrastructure Protection has divided the banking and finance infrastructure into five sectors on the basis of the function or service that each provides. These sectors are banks, non-bank financial service companies, payment systems, investment companies and mutual funds, and securities and commodity exchanges.

1.2.2 Emerging Trends

In comparison with other nations, the United States has a long history of safe and sound banking and financial services. Occasional crises have occurred because of structural imbalances, which were corrected by subsequent legislative and administrative initiatives. However, the banking and finance infrastructure is now at its most potentially chaotic time since the 1930s. Four trends have caused this unrest: (1) deregulation and increased competition, (2) convergence of technologies, (3) internationalization of commerce, and (4) changing definitions of value. These trends are discussed in the following subsections.

Deregulation and Increased Competition

The first driving force in the development of financial services is the movement toward deregulation of the industry. Deregulation has created competitive pressures at every level, as banks, insurers, security and commodity brokers, and issuers of credit search for ways to capitalize on this new freedom to compete with one another. As competition intensifies, margins narrow and risk assessment, on the part of both producers and consumers of financial products and services, becomes more challenging. Another issue is how to determine which entities must be regulated. If, for example, providers of technology and communications services begin to offer financial and banking services, old regulatory paradigms may not be relevant or applicable.

Convergence of Technologies

The second trend consists of (1) the convergence of computer, video, and telecommunications technologies and (2) the increasingly rapid pace at which new technologies are being introduced into the industry. In particular, three technologies are transforming the way in which the banking and finance infrastructure conducts its business:

- Ubiquitous digital broadband links with superfast switching;
- Advanced digital television, desktop video, and high-resolution imaging; and
- Wireless and mobile communications.

These new technologies, which were embryonic a few years ago, present new challenges to those persons involved with banking and financial services. Both those who compete in the nearly limitless marketplace and those who struggle to guide and protect the individuals participating in that marketplace now must contend with these new modes and means of transactions.

Internationalization of Commerce

A third trend also affects the industry. International borders, which were once an effective barrier to financial fraud or persons with malevolent intent, are no longer a deterrent. Today's marketplace is global in time and space: money moves around the world and from time zone to time zone at the "click of a mouse." A single nation with a regulatory and/or law enforcement establishment cannot cope in isolation with the volume and speed of transactions.

Changing Definitions of Value

Finally, the nature of what is being traded in this new virtual marketplace is changing, and its ultimate form is unknown. Walter Wriston said, "Today, information about money is more valuable than money itself" (Wriston 1992). Knowledge about how value is represented, stored, and exchanged is, in itself, a potential new form of wealth. Because this knowledge has value, it becomes a target for theft. It must be protected, as it is stored, moved, and traded.

The potential effects of these forces must be identified, and plans must be made to implement recovery actions. If these actions are not taken, the banking and finance infrastructure, which is a high-reliability/low-consequence system that conducts millions of nearly error-free operations daily with little risk of catastrophic consequences, could change to a lower-reliability/higher-consequence system that has more frequent errors and greater penalties for failure.

Compared with the other infrastructures that support our nation, the banking and finance infrastructure is well protected to withstand all but a full-scale, national-level attack. This protection is the result of our nation's investment in security, which has been fundamental to the development and management of the banking and finance infrastructure for several reasons:

- Accountability and oversight up to the board level;
- Security that is integral to risk management; and
- Major investments in security, diversity, backup and recovery, and policies and legislation, which provide the law enforcement framework for protecting both national security and private interests.

Changes to the banking and finance infrastructure over time have included significant investments in leading-edge technologies. These investments have been made separately by the federal government and private industry and by collaborative efforts between the two. The result has been increased security and a reduction of known and perceived risk in the infrastructure. The federal government, for example, recently issued new $100 bills to provide an additional deterrent to counterfeiting. New bills in other denominations will follow soon. Similarly, private industry has invested in and implemented Cardholder Authentication Verification technologies to thwart attempts to present counterfeit magnetic stripe cards for interacting with the banking and finance infrastructure. For example, financial institutions have added photos and holograms to cards to improve authentication of electronic representations of value (e.g., MONDEX). These institutions were quick to adopt network miniservers and personal computers and are considering the move from magnetic stripe to smart-card technology, which will increase their ability to secure transactions and provide stronger distributed authentication.

1.2.3 Planning for Potential Responses

It is important to consider how the security investments cited in the preceding subsection are justified.

> Industry views security investments as a necessary cost of doing business, to ensure the availability, integrity, and confidentiality of their data. . . . Financial institutions manage risk against known and perceived threats. When the industry becomes aware of new threats or vulnerabilities, firms will quickly move to address the problem. . . . However, in developing their security posture, most network owners and operators do not plan to defend against a structured, deliberate attack or a subtle, non-criminally motivated, confidence-level attack using advanced information warfare tools and techniques. Rather, these firms focus on preventing failures resulting from natural disasters (floods, hurricanes) or preventing financially motivated criminals (not only outsiders but also insiders) from defrauding their business. In short, due to a lack of a business case or data for their risk manage-

> ment models, organizations are not implementing national-security-level protective measures. Rather, they protect business systems from hackers and criminals, who they perceive as the most likely and most damaging threats. . . . Industry currently does not have reliable access to consistent sources of current and accurate vulnerability, threat, and capabilities data to 'feed' into its risk models. Furthermore, there are limited mechanisms for sharing data within, or across industries for assessing systemic vulnerabilities (Booz-Allen and Hamilton, 1996).

Many participants in the banking and finance infrastructure have instituted reliable threat models and mitigation measures that can dramatically reduce the effect of an attack, short of a state-sponsored act of war. The efficacy of these tools depends, however, on having appropriate, accurate, and timely information, including that collected by the U.S. government and international agencies.

Both government and industry need reliable, common access to current and accurate data on vulnerabilities, threats, and capabilities. These data can be "fed" into risk models that will provide information to help ensure continual protection of the infrastructure. Industry and government associations and agencies are being formed to identify requirements and institute processes for sharing information. Examples of such groups are the Federal Agencies United against Fraud, which sponsors the Fraud in Cyberspace Conference, and the Financial Services Technology Consortium.

Few mechanisms, however, are available for sharing relevant data that are not related to law enforcement. Information sharing is critical if today's threat models are to be expanded to defend the infrastructure against terrorist and nation-state attacks. Sharing a broad range of information requires innovative methods to protect the rights of those to whom the information pertains and the exposure of those who provide and use the information. Legal concepts, such as use immunity and statutes of repose from liability, may need to be assessed to determine their applicability and possible implementation.

At this time, government and industry investments in advanced technologies are not sufficiently coordinated to guard against potential terrorist and nation-state attacks—the greatest potential risk to our nation's banking and finance infrastructure. Consider, for example, information system technologies, including distributed network management (improves efficiency and reliability of service), cryptography (secures automated transmissions of monetary value and authenticates the participants in any given transaction), and pattern recognition algorithms (detect indications of fraudulent behaviors). While both our government and industry have invested in R&D for these key technical areas, only ad-hoc mechanisms are available for sharing the results of these investments. As the network of systems underlying this infrastructure becomes more complex, it is critical to coordinate research aimed at coping with the vulnerabilities inherent in that complexity.

1.3 Issues and Trends

1.3.1 Policy Trade-offs

Regulation and Control

The U.S. banking and finance infrastructure is a centrally controlled system backed by the federal government since the 1860s. Since that time, the U.S. Treasury has tightly controlled the representation of money or economic value. Changes in the way that our nation issues coins and currency have been made during the twentieth century to protect against counterfeiting, thereby reducing risks inherent in the infrastructure. Although the policy and legislative guidelines have remained the same, there is a significant precedent for protecting both the interests of the nation as a whole and the interests of our citizens as individuals. Consequently, the behavioral environment for exchanging money for goods and services has had a defined framework within which individuals operate. Modes for spending or exchanging money, investing money, moving money, and communicating the way in which money is moved between exchange entities are based on trust models that are understood by those involved in economic exchange processes.

The purpose of regulating banking and finance in the United States is to maintain the surety, or security, of the system. For banks, regulators have adopted rules based on generally accepted performance indicators:

- Capital adequacy,
- Asset quality,
- Management competency,
- Earnings, and
- Liquidity.

For the investment side, statutes, case law, and regulatory practice have resulted in a standard that balances the protection of investors from fraud and deceit and the promotion of free exchange of value among ready, willing, and able buyers and sellers. The underlying principle is full disclosure of information necessary to facilitate an informed exchange of value. Regulators cannot set the exchange rate for representations of value; investors or purchasers must make that decision. Regulators can only act to ensure that relevant facts are not intentionally withheld from buyers and sellers. This balance between supporting the market and protecting participants has been maintained by focusing on the following elements of financial services:

- *Products*– Most representations of value offered to the public must be registered with federal agencies, state agencies, or both.

- *Practices*—Regulators have attempted to prevent persons with fiduciary or insider status from offering misleading or false inducements or from manipulating buyers and sellers of financial products.
- *Prices*—Regulations set up to limit excessive or inflated pricing of specific representations of value establish limits on interest rates, service fees, and other transaction costs. These rules are intended to ensure that the price paid for any representation of value accurately reflects the true, underlying value of that instrument.

Both managers and regulators of the banking and finance infrastructure are striving to balance four competing goals: security of entrusted value, growth and adaptation of new opportunities, competitiveness in the market, and flexibility to meet uncertainty. The difficulty is that not all financial institutions respond equally to uncertainty or to adaptation of new technologies and products. Likewise, not all regulators are equally able to recognize when a single goal is being overemphasized to the detriment of others. Moreover, not all institutions are subject to the same level of regulation.

The banking and finance infrastructure has an enormous stake in maintaining the trust and confidence of the public in the stability and safety of financial services and products. Members of the industry must balance the severity of a risk against the costs of mitigation. The infrastructure regularly stresses this tenet of operation. Banking, in particular, has developed many techniques and tools to assist managers in analyzing systemic risk. Today, however, the entire infrastructure is constantly under pressure to become more competitive in a continuously shifting marketplace in which the old rules may not apply.

An increasing problem for both industry and regulators is that this new, super-competitive electronic marketplace has little relationship to the location or origin of their products and services. More and more, they are acquiring operational services (e.g., software development, contingency data storage, data processing, communications linkages) needed to support this spatially and temporally disaggregated marketplace from outside sources not directly subject to the standards of the industry. Added to the impact of the electronic marketplace is the industry's response to regulatory pressures to increase competition. To maximize their rate of return, many firms in the industry have concentrated their assets and operations and also reduced their overall workforce. Taking these measures has created more lucrative targets for criminals and generated dissatisfaction among displaced workers, which constitutes an additional threat.

The industry wants the freedom to adopt or exploit opportunities in the new marketplace, but it does not want to be divided by the forces discussed above. Industry leaders want to have a strong voice in shaping whatever regulatory structure is developed to address the new issues in the emerging industry. Of primary concern is that industry leaders do not want to be forced into taking risks that are poorly understood and poorly defined. They would prefer to wait for a regulatory definition, while Congress and the regulators respond to a public demand to "do something."

Regulatory practices can significantly affect the safety and security of the banking and finance infrastructure in terms of balancing economic risks and opportunities. The effects of regulations that would protect the industry as a national infrastructure (that is, in the sense of protecting the industry from intentional ill will) are unknown. However, it is clear that forces shaping the new structure and movement of the industry are already being felt and that to provide significant help, regulatory structure and practices must become more flexible and adaptable.

The banking and finance infrastructure has implemented various security measures and safeguards to protect assets and respond to regulatory pressure. Currently, protecting this infrastructure is affected more directly by regulations established for the information and communications infrastructure. However, changes are expected in the future. Appropriate protective measures may depend on the type of threat, although some measures may be common to all threats. Threats to the banking and finance infrastructure can be categorized as follows:

- *Physical theft or destruction.* Terrorists could attempt to incite financial panic by stealing physical assets or destroying financial data banks or the communication systems that support transactions so that they cannot be used. This type of threat could involve either physical (e.g., bombing a key facility) or cyber attack.
- *Corruption or destruction of data.* Criminals or terrorists could attempt to corrupt or delete information in key systems. For example, they could try to disrupt banking, commerce, or utilities by "hacking" into particular systems. They could then either input false or misleading data, delete data, or deliberately manipulate the system (e.g., "zero out" or increase a bank balance).
- *Unauthorized access to information.* Criminals or others conducting national or industrial espionage could attempt to use information systems to obtain proprietary data or "private" information (in the personal sense).

The greatest damage from any of these threats (physical or cyber) is outright denial of service. The most harmful kinds of attacks against the infrastructure are those that cause the public to perceive the system as unreliable, leading to a serious lack of confidence in the system. Regulatory structure and practice must directly help to define products, practices, and prices in this emerging new structure. To meet this obligation, regulators require new tools with which to assist the industry in defining risk, assessing threats, and responding to crises.

National Security and Promotion of Commerce

A national debate is under way concerning the balance between using technologies to ensure the national defense and to support international competitiveness. Central to this debate for the banking and finance infrastructure are our nation's cryptographic policies. This debate must be resolved before public key systems can be deployed on an international basis with adequate security to protect the assets of the banking and finance infrastructure.

1.3.2 New Technologies

The extent of the interdependence between the information and communications infrastructure and the banking and finance infrastructure is now so significant that it is difficult to conceive how modern banking and finance could be carried out without full and reliable access to a secure telecommunications system. Increasingly, the access to and reliability of that system depend on the same crucial communications and computing technologies. This combination is collectively referred to as the National Information Infrastructure (NII). One group of experts has characterized the importance of the NII to banking and finance in this way:

> Much of the way money is accounted for, handled, and exchanged is now done via the NII. Salaries are directly deposited into bank accounts by electronic funds transfers. Automated teller machines . . . deposit funds, withdraw funds, and make payments. When payment is made for merchandise with debit cards and credit cards, transactions are verified using the public switched [telephone] network. Much of our national economy also depends on the NII. The vast majority of transactions conducted by banks and other financial institutions are done via electronic funds transfers. Over $2 trillion is sent by international wire transfers every day. In addition, most securities transactions are conducted via computerized systems (U.S. Senate 1996).

In the next decade, six trends in technology are probably going to dramatically alter the banking and finance infrastructure:

- Convergence of communicating, computing, and imaging into integrated platforms;
- Proliferation of networks using asynchronous transfer mode cell switching to integrate voice, data, and video for transmission among users;
- Increased reliance on digital communications;
- Increased use of digital signatures for executing agreements;

- Improvements in pattern-directed inference systems for detecting potentially fraudulent or otherwise illegal activities on networks; and
- Deployment of packet-switching protocols throughout the communications and computations networks that support the industry.

The positive effects of these trends on the banking and finance infrastructure are likely to be increased speed, convenience, and openness for all participants. The negative effect is the potential for increased vulnerability to misuse of the systems that comprise the industry's supporting infrastructure. Increased vulnerability could result from more openness, without commensurate attention to security, and disparate rates of introducing new technologies among the many participating institutions and entities. For example, older, slower systems could be overwhelmed by faster, information-dense systems. One expert has defined the issues somewhat differently, but not inconsistently:

> New technology, which includes faster switches, higher speed routers, etc., is being developed, but technology takes time. In the security area, faster encryption algorithms, electronic signatures, cyber notaries, and data compression algorithms need to be developed to send more data in less time while providing secure, confidential, and authenticated network links.
>
> The Internet is technically capable of growing almost infinitely. The major constrictor of growth will be how the user communities will deal with securing intellectual property rights, the security of transactions, and other sociological issues (Kennedy 1998).

The challenge is to ensure that technologies introduced to enhance performance of the infrastructure do not unintentionally reduce the security of the infrastructure.

1.3.3 Internationalization of Information and Trade

The effect of new technologies (e.g., Internet connectivity and the size of the asset pool that is electronically connected worldwide) is significant in many ways. Does greater connectivity motivate criminals to attempt to defraud financial institutions and systems? Furthermore, does greater connectivity lower the risk of exposure because of the potential to remain anonymous over open public networks (e.g., the Internet)? Also, the latest changes in technology allow foreign nation-states to "leapfrog" implementing infrastructure (e.g., investing in pervasive communications systems) by moving to technologies that support electronic commerce, such as the smartcard, cellular phone and satellite communications, and cryptography.

The United States must embrace electronic commerce to participate in international economic exchanges. New technologies are changing the definition of "money" and presenting an incentive for moving toward nontraditional representations of money, such as electronic money (or E-money) and stored-value cards issued with or without bank involvement.

Growth and expansion within this infrastructure are primarily based outside the United States and come at a time when both government and private-sector investments in R&D funding are more limited and in need of reassessment. Decentralization of operations over multiple platforms (rather than being concentrated on a single mainframe with backup capability) makes information at greater risk from tampering, theft, or misuse at any single point.

1.3.4 New Definitions of Value

Efficient commerce depends on well-understood, highly trustworthy definitions of value, financial obligation, money, and legal tender. Value is the underlying utility of an object, for example, weighted by its cost. Just as so many pounds of potatoes are "worth" so many units of money, a given quantity of ownership or control of a financial obligation or expression of ownership (e.g., stocks, bonds, notes, or evidence of debt or guarantee of payment) is also worth so much in exchange.

Money can be any generally accepted medium of exchange or unit of account. A unit of money can represent a certain fixed quantity of a physical substance (e.g., gold, silver, platinum, or potatoes), or it can represent an expectation of value relative to other media of exchange.

The U.S. dollar has value far beyond the intrinsic utility of the paper on which it is printed because, as legal tender (e.g., coins and currency issued by the federal government), it is backed by the full faith in, and credit of, the nation.

Until recently, these relationships among value, financial obligation, money, and legal tender have been clearly defined in the United States because of four stabilizing factors:

- Tightly controlled processes of coinage and issuance of currency;
- Secure and robust communications infrastructures;
- Well-defined authentication practices; and
- Recognizable forms of exchange with known guaranteed exchange values.

Traditionally, the industry has had a clear understanding of the assets within the infrastructure that require protection (Wriston 1992):

> . . . [Technological] developments, generally referred to as the information revolution, are causing a shift in the balance of economic, political, and military power and are changing relationships among government, citizens, and private institutions. Two technological advances –communications technology for transmitting information and modern computer systems for processing data—are driving many of these changes. . . . The systems built around these technologies and the information they process, are now key to delivering the goods and services of the nation. Today, lights would go out, airplanes would stop flying, and financial institutions would shut down if

the supporting computer systems and networks ceased to function. As these changes have evolved, information has become the "capital" for the future; causing a shift in perspective as to the assets that need protection.

We have entered an era in which these traditional relationships among value, financial obligation, money, and legal tender can become unstable because three of the four stabilizing factors are undergoing major changes. The one relatively stable factor –the federal government's minting of coins and issuance of currency—will also have to be adapted to accommodate the new realities.

Section 2
Threats and Vulnerabilities

2.1 Effects of Regulation and Control

The architecture and dynamics of the banking and finance infrastructure are not comprehensively understood. Some components of the systems are static, "stovepiped" items. Discrete functionalities, protocols, and practices are studied independent of the systems into which they are embedded. Regulatory practices and processes are often viewed as hindrances to the efficiency of the marketplace, but can, in fact, add to the confidence and efficiency of the system and contribute to infrastructure assurance.

Because no comprehensive model of the banking and finance infrastructure exists, the impacts of regulatory agencies on this infrastructure are not easily studied. Several issues have become apparent, however. They are listed below along with recommendations to address them.

Issue 1. The lines between federal and state regulatory practices and structures must be as transparent as the lines among local, state, national, and international commerce in financial products and services. It will be necessary to rethink the balance between supervisory and regulatory approaches to practice and the intentional assignment of oversight responsibility to the level closest to where commerce is being conducted.

Recommendation 1. Research should be conducted to define the appropriate structure of oversight agencies for the emerging banking and finance infrastructure at the local, state, federal, and international levels.

Issue 2. More immediate response to problems is needed. Regulators and examiners should begin to monitor the activities of the infrastructure by observing operations in real time, rather than depending on periodic reports generated after the fact.

Recommendation 2. Research should be performed to determine how stakeholders could conduct on-line supervision and oversight. This research should include such techniques as pattern recognition, expert systems, and risk-assessment tools available on-line to both the industry and regulators, so that perceived problems can be recognized and corrected immediately.

Issue 3. Examiners need to have timely and economical training and continuous education. This need should increase as the pace of changes in the industry accelerates. New tools, and the nature of the evolving infrastructure that requires these tools, are complex and unfamiliar to most examiners and regulators.

Recommendation 3. R&D should be conducted to examine distance learning capabilities and on-line expert systems to help to prepare and train examiners and regulators.

Issue 4. The definitions of products, practices, and prices in the industry need to be standardized among state, federal, and international statutes and regulations. All parties involved need to understand what is being regulated, especially because billions of transactions occur in cyberspace 24 hours a day.

Recommendation 4. R&D in model law should be undertaken to clarify regulatory subjects in the emerging infrastructure and standardize the laws and regulations among agencies and between levels of government.

2.2 Effects of New Technologies

The U.S. Department of the Treasury has stated that "[n]ew technology and new ways of using current technology is [sic] making it possible to manage, perform, and create in an environment of shared resources and shared power" (U.S. Department of the Treasury 1993).

While these technologies make financial transactions more efficient, they also make it more difficult to secure the support systems. Each additional point-of-presence in the network of systems and persons in the banking and finance infrastructure creates an additional potential for electronic tampering or attack. The General Accounting Office (GAO) (1996) has stated:

> These advances promise to streamline . . . operations and improve delivery of . . . services. However, they also increase the potential risks that sensitive and critical information could be inappropriately modified, disclosed, or destroyed, possibly resulting in significant interruptions of service, monetary losses, and a loss of confidence in the . . . ability to protect confidential data on individuals.

The efficiency, flexibility, and adaptability that make these new technologies so attractive to the banking and finance infrastructure also create subtle, but potentially catastrophic, weaknesses in the systems. Computerized systems "empower users to perform their jobs more effectively" (Jones and Sicherman 1997). The nexus of communications, computing, and imagery technologies makes it possible, however, for every point-of-presence to have a *custom* approach in interfacing with a network. The flexibility and adaptability create significant problems in attaining desirable states of security for that network, other networks with which it interacts, and the data being handled.

2.3 Effects of Protecting Monetary Information

The GAO (1996) report discusses the vulnerability of government systems, but the warning about vulnerability also is valid for systems that support the banking and finance infrastructure. In addition, this report continues with a statement that parallels the concerns voiced by banking systems experts during Commission interviews; that is,

> . . . the potential risks are increasing because automated systems and records are fast replacing manual procedures and paper documents, which in many cases are no longer available as 'backup' if automated systems should fail. These vulnerabilities are exacerbated because, when systems are interconnected to form networks or are accessible through public telecommunications systems, they are much more vulnerable to anonymous intrusions from remote locations (1996).

The common response to dealing with increased vulnerabilities is to improve encryption, especially for those vulnerabilities that arise from the combined effects of (1) more individual points of presence in a network, (2) faster processors and nearly unlimited storage memory, and (3) greater on-line access to more detailed data. Encryption has been applied in two venues: protection of data and "cloaking" of transactions. The government has invested in extensive research into creating and maintaining cryptographic systems to satisfy the needs of the banking and finance infrastructure. The release of some useful technologies for commercial use has been deterred, however, because the government is required to keep "master keys" for all encryption systems. This requirement is based on law enforcement and national security issues. All security applications are subject to the same vulnerability as systems that provide a "back door" to satisfy this government policy—the concern merely shifts from security of the data and transactions to the security of the master keys. In addition, it is not clear how international companies may react to U.S. policies about key repositories and types of encryption.

The banking and finance infrastructure is becoming more enmeshed with communications technology, which creates an additional security problem. The former has been slower to totally replace physical records and manual procedures and processes than have some of the other service industries. Although the industry is, therefore, relatively more able to respond to system failure, this positive aspect is somewhat offset because of a continued reliance on the integrity of key individuals to authorize and validate certain actions. As a result, the banking and finance infrastructure does not have the advantages of automated audit tracking and surveillance tools. However, such tools cannot replace, but only supplement, trusted employees who operate under dual control systems with stringent audit mechanisms.

2.4 Effects of the International Marketplace

The United States has been the world leader in the "information revolution," which began in 1946 with the invention of the first computer. Since that time, much of our nation's infrastructure has depended on reliable, secure operation of information systems to preserve and protect national welfare and interests.

However, the information revolution is no longer contained within the United States. Persons involved in the banking and finance infrastructure need to recognize the effects of communications technological developments on the international marketplace:

> The globalization of information technology has posed the potential threat of information weapons, which could be one of the most effective, cheapest, and simplest avenues for terrorists and/or nation-states to deploy in order to cripple U.S. defenses. These weapons have been described as great equalizers that help small nations against larger nations. Information warfare attacks could conceivably be conducted with relative anonymity from anywhere in the world (Defense Science Board 1996).
>
> . . . It would be naive to believe that other nation-states, and probably terrorist organizations, are not developing [information warfare tools]. . . . However, lacking credible evidence of existing information warfare attacks on the United States or a physical attack specifically targeting electronic systems, it is unlikely that industry will plan to defend itself from terrorist and nation-state attacks (Booz-Allen and Hamilton 1996).

Section 3
R&D Topics and Activities

3.1 R&D Objectives

The banking and finance infrastructure must preserve the public's confidence in the nation's economy. Management and control of the value of the U.S. dollar are key to the continued confidence of both consumers and international trading partners. National security is, by definition, an underlying goal of this R&D effort.

3.2 Technological Needs

3.2.1 Simulation Model Development

Description

Industry policy makers and planners do not clearly understand the potential impacts and interdependencies of the forces behind the rapid changes within the banking and finance infrastructure. The infrastructure is so diverse that a simple characterization cannot adequately express the potentially complex results from either public or private initiatives that affect components of the infrastructure. Considerable effort is needed to develop a constructive strategic simulation model of this infrastructure. As the model is developed, maintained, and elaborated, analysts can develop increasingly effective strategies that can be used to examine (1) policies and requirements for managing the infrastructure and (2) mechanisms for responding to threats to that infrastructure.

Goals and Challenges

The model must be able to simulate both the technical reactions of the support systems and the probable public and industry reactions to regulatory initiatives and information dissemination initiatives. Other characteristics of the infrastructure also should be modeled. For example, the National Infrastructure Protection Center, which was recently established within the Federal Bureau of Investigation, could use such a model to advise industry on the potential effects of proposed technologies (Reno 1998). This function would require sensitivity in managing and controlling information.

Rationale for the Research and Desired Results

Only a constructive model that can serve as the basis of nondeterministic simulations of the banking and finance infrastructure can satisfy the requirements of the various stakeholders. Such a model, made available through a national user facility, would enable stakeholders to:

- Develop new business risk models;
- Examine the effects of policy trade-offs, shifts in technology, the international marketplace, and various open market standards;
- Validate oversight and training programs;
- Validate intrusion indication and warning tools; and
- Validate system reliability under alternative scenarios, while ensuring that consistent internal logic is used throughout such an analysis.

Timeframe and Resource Requirements

In the near term (before 2002), researchers would engage industry to develop a constructive strategic simulation model (CSSM). Funding required for these efforts is estimated to be $18 million. Before 2005, research activities would include development of the requirements, legal basis, policies, and techniques for protecting data for the CSSM. Funding required for these efforts is estimated to be $10 million. Before 2010, researchers would prepare a field operational model and life-cycle management plan. The cost for this work is estimated to be $1 million.

3.2.2 Information Security Analysis

This topic includes cryptographic research and entity authentication.

Description

Today's approaches for implementing cryptography balance the issues of anonymity and nonrepudiation. Protection of privacy in transactions needs to be balanced with the requirement to be certain of the identities of the parties involved. It needs to be decided whether it is important to maintain an audit (paper) trail to provide evidence of economic transactions (i.e., nonrepudiation) to a third party (someone not involved in the economic exchange). This procedure would support private rights, meet legal requirements for financial reporting, and help to resolve financial electronic crimes.

If it is determined that an audit trail is of paramount importance, secondary or less importance can be placed on anonymity. In a paper cash system, anonymity in the transaction is possible. Persons pay in cash for goods and services without proving their identities. If paying cash is of paramount importance to an E-money-based economy, nonrepudiation must be less important. Certainly a trade-off is inevitable between anonymity and nonrepudiation. Research needs to be conducted to determine the best ways to support both interests simultaneously.

Goals and Challenges

Cryptography allows party A to send information to party B across open public networks or communications channels. It gives a defined level of confidence that the data received by party B actually came from party A and not from someone masquerading as party A. It also ensures that the information received has not been altered during transmission and that another party has not substituted a false message for a legitimate one. Most important, by applying an encryption algorithm, cryptography ensures that intruders or unauthorized parties cannot read the message.

Issues that arise in the management of public keys, which are used for encryption purposes, can become onerous. Research is needed to study, develop, pilot test, and investigate the liabilities associated with public key infrastructures to enable secure electronic commerce. Financial standards are in place in this area; however, they need to be assessed before being applied in the future secure financial environment.

"Entity authentication" refers to a person or an organization (e.g., bank or merchant); it also refers to authentication of a device as a deterrent to counterfeit smartcards, cash, or tokens of any kind required to confirm a person's identity. Authentication is best provided by presenting three types of personal signatures in an integrated architecture: (1) informational, something that you know (e.g., a personal identification number [PIN] or a password); (2) credential, something that you have in your possession (e.g., a card, key, or badge); and (3) biometric, something that you are (e.g., fingerprints, DNA, or other bio-physical characteristics unique to an individual). The authentication system should require simultaneous presentation of all three signatures.

Research is needed to reduce ambiguity in these measures and to ensure that an unauthorized person cannot take another person's property. Research in authentication is key to the future of the banking and finance infrastructure because of the lack of personal relationships with clientele, especially when trading partners are geographically distant, which is common in international electronic commerce. Research also is needed to prevent persons from manipulating the system to discover combinations of specific data (see numbered items above) about an entity that can compromise authentication.

Rationale for the Research and Desired Results

Scalable public key management systems are necessary to address top-priority management issues posed by the broad reach of principal players in the banking and finance infrastructure. Some entities have to be trusted to manage keys (e.g., key generation, key storage, key delivery), and trust can be a difficult problem in international systems.

Some entity or group of entities must be responsible for validating private or public key pair holders and certifying electronic identities. These certificates can expire or be revoked. This entity often is referred to as the "certificate authority." Very large, scalable systems could require multiple certificate authorities in a network. How will users certified by one certificate authority trust users certified by another certificate authority (i.e., cross-certification issues)? Interoperability issues must be addressed in international environments. They are difficult problems, not only technically, but also politically. National interests and interest in international competitiveness and interoperability must somehow be reconciled to support, if not facilitate, international economic exchanges.

If the banking and finance infrastructure is characterized by E-money systems and nonstandard representations of money, by both banks and non-banks, how will recipients of electronic commerce messages verify the integrity and originator of these messages? Authorization is an important function in the banking system, so the meaning of identity certificates needs to be understood, and the use of other types of certificates (e.g., attribute or capability certificates for authorization) needs to be researched and pilot tested.

The enormous trust placed in information systems mandates far more security than is currently in place. R&D is needed for key management, cryptographic functions, key generation, and storage and manipulation of fungibles (e.g., items capable of mutual substitution; they are interchangeable). More secure computer hardware and software, and capabilities in operating systems, networking, and operations, need to be developed. Without such advances, cryptography will fail to meet the needs identified.

Timeframe and Resource Requirements

In the near term (before 2002), research would focus on developing a legal and procedural basis for expediting access to government off-the-shelf cryptographic analysis and surety analysis technology. Security standards would be developed and validated, and the efficacy of implementing cryptographic and surety technologies would be analyzed. Funding required for these efforts is estimated to be $32 million. Before 2005, research would focus on implementing a balance in anonymity and fielding scalable key public management systems. Funding required for these efforts is estimated to be $6 million. Before 2010, researchers would field entity authentication technologies. The cost for this work is estimated to be $1 million.

3.2.3 Intrusion Indication and Warning Tools

Description

The current banking and finance infrastructure is capable of indicating problems and issuing warnings based on physical attributes and documented evidence. For example, these attributes and evidence imbalances alert security teams, who then review physical evidence and electronic indicators and begin corrective measures (as needed). People monitor the integrity of sections of the infrastructure and provide warnings and indications of problems. The borders of our nation and the redundancy of systems that must integrate to verify operational integrity (e.g., output from information systems, paper reconciliation processes, telecommunications confirmations and authorizations) are helpful in this process. The federal government monitors the economy and makes adjustments and modifications to control inflation on the basis of similar mechanisms and indicators, but on an international level.

Goals and Challenges

Changes in the banking and finance infrastructure have resulted from (1) emerging technologies (e.g., network connectivity, satellite communications, new forms of monetary value) and (2) new entries to the competitive marketplace both nationally and internationally (e.g., the insurance industry and non-bank providers of bank cards). These changes preclude the need for, and the effectiveness of, many of the physical control processes that the infrastructure depends on for assurance of faithful execution. Total dependence on information systems data for indications and warnings is a possible solution; however, it requires a more careful look at security, integrity, authentication, reliability, and availability. Other solutions for redundant indicator paths need to be evaluated and instituted, not only at the industry level, but also at the national and international levels.

Rationale for the Research and Desired Results

The United States needs to plan for the security of the banking and finance infrastructure to protect our national interests and ensure public confidence in an international electronic commerce exchange environment. To design and operate such a framework, evaluators need to assess vulnerabilities and threats on a regular basis so that prudent risk management mechanisms can be implemented. Furthermore, the government needs to know when a nation-state or a terrorist attack causes discrepancies in the infrastructure. This information is valuable in terms of supporting not only our national defense, but also retaliation, as appropriate. Infrastructure principals also need to know when natural disasters or operational errors cause discrepancies so that they can deal appropriately with public reaction. Part of this effort should include research into ways of dealing with disseminating information to the public; in addition, panic management planning should be a part of this effort.

For the government to protect our nation by means of financial crime prevention and law enforcement, the operations of the Financial Crime Enforcement Network (FinCEN) and the Secret Service Financial Crimes Division must be redefined. These agencies focus on combating money laundering and counterfeiting, respectively, but currently are not specifically authorized to protect our infrastructure. Their internal processes and controls are based on the physical borders and boundaries that provide for checks and balances within the system. Given that physical boundaries do not exist in cyberspace, their primary functions need to be reexamined for the benefit of the country. Our new environment has generated a need for tools to assess national vulnerability and threats; these tools also support the design of threat mitigation techniques that can be used not only by FinCEN and the Secret Service, but also by industry security teams and services.

Timeframe and Resource Requirements

In the near term (before 2002), research would focus on using insight gained from work on the CSSM to determine where sensitivity tools and techniques within I&W are applicable. Researchers also would determine what data are required to implement those tools. Funding required for these efforts is estimated to be $9 million. Before 2005, research would focus on development of an initial set of tools. Funding required for this timeframe is estimated to be $7 million. Before 2010, researchers would field all operational tools. Funding required for this effort is estimated to be $1 million.

3.2.4 Systems Reliability Enhancement

Description

Research into issues that affect the reliability and recoverability of the banking and finance infrastructure should produce the following:

- "Reliability-increasing" techniques for continuing transactions through interruptions;
- Alternative routes, tools, and techniques for dealing with interruptions;
- Alternative routes, tools, and techniques for seeking alternative routes;
- New methods for recording the state of transactions;
- Automatic detection of attempts to overload the system and automatic healing around these attempts;
- Capabilities for detecting new ways to commit fraud or defeat the system and for adapting continuously with new defenses;
- Operations in the event of compromise (e.g., a root certificate);
- Operations in the presence of a communications outage; and
- Degraded mode operations.

The critical functions of secure systems typically operate on a trusted computer system to ensure that the authority for degradation can be validated. Technologies that should be explored as tools to deal with system reliability issues include the following:

- Design and deployment of dynamically configurable firewalls to protect against specific attacks while allowing authenticated transactions to continue;
- Network agents or "benign viruses," which are used for data aggregation (studied from both an offensive and a defensive perspective to support infrastructure surety); and

- Information systems that "heal" themselves or can be designed to facilitate recovery.

Goals and Challenges

Technology evaluations and integration surety issues need to be studied, and recommendations need to be made available to managers of the infrastructure. Effective analysis of these issues must be based on the constructive simulation model. A "trusted computer system" needs to be mapped to incorporate "a trusted computer network" in support of the banking and finance infrastructure. Accomplishing this mapping—and understanding its implications—requires significant effort because of the complexity and interdependencies involved. Effective and timely analysis is nearly impossible if a constructive simulation model is not available.

Rationale for the Research and Desired Results

Trusted systems traditionally have provided the basic capability for computer systems that have ultra-high requirements for availability and reliability. Trusted systems have been accredited to perform their required tasks in the presence of failures. Failures can be manifested in several ways: intrusion by unauthorized users, design errors, or the erroneous functioning of a component.

A current trend in the design of computer-based information systems for application in critical systems is to construct a reliable system from unreliable parts. Providing secure methods for transferring information over open public networks is critical for the banking and finance infrastructure because it must maintain the trust of its customers. Because open public networks are not secure, research must be increased to develop and implement new design techniques. These systems use redundancy, layering, and diversity paradigms to detect failures in a hierarchy and gracefully degrade to a state that provides a less functional, yet more trusted, configuration for operation.

Timeframe and Resource Requirements

In the near term (before 2002), research would focus on developing, publishing, and initiating implementation of standards and specifications. The focus would then turn to developing prototypes of network security agents. Funding required for these efforts is estimated to be $54 million. Before 2005, researchers would complete implementing the standards and specifications, as well as the prototypes of network security agents. Funding required for these efforts is estimated to be $15 million. Before 2010, the prototypes of self-healing systems, configurable firewalls, and network security agents would be "fielded." Funding required for these activities is estimated to be $2 million.

3.2.5 Information System Standardization

Description

Because new employees, customers, and other individuals; products; and technologies are introduced regularly into the banking and finance infrastructure, the industry and its regulators need to establish new standards for defining risk, assessing threats, and specifying required responses to crises. These standards must result from a collaborative effort and be administered in the same way. New organizational designs must be conceived for overseeing the infrastructure. These designs must effectively allocate responsibilities and authority among federal and state agencies, international treaty organizations, and industry associations. All standards and organizational templates must be as open and flexible as possible to accommodate the rapid changes and increased complexities, which are characteristic of this industry.

Goals and Challenges

Currently, elected officials—particularly members of Congress—and regulators are struggling to agree on ways to protect the banking and finance infrastructure. The elected officials are considering making the regulatory agencies more accountable for the health and safety of the banking system. Their approach is to consolidate the regulatory agencies and implement strict codification of standards and procedures, with fewer regulations and regulators. Appointed officials who manage the regulatory system have a different solution—greater autonomy for examiners and less reshuffling and reorganization of authority and responsibility. The trade-off is between accountability and flexibility.

The U.S. banking regulatory structure is much like it was in 1950. The Federal Reserve, the Office of the Controller of the Currency, and the Federal Deposit Insurance Corporation have divided responsibilities for overseeing a rapidly changing and growing industry. Rather than stressing the need for training and experience in bank supervision, which would allow more flexibility in meeting the expected changes, the law now emphasizes across-the-board standards and strict adherence to regulations developed in response to the last banking crisis. One industry expert said that a trade-off occurs between strict political accountability and freedom of action in response to reforming the U.S. banking regulations.

The U.S. banking and finance infrastructure has evolved slowly. However, increased competition, new technology, and the amendment and revision of the law in the late 1990s have introduced substantial changes. The banking environment has moved from a fairly static, predictable industry to a dynamic, rapidly developing new structure. The regulatory scheme in 1975 probably will not be evident in 2000.

Although federal agencies continue to have the same compartmentalized responsibilities, dramatic changes probably will be made, as it becomes obvious that this structure may not be responsive and flexible enough to cope with the rate of change expected in the next two decades. Regulators must be free to apply different approaches to supervision and regulation, as appropriate, for a defined set of facts concerning a specific banking activity or bank. They must not be hampered by either bureaucratic intransigence or political expediency.

Rationale for Research and Desired Results

Open standards for the information infrastructure are important for interoperability and free-market competition. Rather than relying on many sources to develop software elements, banks and their customers increasingly depend on a handful of software suppliers—a new vulnerability that can affect the infrastructure. Government encouragement and support for open standards can strengthen the free-market environment and help to provide an infrastructure that is not constrained by a few entities.

Timeframe and Resource Requirements

In the near term (before 2002), research would focus on developing and publishing standards and specifications for the infrastructure. Funding required for these efforts is estimated to be $6 million.

3.2.6 Information Security Support for Electronic Commerce

Description

The U.S. financial payments architecture needs to be redesigned to support the national interests with respect to new international exchange environments and technologies. The technical options available for use by government, industry, and individual consumers need to be evaluated on the basis of their ability to support the security requirements yet to be defined for this infrastructure. The National Institute of Science and Technology and the National Security Agency have performed Underwriters Laboratory functions for these technologies on the basis of their potential impact on the surety of the banking and finance infrastructure. This arrangement should be fostered and enhanced.

Goals and Challenges

To remain competitive, the U.S. banking and finance infrastructure must be able to access cryptographic and surety technologies sufficient to maintain efficiency and effectiveness in protecting its customers' interests. These needs must be balanced against other national security interests.

Rationale for Research and Desired Results

The appropriate level of cryptographic technologies used in commercial applications must addressed immediately if the United States is to continue to be an economic world leader. International electronic commerce increases requirements for the robustness and surety of authentication mechanisms, for information systems and data integrity, and for innovative solutions to the trade-offs in balancing privacy and nonrepudiation. To support authentication requirements, biometric research needs to continue. Research also is needed to consider the applications of existing and developing technologies to satisfy more stringent requirements in infrastructure surety. Standards for integrating these technologies into system design should be developed as an incentive for industry to fill any gaps.

Timeframe and Resource Requirements

In the near term (before 2002), research would focus on publishing initial standards and specifications for equipment and support tools for the banking and finance infrastructure. Funding required for these efforts is estimated to be $9 million. Before 2005, researchers would field the standards and specifications. Funding required for these efforts is estimated to be $9 million. Before 2010, operational tools would be tested in the field. Funding required for these activities is estimated to be $3 million.

3.3 Technology R&D Shortfalls

Current commercial technologies may or may not be sufficient to protect the banking and finance infrastructure in the future. Various commercial off-the-shelf and government off-the-shelf products have been developed to provide security to financial information systems. However, most of these products lack the robustness and scaleability to secure our nation's information economy.

In addition, it is not clear that the private sector has the necessary motivation or incentive to develop the level of services that may be required to protect the infrastructure at the national level. Most private-sector parties work to capture market share or some other competitive advantage through their information technology innovations. Therefore, it is unlikely that the private sector would develop the open, scalable, and robust information technologies needed to foster a widespread competitive information economy.

Although the private sector apparently lacks sufficient incentive for developing certain technologies of importance to our national security, private/public-sector partnerships can play an active role in developing the necessary technologies. Areas in which partnerships are needed to help the banking and finance infrastructure to reach its full potential are described below.

3.3.1 Modeling and Simulation

It is unlikely that a single entity in industry can develop, maintain, and elaborate a scalable, flexible, and comprehensive constructive model of the entire banking and finance infrastructure because of the costs and complexities of such an enterprise. Industrial entities have few incentives for sharing information about their operations and structures. An industry/government consortium could develop such incentives; however, sufficient guarantees would have to be in place to protect proprietary business information. Moreover, the intent would have to be clear that the model and information would be used solely for analyzing technologies, making business arrangements, and developing regulatory schemes. These tasks would be directed at enabling the banking and finance infrastructure to move forward, not for surveillance or taxation of industry.

3.3.2 Key Management Systems

Cryptography plays a prominent role in most information security technologies. However, cryptographic methods are difficult, if not impossible, to implement without efficient, scalable mechanisms for managing key components. In particular, the banking and finance infrastructure of the future needs standard, open mechanisms for certifying public keys and cryptographic credentials. The industry must have access to better tools for evaluating cryptographic systems and have a well-defined method for comparing the appropriateness of such systems for specific applications.

3.3.3 Authentication Technologies

Our future information economy cannot reach its potential until science and industry develop better techniques for identifying and authenticating individuals and entities to information systems. The industry needs inexpensive, reliable, and scalable techniques to support the vast number of individuals who present themselves to information terminals or appliances for many reasons. Biometric identification techniques must be developed to meet these needs. Researchers also must concentrate on developing better sensors that can become as common as keyboards and touch-pads are today.

3.3.4 Intrusion and Anomaly Detection Tools

Tools that combine automated pattern recognition, sensitivity analysis, and nonlinear correlations are desperately needed to aid in deciding when an event is a systemic anomaly as opposed to when it is evidence of intentional malfeasance. It is unlikely that the banking and finance infrastructure could justify the necessary R&D as a purely private matter; it would require a strong government support program. The need for such tools is not unique to this infrastructure, and the specification for, and costs of, such research, therefore, should not be borne solely by this infrastructure.

3.3.5 Computer and Network Security

All applicable technology areas depend significantly on research on computer and network security. Details of R&D requirements in security (Chapter 5, *Preliminary Research and Development Roadmap for Protecting and Assuring the Information and Communications Infrastructure*) should be reviewed for specific interdependencies with the banking and finance infrastructure. Any technologies that affect the robustness of the communications and computation systems that support banking and finance have a critical effect on this industry.

3.3.6 Physical and Electronic Protection Technologies

It is difficult to imagine that citizens and commercial entities would welcome an open electronic banking and finance infrastructure if the community had to rely on current technologies for protecting data stored in information systems. In particular, the community needs better techniques for keeping sensitive data safe from exposure, even when the same parties want to use open public networks and standard computing platforms for managing these data. Research is needed into highly secure, portable data storage, such as smartcards, cryptographic storage, and security-enhanced memories for microcomputers.

3.3.7 Electronic Payment Systems

The banking and finance infrastructure could make the transition from current concepts of electronic cash—and other unique tokens that can be converted to real currency—to the concept of electronic cash minted by the U.S. government. Electronic cash would provide the same full trusts and guarantees as physical currency carries today. Meanwhile, however, the industry needs payment mechanisms that enable an orderly transition from physical instruments to high-confidence electronic instruments, such as electronic checks and other widely accepted standard electronic payment mechanisms.

3.3.8 Network Security Management Systems

Finally, these technologies are not useful until they can be integrated into transaction support systems that are as available and robust as we have come to expect. Tomorrow's technologies must be integrated so that they enhance the trust placed in today's banking system.

3.4 R&D Topics and Roadmaps

In meeting its responsibilities, the government must combine patience with aggressive fact finding, study, and coordination among government units, both nationally and internationally. Premature action by government agencies, or decisions based on incomplete analysis, could "thwart innovation and its benefits, including, perhaps, the ability of U.S. firms to compete effectively in global markets" (U.S. Department of the Treasury 1996).

To protect national interests in an economic infrastructure characterized by international electronic commerce, the government must understand the existing infrastructure and its implications. These implications include its vulnerabilities and the changes in threat profiles that can develop as electronic commerce emerges. Table A.1 provides a summary description of the research topics and their interrelationships. This table summarizes programmatic expenditures for certain timeframes to address the vital issues raised above. The necessary R&D is grouped into clusters of technically related topics.

Table A. 1 Summary of Banking and Finance R&D Topics

Research Topic					
No.	Title (Type[b])	Product	Goals and Challenges	Threats and Vulnerabilities	Priority Category
1	Simulation Model Development[c] (A,ATD, POP)				
1.1	Specify and collect the minimal data set needed to describe the infrastructure. Develop a constructive strategic simulation of this infrastructure.	Scalable, constructive models capable of supporting useful simulations	Specify and collect data. Specify and characterize functional flow on how to engage the industry, protect information, determine inter-dependencies, identify available data and what is needed, and identify available and appropriate modeling techniques.	Complexities, inter-dependencies	Most important.

Research Topic						
No.	Title (Type[b])	Product	Goals and Challenges	Threats and Vulnerabilities	Priority Category
1.2	Create, develop, and evaluate a process for engaging industry in developing, designing, and maintaining a constructive strategic simulation model (CSSM) for the U.S. government and banking and finance stakeholders.	Concept/ strategy paper: process, set of recom- mendations (validated in industry forum), and an implementa- tion plan	Determine the uses for the model. Define CSSM requirements, including interdepen- dencies. Determine the architecture of the CSSM, especially protection of information		
1.3	Develop the requirements, policies, legal basis, and techniques for protecting sensitive, proprietary, and classified data required for the CSSM (e.g., leverage existing work, models, mechanisms). Phase 1 involves historical and contemporary research. Phase 2 identifies gaps for making recommendations. Phase 3 gives iterations of Phase 2 during model development.	End-to-end model of the banking and finance infrastructure that can support non- deterministic simulations	Define required data. Identify available data and gaps. Determine available tech- niques/ tools and gaps. Develop prototype CSSM. Test, validate, and develop life-cycle management methodology. Ensure that all developments are accurate, efficient, respond rapidly, and are timely.		
1.4	Specify, design, and code the CSSM.				
2	Information Security Analysis (A, ATD, POP)				

Research Topic					
No.	**Title (Type[b])**	**Product**	**Goals and Challenges**	**Threats and Vulnerabilities**	**Priority Category**
2.1	Analyze and evaluate the degree to which national strategic interests are adequately addressed by current cryptographic and surety analysis technologies, policies, and practices. If the answer reveals gaps, continue with topics 2.2-2.7.	Policy paper, including both legislative and procedural recommendations; information, hardware, and software	Find an independent, yet sufficiently knowledgeable team to do a reasonable analysis, given that full data for analyzing the problem might require sensitive and classified information. Acknowledge that this topic is a political "hot potato;" the intelligence agencies might object to this analysis. If gaps are found, making recommendations will be difficult, because it requires dealing with "equities" in National Security goals.	Cyber, complexities, inter-dependencies	Most important

Research Topic					
No.	Title (Type[b])	Product	Goals and Challenges	Threats and Vulnerabilities	Priority Category
2.2	Develop a legal and procedural basis for expediting access to government off-the-shelf cryptographic analysis and surety analysis technology.	Development guidelines, metrics for judging the effectiveness of implementations, analysis techniques, and methodologies	Develop the means to allow effective and efficient analysis metrics to assure sound information system processing of banking and finance data with the appropriate level of security.		
2.3	Analyze and evaluate the efficacy of implementations of cryptographic and surety technologies.		Avoid the pitfalls from the "Rainbow Series" security guidelines in which evaluation processes cause unacceptable product cycle times. Include much more than algorithmic standards; allow judgment of the actual implementations of the systems. Support variable security levels required for variable data sensitivity.		

Research Topic					
No.	Title (Type[b])	Product	Goals and Challenges	Threats and Vulnerabilities	Priority Category
2.4	Develop and validate security implementation standards for banking and finance information applications (scalable, supporting variable security levels).		Note that the InfoSec community has struggled with variable security levels before, and it is not easy. Need to focus on the real requirements of the banking and finance infrastructure and find solutions that are much more efficient than those in place for defense applications today.		

Research Topic					
No.	Title (Type[b])	Product	Goals and Challenges	Threats and Vulnerabilities	Priority Category
2.5	Develop scalable public key management systems that are (a) applicable and usable for local, small-scale, and global banking and finance infrastructure; (b) capable of operating with other key management systems implemented for the information and communications infrastructure (the banking and finance community will rely on these systems); and (c) be useful and usable today and in the future.	Improved public management systems with listed properties. Policy papers and recommendations for handling liabilities if any key management systems fail. Specifications and designs for better entity identification technologies.	Keep in mind that all developers of standards have traditionally been very slow in taking actions. Develop effective public management systems for information security applications that process banking and finance data. Avoid developing many noninter-operating certificate authorities that make assured operations risky. Look at scaleability of solutions—both large and small systems. Assign liabilities involved in potential failures in certificate authorities.		

Research Topic					
No.	Title (Type[b])	Product	Goals and Challenges	Threats and Vulnerabilities	Priority Category
			(Many are developing certificate authority systems, although not all are suitable for the banking and finance infrastructure. The industry is investing in the area, but federal dollars might ensure interoperability and better security features in most systems. This is why the dollar amount is relatively small. [Work in key recovery will be a part of this, but other R&D efforts are important.])		

Research Topic					
No.	Title (Type[b])	Product	Goals and Challenges	Threats and Vulnerabilities	Priority Category
2.6	Develop more effective ways to authenticate entities—persons and systems—that use the banking and finance infrastructure. Improve "biometric" identity systems for individuals —strongly linked to physical tokens that present these individuals in a system. Develop mechanisms for authenticating authorized users of the equipment in systems.	Position paper evaluated by the stakeholders on the policy of the U.S. banking and finance infrastructure with respect to this issue. Recommendations for required legislation to cover this policy. Prototypical solutions that provide a balance of technical support.	Develop better, cost-effective biometric systems. Be more careful in linking biometrics of the individual to the physical token used by systems to identify individuals. Implement stronger methods for verifying that certain equipment used in remote systems has not been modified in an unauthorized manner. Find cost-efficient methods to identify unauthorized changes to equipment.		
2.7	Clarify and resolve to achieve an appropriate balance between the need for anonymity and nonrepudiation in information security systems for the banking and finance infrastructure.		Analyze the issues involved. Develop cryptographic and system solutions for balancing competing issues. Develop legislative actions to support these solutions.		

Research Topic					
No.	Title (Type[b])	Product	Goals and Challenges	Threats and Vulnerabilities	Priority Category
3	Intrusion Indication and Warning (I&W) Tools (B, A, ATD, POP)				
3.1	Determine where I&W tools and techniques are applicable	Information, hardware, software	Aim for accuracy, efficiency, and rapid response time.	Cyber, inter-dependencies	Very important
3.2	Develop a suite of intrusion and anomaly detection tools.				
3.3	Develop suite of technology sensitivity analysis tools.				
4	Systems Reliability Enhancement (B, A, ATD, POP)				
4.1	Develop standards for high-availability/high-reliability systems	Information, hardware, software	Understand the environment.	Complexities, inter-dependencies	Very important
4.2	Develop standards for dynamically configurable firewalls.				
4.3	Analyze the utility and efficiency of network agent defenses.				
4.4	Develop standards for self-healing systems.				
5	Information System Standardization (A)	Information, policy, documents	Determine how to engage the industry.	Complexities, inter-dependencies	Important
6	Electronic Commerce Security Enhancement (B, A, ATD, POP)	Information, hardware, software.	Understand the environment. Determine how to engage the industry.	Complexities, inter-dependencies	Important

Research Topic					
No.	Title (Type[b])	Product	Goals and Challenges	Threats and Vulnerabilities	Priority Category
6.1	Develop standards for user equipment and network security,				
6.2	Implement authentication tools and techniques. (7 years, $15 million)				

[a] The order of the R&D topics within a Priority category (i.e., most important, very important, important) does not imply relative importance. Some of these tasks must be done in parallel—some are iterative

[b] B = basic; A = applied; ATD = advanced technology development; and POP = proof of principle and validation.

Section 4
R&D Topic Roadmaps

The suggested roadmap for each of the R&D topics identified and presented by the Banking and Finance R&D Roadmapping Team is summarized in Table A.2. The accomplishments during three phases of research (i.e., near term [before 2002], by approximately 2005, and by approximately 2010) are summarized. More detailed information can be found in Section 3, which contains more detailed topic description.

Table A.2 Summary of the Banking and Finance Infrastructure R&D Roadmap

R&D Topic				
No.	Title	Near Term (Resource Estimate[a])	Achieved by ~ 2005 (Resource Estimate[a])	Achieved by ~2010 (Resource Estimate[a])
1	Simulation Model Development	Engage industry and design and develop a constructive strategic simulation model (CSSM). ($18 million)	Develop the requirements, legal basis, policies, and techniques for protecting the sensitive, proprietary, and classified data required for the CSSM. Leverage existing work, models, mechanisms, etc. ($10 million)	Prepare field operational model and life-cycle management plan. ($1 million)
2	Information Security Analysis	Develop a legal and procedural basis for expediting access to government off-the-shelf cryptographic analysis and surety analysis technology. Analyze and evaluate the efficacy of implementations of cryptographic and surety technologies. Develop and validate security implementation standards for banking and finance information applications (scalable, supporting variable security levels). ($32 million)	Implement anonymity balance. Field scalable key public management systems. ($6 million)	Field entity authentication technologies. ($1 million)

R&D Topic				
No.	Title	Near Term (Resource Estimate[a])	Achieved by ~2005 (Resource Estimate[a])	Achieved by ~2010 (Resource Estimate[a])
3	Intrusion Indication and Warning (I&W) Tools	Use insight from the development of the CSSM to determine where within the system I&W and sensitivity tools and techniques are applicable. Determine what data are required to implement those tools and techniques. ($29 million)	Develop an initial suite of tools. ($7 million)	Field operational tools. ($1 million
4	Systems Reliability Enhancement	Develop, publish, and begin to implement initial standards and specifications. Develop prototypes of network security agents. ($54 million)	Complete implementation of standards and specifications, and prototypes of network security agents. ($15 million)	Field prototypes of self-healing systems, configurable firewalls, and network defense agents. ($2 million)
5	Information System Standardization	Publish initial standards for open architecture. ($6 million)		
6	Electronic Commerce Security Enhancement	Publish initial standards and specifications for equipment and support tools. ($9 million)	Field standards. ($9 million)	Field operational tools. ($3 million)

[a] Resource estimates reflect qualitative, order-of-magnitude judgments. They are intended to be representative of the resources needed for the R&D topics and are based on assumptions concerning the scope, the expected level of effort, and the pace of the research. Detailed cost estimates must be prepared in concert with the development of detailed R&D plans.

Section 5
References

Booz-Allen and Hamilton, Inc., 1996, "Executive Summary—U.S. Banking and Finance Infrastructure Security Assessment."

Defense Science Board, 1996, Task Force on Information Warfare, Nov. (http://www.infowar.com).

General Accounting Office, 1996, *Information Security-Opportunities for Improved OMB Oversight of Agency Practices,* Washington, D.C., Sept.

Jones, E., and A. Sicherman, 1997, *Evaluating and Managing the Integrity of Computerized Accountability Systems Against Insider Threats,"* Lawrence Livermore National Laboratory, Livermore, Calif.

Kennedy, J.T., 1998, "Internet Intricacies: Don't Get Caught in the Net," *Contingency Planning and Management* III(1): 12–18, Jan.

Reno, J., 1998, speech presented by the U.S. Attorney General at Lawrence Livermore National Laboratory, Livermore, Calif., Feb. 25.

U.S. Department of the Treasury, 1993, *Future Trend Alert,* Nov.

U.S. Department of the Treasury, 1996, "An Introduction to Electronic Money Issues," *Toward Electronic Money and Banking: The Role of Government,* Conference held in Washington, D.C., September 19–20.

U.S. Senate, 1996, Permanent Subcommittee on Investigations, Hearings on Security in Cyberspace (Minority Staff Report), June 5.

Wriston, W., 1992, *The Twilight of Sovereignty,* Charles Scribner's & Sons, New York, N.Y.

CHAPTER 4

PRELIMINARY RESEARCH AND DEVELOPMENT

ROADMAP FOR PROTECTING AND ASSURING THE ENERGY INFRASTRUCTURE[1]

1 This document is one component of a longer report entitled Preliminary Research and Development Roadmap for Protecting and Assuring Critical National Infrastructures (Transition Office of the President's Commission on Critical Infrastructure Protection and the Critical Infrastructure Assurance Office. Washington, D.C. July 1998).

Contents

Section 1 Introduction

1.1 Scope of the Infrastructure

1.1.1 Electric Power

1.1.2 Oil and Natural Gas

1.2 Characterization of the Infrastructure

1.2.1 Electric Power

1.2.2 Oil and Natural Gas

1.3 Issues and Trends

1.3.1 Electric Power

1.3.2 Oil and Natural Gas

1.3.3 Challenges in the Energy Industry

1.3.4 Ultimate Energy Industry Configurations

Section 2 Threats and Vulnerabilities

2.1 Threats

2.2 Vulnerabilities

2.2.1 Electric Power

2.2.2 Oil and Gas

Section 3 R&D Topics and Activities

3.1 Electric Power Systems

3.1.1 Real-time Control Mechanisms

3.1.2 Analysis of Scale and Complexity

3.1.3 Vulnerability Assessment

3.1.4 Information Assurance and Cyber Security

3.1.5 Emergency Response and Recovery Information Technologies

3.1.6 Transmission and Distribution Technologies

3.1.7 On-line Security Assessment

3.1.8 Dispersed Generation and Backup Infrastructures

3.2 Oil and Natural Gas Systems

3.2.1 Critical Consequence Analysis

3.2.2 Decision Support Systems
3.2.3 Physical Protection Assessment
3.2.4 Multisensor and Warning Technologies
3.2.5 Emergency Response Capability Enhancement
3.2.6 Cyber Protection Enhancement
3.3 Joint Topics
3.3.1 Evaluation of Policy Effects
3.3.2 Institutional Barriers
3.3.3 Infrastructure Interdependencies
3.4 Summary of Research Topics

Section 4 R&D Topic Roadmap

Tables

B.1 Estimated Timeframe for Developing Real-time Control Technologies

B.2 Estimates of Timeframe and Cost for Information Assurance and Cyber Security

B.3 Assessment of the Complexity of Decision Analysis Models by Industry Sector

B.4 Summary of Research Topics

B.5 Summary of Funding Requirements by Research Topic

B.6 Summary of the Energy R&D Roadmap

Figures

B.1 U.S. Bulk Electric Power System Interconnections and Reliability Coordinators

B.2 Spectrum of National Security Preparedness and Government Roles for the Electric Power System Infrastructure

Section 1
Introduction

The security, economic prosperity, and social well being of the United States depend on a complex system of interdependent infrastructures. Their lifeblood is energy, an infrastructure composed of industries that produce and distribute electric power, oil, and natural gas.[2] Individuals and organizations in the United States spend approximately $500 billion per year, or about 7.5% of the gross national product, on electricity and fuels. Because specific complexities and characteristics of the electric power system (EPS) infrastructure differ from those of the oil and gas transportation and storage infrastructure, they are often described separately in this report.

1.1 Scope of the Infrastructure

1.1.1 Electric Power

The EPS infrastructure includes generation stations, transmission and distribution networks, and transport and storage of fuel needed to make and supply reliable electricity to customers at a reasonable cost. Electric utilities estimate that revenue from retail sales of electricity totaled $208 billion in 1995. More than one-third of the nation's primary sources of energy (i.e., coal, oil, gas, nuclear) is consumed to generate electricity.

Without electric power, other critical infrastructures, such as telecommunications, banking and finance, and segments of the transportation industry, could not function at an acceptable level. For example, power outages affect virtually all modes of transportation, including subways, elevators, and street traffic (e.g., traffic lights, gasoline pumps). Some infrastructures have invested in backup generating equipment to minimize the impact of a serious outage.

Consumers expect electricity to be available instantly—at the "flick of a switch." Major outages, such as those in the western United States on July 2 and August 10, 1996 (which affected 7.5 million customers), led to follow-up investigations to pinpoint causes and suggest responses to reduce the possibility of future outages. President Clinton noted in his July 3, 1996, memo to the Secretary of Energy that the July 2 outage:

> . . . had a ripple effect as power stations across the vast grid automatically shut down as the result of experiencing a surge. The outages caused numerous problems in the region, including disruptions of train service, traffic problems, loss of air conditioning, interruption of telephone service, and interference with water supplies. . . . A steady supply of power is a vital

---

2 Coal-related issues were not addressed directly, but Chapter 6, which discusses the transportation infrastructure, covers many issues related to coal delivery.

factor in both the local and national economies and is essential for the safety of all Americans.

An electrical outage can result in both direct impacts (e.g., malfunctioning alarm systems) and indirect impacts (e.g., traffic accidents, looting). Analyses have shown that electrical power outages incur substantial costs. The 1977 New York City outage affected about 3 million customers and cost nearly $800 million (1995 dollars). Cost estimates from the August 1996 outage in the western United States have ranged from $700 million to $4 billion.

1.1.2 Oil and Natural Gas

Industry and consumers use petroleum as fuel and as lubrication for many modes of transportation (e.g., automobiles, commercial vehicles, agricultural equipment, trains, ships, aircraft) and industrial machinery. Petroleum products provide heat for residential, industrial, and commercial buildings and for producing, processing, packaging, distributing, and preparing food and food products. Petroleum also is used in the textile and clothing industries to manufacture synthetic fabric, detergents, and dry-cleaning solvents. Other uses for petroleum are with chemicals for cosmetics and pharmaceutical products, and with plastics in manufactured products. Petroleum also helped to generate 3% of electricity in the United States during 1996.

Natural gas is delivered to millions of consumers through the nation's 1.3-million-mile network of underground pipe (e.g., gathering, transmission, distribution). In 1995, the industry served 58.7 million customers: 53.9 million residential customers, 4.5 million commercial customers, 180,900 industrial end users, and 61,300 other customers. Electric power generators increasingly use natural gas. Also, gas technologies are increasing the market share in cooling applications and in gas-fueled vehicles. Furthermore, natural gas is the primary fuel used in cogeneration, capturing about 60% of the market. It is the cleanest burning fossil fuel, producing primarily carbon dioxide (CO2), water vapor, and small amounts of nitrogen oxides.

The oil and gas industries are vital to the U.S. economy because they provide:

- Energy to more than 260 million Americans,
- 65% of the nation's energy needs,
- 1.5 million jobs, and
- Annual revenues of almost $400 billion.

The shock of rapid increases in the price of oil in the 1970s demonstrated that large, sudden price increases erode purchasing power and may drive the global economy into recession. Between 1972 and 1991, price shocks alone cost the U.S. economy $4 trillion. Underneath the economic issues lie hard facts. Most Americans could not heat their homes, cook their food, or drive their vehicles without oil and gas. These infrastructure commodities are the foundation of modern society, and the United States is highly dependent on them.

Despite this dependence, the U.S. energy infrastructure is among the most reliable and robust in the world. While widespread energy shortages and outages make national and international news, they are rare. Most incidents occur at the local level and do not propagate. Despite the reliability of the U.S. energy infrastructure, however, challenges exist for sustaining this resilience as our nation enters the millenium. The oil and gas infrastructures represent a large capital investment and have become increasingly vulnerable to outside forces.

1.2 Characterization of the Infrastructure

1.2.1 Electric Power

The U.S. electric power system is complex. Generating units produce electricity; transmission lines transport large quantities of electricity long distances over high-voltage lines; and distribution lines deliver small amounts of electricity to individual customers over low-voltage lines. Substations, or places where power transformers increase voltage to transmit electricity or decrease voltage to distribute power, link the system. Energy or utility control centers coordinate operations.

The EPS includes approximately 3,200 electric utilities throughout the 50 states, the District of Columbia, and Mexico and is closely tied to Canadian power systems. Traditional electric utilities generate, transmit, and distribute electricity and other energy services in designated service territories. Restructuring has encouraged new entities, such as nonutility power producers, power marketers, and power brokers, to enter the emerging market.

At the end of 1994, U.S. electric utilities owned 10,427 generating units. The total installed capacity in 1995 exceeded 769,000 MW, and net generation totaled 3,356 billion kilowatt-hours. Total generation increased by approximately 3% in 1995.

Coal generating units continue to provide the largest share of electric energy (55%) and have the largest share of generating capacity (43%). Nuclear power accounts for 22% of generation and 14% of capacity. Oil and gas units provide 12% of energy but have a 29% share of capacity because these sources are used more for peaking and daily cycling. Renewables (primarily hydroelectric) represent about 10% of generation and 11% of capacity. The remaining capacity (3%) is hydroelectric pumped storage.

Electric utilities use the ultimate "just-in-time" delivery system. Consumers challenge the system by using lights, appliances, motors, and other electrical equipment. In the aggregate, the instantaneous turning on and off of lights, appliances, computers, and other equipment connected to the EPS requires rapid response by the combined generation, transmission, and distribution portions of the system to maintain frequency, voltage, and dynamic stability. With more and more devices being produced to operate using electricity, more remote controls and more reliance on computers, the U.S. has become increasingly dependent on electricity. The continuity of high-quality electricity is more critical than ever to ensure electric power to our electronically dependent society.

As shown in Figure B.1, bulk EPSs in the United States and Canada are structured into four major networks: Eastern, Western, ERCOT, and Quebec Interconnections.

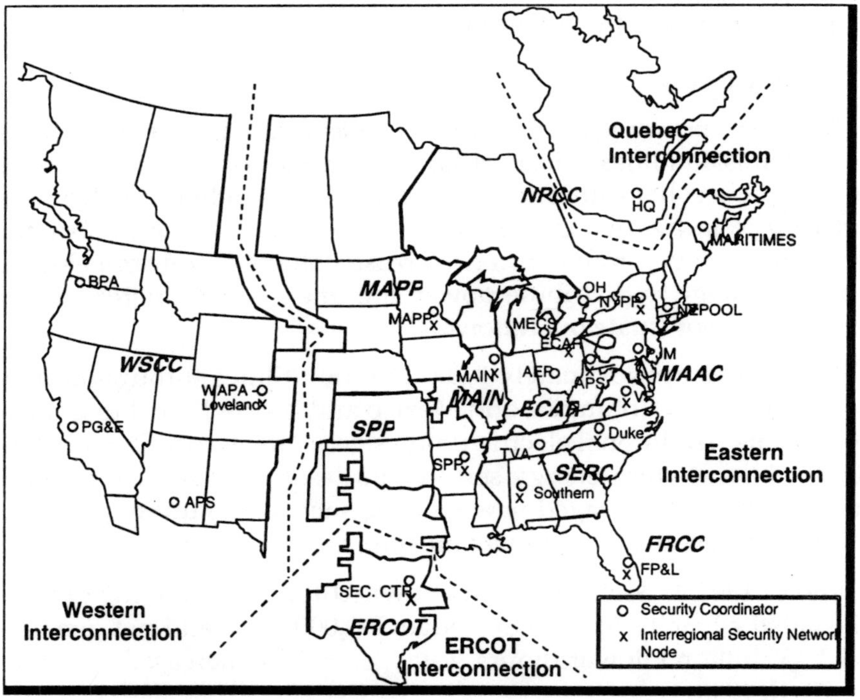

Figure B.1 U.S. Bulk Electric Power System Interconnections and Reliability Coordinators

Each interconnection consists of extra-high voltage connections between individual utilities, which transfer electricity from one part of the network to another. These interconnections are monitored and controlled to ensure safety and dependability. Each interconnection must balance supply and demand. Even the power exchanger between these interconnections must be carefully regulated in real time.

The North American Electric Reliability Council (NERC) is composed of 10 regional reliability councils shown in Figure B.1 (e.g., MAPP is the regional reliability council that covers five north central U.S. states and two Canadian provinces). Within each council are security coordinators, interregional security network nodes, and 146 control areas.

The EPS relies on a centralized control center (command-and-control infrastructure) to coordinate the overall operation of the system within control areas. A key component for communication between the control center and important equipment is the Supervisory Control and Data Acquisition (SCADA) system. Its primary purpose is to control generation and the transmission network directly within the area to balance power flows, regulate voltage, and control frequency. Imbalances between loads and generation are managed through real-time control of selected generators and, during severe emergencies, by controlled load shedding. System control in a restructured industry may change some of these responsibilities.

1.2.2 Oil and Natural Gas

The oil and natural gas industries are complex, robust networks that have proved to be extremely reliable over time. The industries can be characterized by production, transportation, processing, distribution, and end use activities. Production involves well-heads that feed into gathering pipelines. These pipelines carry the crude oil or gas to processing centers: crude oil to a refinery and natural gas to a gas processing plant. Transmission pipelines deliver the gas or refined petroleum products to distribution pipelines that provide products to customers that range from bulk terminal operators to end users.

The delivery systems for natural gas and petroleum products include (in varying levels) compressor stations for natural gas and pumping stations for liquid products, storage capability, and market hubs. Both gas and oil systems use physically manipulated and automated controls, including SCADA. The natural gas system has city gates –transfer and transaction points for gas from the pipeline company to the local distribution company. Barges, trucks, and railroads also transport liquid products. End users include residential, commercial, and industrial customers, as well as electric utilities.

The gas and oil infrastructure is vast and reaches into every region of the country. About 22 trillion cubic feet of gas and 6.6 billion barrels of refined oil products are delivered annually in the United States. In 1996, the oil and gas infrastructure included the following capabilities:

- Operation of 161 domestic refineries with crude distillation capacity of more than 15 million barrels per day. Refineries represent an infrastructure in their own right; the typical refinery is a collection of many manufacturing plants and supporting facilities, which operate interdependently. They convert crude oils and other raw materials into petroleum products.

- Crude oil and petroleum products pumped through about 220,000 miles of pipelines.
- Natural gas collected, transported, stored, and delivered through approximately 62,000 miles of gathering pipelines; 265,000 miles of transmission pipelines; and 935,000 miles of distribution pipelines.
- 375 natural gas storage fields.

1.3 Issues and Trends

1.3.1 Electric Power

When the EPS fails to meet our expectations, it can lead to significant personal or economic losses. Since the nation has entered the "communication age" and our society is increasingly dominated by "silicon-based" technologies, the requirements for electricity have changed. Our society previously needed large amounts of electricity to support our economy (primarily quantities of electrical supply). Now we not only require large amounts of electricity, but also a more reliable supply (both quantity and quality of supply are critical). Thus, the requirement for electric power assurance has increased and is likely to continue to increase. Reliability is a concern, and future reliability could be impaired by the increasing complexity of the grid, by various side effects due to restructuring, and by deliberate attacks.

Factors that could affect the traditional reliability and security of the EPS infrastructure include the following:

- Business elements, including new information systems for electronic commerce, data interchange, and improved operational efficiencies, are essential because of the rapid restructuring of the electric power and natural gas industries.
- Electric utility and natural gas companies are consolidating resources, but finding it nearly impossible to obtain new transmission line rights-of-way because of a prevailing "not-in-my-backyard" (NIMBY) attitude.[3]
- With the advent of natural gas and electricity commodity markets, marketing companies have increased from 8 in 1992 to more than 250 in 1996. This increase has caused an exponential growth in the number and magnitude of power transactions and the resulting demands on the

---

3 If everyone applies NIMBY, the result is BANANA (build absolutely nothing anywhere near anyone).

physical grid and its control system and on the information system needed to manage the transactions.

- Additional vulnerabilities have created a dependence on industry-wide information systems based on open-system architectures, centralized operations, increased communications over public switched networks, and remote maintenance.
- Downsizing in the industry has increased the probability of disgruntled "insiders" and has created a loss of expertise.
- A possible reduction in maintenance after restructuring could result in Auckland-type failures (e.g., cascading, or progressive, failure of a system).
- Because change has occurred so rapidly in the electric industry, vulnerabilities have been introduced (e.g., those related to restructuring and rapid proliferation of industry-wide information systems based on open-system architectures).
- Regulatory requirements for restructuring the industry have increased the size of the community that needs to be able to access industry data, while at the same time system control operations have been concentrated into fewer locations. Increased connectivity and a smaller number of increasingly critical sites create more opportunities for malicious acts.

Electronic power components also are changing the nature of the demand for electricity in less obvious ways, such as adjustable speed drives, which can destroy the overall integrity of the system. While these drives generally are desirable from the user's viewpoint because they eliminate problems associated with slight variations in the voltage or frequency of the grid, they also remove the "natural" tendency of loads to reduce their value as either the voltage or the frequency is reduced. Generally, a system under near-failure conditions reduces voltage and frequency. However, adjustable speed drives do not perform in this way unless they are programmed to do so. Adjustable speed drives not only compromise system integrity, but they also are applied when simpler solutions are available. Finally, top-changing transformers automatically switch secondary winding tops to sustain voltage or feeders.

1.3.2 Oil and Natural Gas

The future reliability of the oil and natural gas infrastructures may be a challenge in the future. Many factors could affect the traditional reliability and security of the oil and natural gas transportation and storage infrastructure, including the following:

- Competitive markets in the natural gas industry are growing so rapidly that system use is increasing.

- The age of both oil and gas pipelines is a potential safety concern: most pipelines are more than 30 years old. Risk assessment and leak management programs are frequently used to help to determine when pipelines become unsafe, particularly in urban or sensitive areas.
- Compliance with environmental regulations increases operating costs in both industries. The oil industry also is driven to produce "greener" products.
- U.S. dependence on foreign supplies has increased significantly: more than 50% for oil and 13% for gas.
- Reduced investments in new technology and its applications are barriers to efficient operation and reliable protection of operations and the infrastructure.
- Both industries increasingly reduce costs through automation and downsizing. As these industries rely more on computers and automation, the possibility of a cyber attack increases.
- Concern over pipelines and production expansion has led to the NIMBY attitude. Permitting and siting issues are expected to grow in importance because of increases in oil imports, shifting population, and increases in the use of natural gas.

1.3.3 Challenges in the Energy Industry

The entire energy industry faces many significant challenges:

- Maintaining reliable energy delivery systems, while undergoing restructuring and change.
- Understanding the complexity and identifying the vulnerabilities of the emerging system and managing the inherent vulnerabilities cost-effectively.
- Preventing the spread of disturbances (either natural or man-made) to transmission systems to avoid widespread outages and long-lasting disturbances.
- Developing and implementing real-time control and communications systems to help to ensure a reliable supply of energy.
- Developing and implementing information security technologies to protect energy system information and communication systems from disruptions.
- Ensuring that our nation is protected against disruptions in fuel supply.
- Developing appropriate policies, incentives, and, where necessary, standards to assure the integrity of energy transmission systems.

- Ensuring that the energy industry's evolution enhances industry's competitive position in the world marketplace and increases our quality of life.
- Creating an atmosphere in which government and private industry share information to improve infrastructure assurance.

1.3.4 Ultimate Energy Industry Configurations

Recommendation of specific energy research areas depends in part on assumed results of rapid changes in the industries. That is, will restructured energy industries be a slightly modified version of historical vertically integrated industries or will they be horizontally integrated? One characteristic of a vertically integrated industry is that all controls, all control variables, and all system states are measurable and available to a central entity. The horizontally integrated industry is characterized by a high degree of uncertainty, and most services are acquired through the market. No position has been assumed for this report, and therefore some R&D recommendations are more appropriate for industry configurations than for others. As the recommended R&D topics undergo further study, specific "end games" for the restructured industries should be examined to identify the most relevant R&D activities.

Section 2
Threats and Vulnerabilities

Energy systems in the United States are normally reliable and economical. Energy companies can minimize the impacts of highly unlikely events, such as multiple simultaneous equipment failures at a single site. However, sabotage, terrorism, or a major natural disaster can inflict unprecedented damage.

Although U.S. energy companies have performed well, restructuring and competition have increased the stress on the energy system infrastructure, and it is uncertain how these systems would work under extreme circumstances. Therefore, both industry and government must investigate the likelihood of such potential damage, and, if warranted, develop ways to reduce risk, minimize damage, and mitigate the effects of outages.

The U.S. energy system is vulnerable to disruption and destruction from multiple threats and actions. Physical threats include terrorists and insiders, natural hazards, and accidents. Cyber threats originate from routine technical problems or from sabotage to information networks, energy management systems (EMSs), and SCADA systems.

2.1 Threats

Threats to the U.S. energy system arise from various sources, including hostile governments, terrorist groups, other organized groups or individuals, disgruntled employees, malicious intruders, natural disasters, accidents, system complexities, and dependence on other infrastructures. The U.S. Department of Energy (DOE) has documented more than 1,000 incidents against the U.S. energy system over the past 15 years; some supply disruptions have caused significant damage. In recent years, cyber incidents, including deliberate and accidental malfunctions, also have been documented.

Terrorists are not known to have caused any long-term energy outages in the United States. However, energy system components have been the targets of numerous isolated acts of sabotage. Several incidents have resulted in multimillion dollar repairs. For example, a 90-minute blackout that disrupted San Francisco on October 23, 1997, was attributed to sabotage.

Well-organized groups (perhaps working with insiders) could cause massive physical and cyber damage to our energy supply systems. These groups could damage the system so severely that major cities or multistate regions could suffer severe, long-term energy shortages. By carefully studying open-source information, such groups can increase their chances of causing major damage.

Cyber threats are rapidly increasing, as the industry becomes automated and interconnected, and more entities can access information that could be used to attack the system. While documented cases of insider attacks on computers are basically few, a knowledgeable insider has almost unlimited ability to cause problems, from bypassing access authorization to subverting systems. The rationale for an insider attack ranges from disgruntlement to financial gain and is the subject of much conjecture.

The Defense Science Board (DSB) concluded that threats to the national and defense information infrastructures include:

- Incompetent, inquisitive, or unintentional blunderers; mischief makers; and pranksters.
- Hackers driven by technical challenge.
- Disgruntled employees or unhappy customers seeking revenge for perceived wrongs.
- Criminals seeking personal financial gain.
- Organized crime seeking financial gain or trying to conceal crimes.
- Individual political dissidents attempting to draw attention to a cause.
- Organized terrorist groups or nation states trying to influence U.S. policy through isolated attacks.

- Foreign espionage agents seeking to exploit information for economic, political, or military purposes.
- Tactical countermeasures for impairing U.S. military weapons or command systems.
- Multifaceted tactical information warfare aiming to disrupt a major U.S. military mission.
- Large, organized groups or major nation states intent on overthrowing the U.S. government by crippling the national information infrastructure.

On the basis of validated incidents, the DSB concluded that some threats exist, while others are possible in the near future.

Threats can be "incidental" (or "inadvertent") or "malicious" (or "deliberate"). Many threats (particularly complex threats) result simply from a lack of understanding about how things work or may work. As a result, malicious parties can exploit new vulnerabilities. Research can be a significant help in this area.

2.2 Vulnerabilities

The vulnerabilities that the energy infrastructures must face are described below:

- Vulnerabilities are created in the operating environment because of the rapid proliferation of industry-wide information systems based on open-system architectures, centralized operations, increased communications over public telecommunications networks, and remote maintenance.
- SCADA systems are not protected by encryption or authentication; however, they typically use proprietary message protocols and dedicated communication systems. Pressure to reduce costs is driving the industry toward open systems and shared communication networks. Data will be required from an increasing number of field devices, but competitive pressures will limit information security expenditures. SCADA systems are vulnerable because (1) the industry has not increased security measures in the configuration and implementation of commercial-off-the-shelf (COTS) hardware and software, (2) connections are made to other company networks, and (3) the industry relies on dial-back modems that can be bypassed. (These COTS systems may be more reliable than the customized versions, but their widespread use introduces new vulnerabilities.)
- The availability of information that can be used to identify vulnerabilities has increased, and much more is mandated by regulatory bodies to facilitate competition. In addition, tools are available for exploiting

those vulnerabilities. Easy availability of information is a major concern to the industry.

- Advanced technologies, with inherent complexities, are rapidly assimilated.
- Infrastructure corridors (e.g., communications, electric transmission lines, pipelines) are being consolidated.
- The industry as a whole has not adequately addressed previously identified physical vulnerabilities of critical assets, such as control centers.
- Few technical and operational standards for specifications, system measurements, and codes of practice are in place.

2.2.1 Electric Power

The physical vulnerability of greatest concern to the EPS is a cascading failure. A cascade is the progressive failure of the system, as sequential outages of individual components result in widespread voltage collapse and system de-integration. When a large power system is stressed, cascades can be initiated by coupled failures of single components that, taken individually, represent minor problems. Cascades typically involve minimal equipment damage and are resolved within a few hours. However, when significant damage to equipment occurs (e.g., 1998 outages in Auckland and Quebec), the time and expense of restoration increase significantly. The initiating events of modern cascading outages have been accidental failures during infrequent periods of high system stress or unusual operating conditions. Deliberate attacks under such conditions, however, would have the same effect. Periods of high system stress will likely become more frequent as the restructured competitive electric market develops. Other physical vulnerabilities of concern include control centers and substations, although certain generation facilities and transmission lines also are of concern.

Deliberate attacks on the integrity of the grid require coordination. Because more information about electric power grids is available, it is possible for knowledgeable individuals to coordinate devastating attacks by targeting a few selected components (e.g., control centers). It is thus important to study countermeasures to such attacks. The nature of power systems means that effects multiply over long distances very quickly.

SCADA systems are among the most attractive cyber targets to disgruntled insiders and saboteurs intent on triggering a catastrophic event. Because of the exceptional growth of information system networks needed to interconnect business, administrative, and operational systems, intruders could disrupt them easily by accessing a SCADA system and modifying the data used for operational decisions, the programs that control critical industry equipment, or the data reported to control centers.

2.2.2 Oil and Gas

Both the oil and the gas infrastructures are vulnerable targets. Their systems are extensive and generally accessible to other utilities – and often to the public. Protective fences and security along all production, transportation, and processing points are not feasible because of costs.

These highly complex infrastructures rely on production and gathering, processing and storage, and transmission and distribution to move oil and gas and to the marketplace. These infrastructures are extremely capital-intensive; a single oil platform can cost $50 million or more, with deep-water platforms costing 10 times that amount. Tankers can cost millions of dollars—liquefied natural gas (LNG) tankers are the most expensive vessels, except for military ships. Construction of transmission pipelines can cost up to $1 million per mile, not including the compressor or pumping stations, which can exceed $40 million and are required approximately every 50 miles. Petroleum refineries, gas processing centers, tank farms, gas storage fields, odorant facilities, and distribution systems are other costly investments.

These infrastructures are difficult to protect. For example, the United States has enough gas pipelines to encircle the earth more than 7.5 times. Security measures, such as fences and guards, are not economical because of the large area in need of protection. Currently, no mandatory or voluntary security standards (except for LNG facilities) exist for these infrastructures nor is there a regulatory body that oversees security issues.

Well-heads, gathering pipelines, waterborne vessels, control centers, tank farms, transmission lines, pumping stations, compressor stations, refineries, gas processing centers, city-gate stations, distribution pipelines, LNG facilities, and odorant facilities also are vulnerable to threats. The degree of vulnerability depends on the importance of each component to its respective infrastructure and the amount of redundancy. For example, well-heads are less vulnerable than other components because of the large number of wells and the ability to extract oil or gas from substitute wells. City-gate stations are highly vulnerable because they are few in number; however, they are important because they connect to distribution pipelines.

One of the infrastructure's greatest vulnerabilities is the nation's dependence on foreign oil. The 1973–1974 Arab oil embargo made it obvious that oil shipped from an unstable area halfway around the world can be cut off at will, priced almost at will, and cause major economic hardship. Also, in 1979, a 1% reduction in the availability of oil worldwide during the Iranian revolution triggered long lines at gas stations and a 120% price increase in the United States. Despite these major supply disruptions (and the Gulf War), the nation is at an all-time high (more than 50%) in depending on foreign oil.

As in the electric power industry, SCADA system used in the oil and gas industries are subject to electronic intrusion. If accessed, information could be manipulated or control programs could be modified. Under certain circumstances, a hammering effect could be induced in pipelines, possibly leading to breaks. Similarly, remote-controlled pressure regulators could be manipulated to cause over- or under-pressurization and explosions. More research is needed to determine the feasibility of such attacks.

To minimize costs and increase efficiency, many companies are expanding their automation and networking systems dramatically and linking their control, administrative, and business information systems. Cyber threats represent unique vulnerabilities to these infrastructures. As these systems move to open-system architectures that use standard protocols and interconnected systems, hackers find it easier to access most systems because they are based on personal computers. Various Internet forums provide "cookbooks" that explain how to break into systems; some even provide access passwords. As systems become highly interconnected, access to multiple systems across multiple computers would become easier, which would increase the effects from hackers who access the system.

- Joint Topics

  15. Evaluation of policy effects
  16. Institutional barriers
  17. Infrastructure interdependencies

All of the R&D topics discussed in this section are worthy of federal assistance to improve energy infrastructure assurance. Substantial industry efforts are underway for some research topics; additional federal support is necessary and appropriate to achieve timely results and provide for energy infrastructure assurance. Some of the research topics have primary objectives in addition to infrastructure assurance. In those instances, federal support on the infrastructure assurance aspects is encouraged. In other cases, the proposed research is pioneering, so the federal government must initiate this effort. Industry presumably would participate and contribute financially as the research proceeds.

Some R&D topics listed in Sections 3.1 and 3.2 are partially relevant for the oil and gas infrastructure and vice versa. Joint (interdependency) topics listed in Section 3.3 apply entirely to both the electric and the oil and gas infrastructures.

3.1 Electric Power Systems

3.1.1 Real-time Control Mechanisms

Description

Although utilities provide on-line control of the major features for operating the electric system, man-in-the-loop operator control, automated control for limited functions (e.g., automatic generator control), and locally activated control for protection are typically combined. In the future, increases in the interconnected complexity of the power system, the introduction of new distributed resources (e.g., generation, storage, load control), and increased stress on existing grids will make real-time automated control a necessity. Coordinated control over larger portions of the grid will be required (coincidentally being mandated under Federal Energy Regulatory Commission [FERC] regulations). Dramatic enhancements in technology and its implementation will be needed to ensure reliable service.

Currently, the only available control is generation set-points (real power and voltage). A more flexible alternating current (AC) transmission system is necessary because in the future generation control may not be available and the market, whatever it is, works best with an unconstrained delivery system. The current control philosophy is assessment and avoidance; it must be replaced by identification and control. However, control methods are needed that can tolerate a large degree of uncertainty and complexity. Methods that allow control on the basis of data rather than on models are needed because it is unlikely that sufficiently complex and/or detailed models would be available.

Several topics included in the suite of technology R&D required for real-time control have been addressed because of their importance. These topics include on-line security assessment, advances in computational algorithms, advanced high-power electronic switching technology, and approaches for dealing with complexity. Additional development is needed in four areas, which are described in greater detail in the following subsections.

Instrumentation and Monitoring for Distributed Control. Monitoring is unique in its relation to real-time system control in that the required decision making is inextricably linked to the quality and timeliness of the information received. "What cannot be measured cannot be controlled" is the basic axiom of decision and control. Monitoring includes systems for collecting time-synchronized data gathered from disparate points in the system, as well as tools to extract and disseminate the data for a given application. This definition implies that raw information, such as that obtained from the terminals of a transducer, is not very useful to the decision maker.

Applied research and advanced technology development are required to upgrade these large-scale data collection systems to the level required for implementing real-time power system control. The objective of this research would be to design hardware and software systems that can accurately collect and manage large data streams that emanate from geographic locations throughout the grid.

Analysis and Computation for Large-scale Systems. Production and delivery of electricity are data-intensive industries. Real-time control requires massive data sets in addition to those used by electric utilities.[4] Advanced visualization techniques, user-friendly human/machine interfaces, and expert systems must be developed to process this volume of information. Basic and applied research, advanced technology development, and proof of principle and validation can produce software systems capable of conveying complex detail and intricate dependencies to utility engineers and operators.

Advanced Control Methods. As more large-scale control devices are developed to enable systems to operate closer to theoretical limits, the role of stability control systems significantly expands. The control of future large-scale devices affects the behavior of the system. Proper controls produce beneficial results; whereas improper controls result in disaster. Therefore, the control system must be reliable and resilient as operating conditions change. Meeting these needs requires advancements in, for example, communication and coordination between central and local controllers, coordination between different local control stations, robust control theory of large-scale systems, and intelligent hierarchical supervision of local controllers. The ideal real-time stability control structure is decentralized; that is, most decisions are made locally, which minimizes dependence on communications. Communicated information and control at different hierarchical levels enhance the performance of the local control systems and ensure optimal system-wide control.

Proper disposition of the themes covered by this topic requires all types of research, especially basic research. The product of the R&D conducted under this topic will be a new body of control theory specifically developed for large-scale systems, but applicable to other large-scale nonlinear systems (e.g., the stability of space structures).

Decision Support Tools. Decision support is a critical element for real-time control architecture. Like any other critical infrastructures, the EPS relies on human engineers and operators to use good judgment to ensure reliable

---

4 As used in this report, "utility" refers to the system operator, generator, or supplier in the restructured environment.

service. They need the best tools available to take informed actions to manipulate and protect the bulk grid.

The decision support architecture for real-time control should be both distributed and hierarchical. In general, modules of the decision support system should be physically located with individual components, major component groups, substations, regional offices, and the central distribution center. Reasoning requirements and the scope of influence increase for modules as they progress up the hierarchy, from the component groups to the distribution center. Component modules "reason" about their respective components and pass conclusions up the hierarchy or request that information be sent down the hierarchy. At the other end of the hierarchy, the scope of the central distribution decision support module includes the entire distribution system and, for the most part, addresses issues involving the high-level power distribution network.

This topic requires a broad array of research activities from basic research to advanced technology development and proof of principle and validation. The new hardware and software systems will enable real-time control for people charged with seeing that the system operates continuously and efficiently.

Goals and Challenges

Instrumentation and Monitoring for Distributed Control. A set of fully compatible EPS models is needed to coordinate control over broader areas and to distribute intelligent real-time control into the distribution systems. Information across traditional organizational and topological boundaries would be shared in real time. The EPS models need protocols for data acquisition, communication, storage, access, and dissemination. Important operational information must be available in a distributed manner. Both local decisions and control actuations must lead to optimum use of emerging technologies for distributed resources and stability enhancement, but, in particular, to enable control during emergencies.

Measurements must be made with timing accuracies that have not been required in the past. The system must provide much larger volumes of information, sufficient to characterize events at higher control levels, both locally and collectively, as they are developing, progressing, or being analyzed in detail. Better optical measurements of EPS behavior are required. They must provide temporally precise data at costs comparable to, or lower than, those of conventional transducers. Measurement devices that enable adaptive monitoring, by using complex pattern-based event recognition filters and triggers, are also required.

The large amount of information to be gathered at distributed points in the grid requires very high bandwidth communication systems. Although early wide-area measurement systems can require only episodic communication when events occur, real-time communication should be anticipated and necessary bandwidth secured. A significant investment can be required for communication systems; therefore, methods and algorithms should be explored that reduce or condense measurement information (such as wavelets). Consistent with communication requirements, new protocols are probably necessary to meet progressive and expanding needs in this area. Finally, the means for coordinating information exchange in highly dynamic circumstances are required.

Analysis and Computation for Large-scale Systems. Current efforts in this area focus on developing methods for extremely fast simulation of potential contingencies, starting from a known operating point (typically the current operating point). Known as on-line security assessment (OSA), this area of research requires accurate models of the system under study. As with all large-scale systems, it is challenging to develop models with the degree of accuracy required to result in meaningful OSAs. It is essential that "measurement-based" methods are used with "model-based" methods such as OSA. The effort in this area must focus on measurement-and model-based methods to (1) compute the necessary stability indices more quickly than is possible at this time and (2) accommodate uncertainty in system analysis.

A stability index is a metric that defines the ability of the bulk power grid to remain interconnected, given the introduction of a known disturbance. The development of one or more good indices gives operators new tools to use in making switching decisions or manipulating line loadings. Uncertainty is a factor in all dynamic systems, but the magnitude of the uncertainties in large-scale systems presents unusual challenges in signal processing, simulation, and other types of analysis. Consider modeling a refinery with thousands of dynamic elements—a challenging process. The interconnected power system has thousands of assets, such as a nuclear power plant, with at least the level of sophistication of a refinery. With only a slight uncertainty in each modeled element, the magnitude of the aggregate uncertainty often makes the analysis meaningless.

New effective paradigms are needed by which the results of complex, large-scale computations that involve great uncertainty can be meaningfully conveyed to operators and others in an intuitive and comprehensible manner. For example, newer and better indices of the system's performance under expected and/or anticipated conditions may be warranted. However, more effective means for conveying this information may require significant additional research and experimentation.

Computationally robust and verified solution methods are needed for large-scale systems. These methods must not only consider uncertainties in the computation, but also uncertainties in the data and the models.

Advanced Control Methods. Although an abundance of scientific literature in control theory is available, the control of large-scale systems is especially challenging. To achieve the principal goal of this effort, it may be necessary to extend existing control theory in new directions or develop new approaches to better address some of the unique challenges of controlling a highly dispersed structure. The effects (1) of one actuator on an actuator hundreds of miles away, (2) of losing a control actuator, (3) of losing an information link critical to controller operation, and (4) of changes in power system topology on a control algorithm must be taken into account in ways never before conceived.

Robust control theory refers to control theory that deals with maintaining effective control in an environment of changing system parameters. In the EPS, grid topology constantly changes, as lines, generators, and loads are switched in and out of service. One of the goals of this research to advance robust linear and nonlinear control theory to reduce the grid reserve margins.

Finally, implementation of a decentralized control scheme requires the development of methods for dealing with degraded knowledge or power system capability. An autonomous controller must not fail because of a lack of knowledge of parts of the surrounding system. Methods must be developed to ensure that this type of information system failure does not form a "rogue" controller that acts contrary to goals of the remainder of the interconnected control hierarchy. This problem, in the form of "over-reaching relays," played a role in the 1996 western U.S. outages. In effect, the team proposes to conduct research on revamping, upgrading, and refining the conceptual design of the relay and control structures of the system.

Decision Support Tools. The reasoning element is the heart of any decision support module. It transforms data into information, analyzes data and information, draws conclusions, solicits information from other modules and from the system operators, and develops recommendations. The goal of this research is to develop technologies required to implement a functional reasoning element for decision support on a large-scale, widely dispersed system such as the electric power grid.

The reasoning element must use some form of artificial intelligence (AI). To date, applying AI tools to power system problems has had mixed reviews. AI-based tools have been applied only to well-defined problems, such as processing alarms. New AI tools are needed to aid human operators in the overall decision-making process. A key element is developing multiconstraint optimization tools that accommodate all the relevant objectives for operating a power system, in particular, situationally adaptive optimization tools.

An additional goal is to develop autonomous agents for reasoning and optimizing system operations. These agents would operate at the higher levels of the control hierarchy and assist in the decision-making process for mundane, but critical, system performance measures. The logic for these autonomous agents would extend down to the delivery level, where they could assist operators with complex circuit diagnostics. They could help to minimize customer outages (e.g., through adroit circuit switching), maximize asset use, and improve many operational procedures currently carried out ad-hoc.

Rationale for the Research and Desired Results

Instrumentation and Monitoring for Distributed Control. Advanced instrumentation and monitoring systems, including the data systems that support their effective use, require vital R&D to enable the required greater utilization of the existing electric system (i.e., providing information essential for operating at inevitably lower reserve margins, for prompt avoidance of cascading events, effective management of emergencies, rapid recovery from major events). The degree to which power system reliability can be operationally managed depends on instrumentation and monitoring. On-line reserves increase the inertia of the system, which makes it more stable in the presence of disturbances.

Analysis and Computation for Large-scale Systems. Another reason the United States maintains significant capacity reserves today is that on-line information cannot be used effectively to calculate stability margins online. The computational challenge is too great for conventional algorithms and workstation platforms. While computational capacities continue to increase, work needs to be done to develop more effective algorithms and methods for computing stability indices, particularly for increasingly complex systems. Also, significant evidence shows that present models do not accurately predict power system behavior during stressed conditions because of assumptions made in the models and inherent nonlinearity exhibited during stressed conditions. In addition, no methods incorporate uncertainty in on-line dynamic stability tools. Such advances are essential for both preventing and recovering from significant power system outages.

There is a need for better understanding of uncertainty. Low-probability, but high-damage, events are most important for infrastructure assurance analysis, but traditional analysis methods do not effectively capture these effects. Thus, not only are risks present in using the system, but they also are not apparent. How close we are to safe limits depends on knowing where we are and what the limits are.

Advanced Control Methods. Trends in technological and infrastructural development have changed the landscape of power system topology and control. These trends enable greater use of distributed elements of the system for control (e.g., development of flexible AC transmission system devices and distributed load control), while also increasing the need for projected widespread implementation of distributed generation. New control methods are essential for enabling the use of such devices. With these control systems and devices (systems of devices), reliability can be managed to minimize the effects of undesirable incidents or events. These devices increase the options that operators and their automated agents have to prevent or manage a potential outage. Recovery also is substantially enhanced if an outage occurs.

Decision Support Tools. Substantial improvements in the type, quality, and quantity of information available for operating the increasingly complex power system in real time would be lost if the information could not be used to make prompt, accurate decisions related to control. The massive amounts of information processing, calculation, analysis, and reasoning required to manage the power system would overwhelm present operators if they did not have additional automated decision support tools. If the operators or yet-to-be-developed automated agents are not able to make decisions with confidence and at the appropriate time, many operational options will remain beyond implementation, and advances in each of the areas above would have limited effect. Decision support tools being developed would be of particular value for diagnosing problems and would be of immense value during emergencies, when most control rooms overwhelm operators with information (much of it irrelevant).

Timeframe and Resource Requirements

Because of the complexity of the EPS and because the United States relies on it for our entire well being, the development and demonstration of systemic technologies are long, frequently expensive processes. The electric power industry is the most capitalized in the nation and has equipment lives often measured in decades.

Table B.1 provides estimates of the timeframe and resource requirements for developing real-time control technologies.

3.1.2 Analysis of Scale and Complexity

Description

Scale and complexity primarily involve issues and vulnerabilities caused by the sheer size of the interconnected transmission grid, along with the increasing use of more sophisticated components and technologies within the grid (for example, an increased use of power electronic components). In almost all cases, a larger grid with more technologies in use leads to more complex and less intuitive situations. The objectives of an R&D effort in this area are as follows:

- Develop a better understanding of the stability characteristics of very large systems, which integrate economics, physical energy delivery, communications, and computation.

Table B.1 Estimated Timeframe for Developing Real-time Control Technologies

Technology Area	Timeframe	Cost[a]
Instrumentation and Monitoring for Distributed Control	3 yrs: first field test of WAMS 5 yrs: first incorporation in operator-assisted control 10 yrs: first use in large-scale automated control 15 yrs: first coordinated use at multiple scales	5 20 60 45
Analysis and Computation for Large-scale Systems	3 yrs: near-real-time stability computation for 1,000-bus system 5 yrs: 10,000-bus system 10 yrs: incorporation of uncertainty in on-line calculations	15 25 60
Advanced Control Methods	3 yrs: next-generation architectures detailed 5 yrs: first subcomponent field trials 10 yrs: first field trials of full multilevel hierarchical systems	8 20 60
Decision Support Tools	5 yrs: first field trials of AI tools in control room 10 yrs: first automated agents in control rooms 15 yrs: first coordinated intelligent control optimization tools at multiple scales	10 30 45

[a] Costs are estimated in millions of U.S. dollars.

- Study countermeasures to avoid or mitigate malicious control.
- Study technologies that might reduce, or help to cope with, complexity.
- Develop tools for very large-scale computation.
- Study large network interactions, voltage collapse, and network security.
- Study the effect of uncertainties and changing conditions on systems.
- Study the effect of complexity and scale on human behavior.

Complexity need not imply numerous components (though power systems have that challenge, too). Even very simple nonlinear systems can be difficult, if not impossible, to analyze and can demonstrate very complicated (i.e., chaotic) behavior. Local linearization (or piece-wise linearization) enables treatment of nonlinear systems as linear systems over certain operating regions where the system is "well behaved." However, characterization of the appropriate operating regions is not well developed and varies on the basis of changing parameters that characterize the system. For instance, as stress on the system increases, nonlinearities are expected to become more important in characterizing system behavior. Compelling evidence shows that months after the massive outage in the western U.S. grid on August 10, 1996, transmission planning staff still could not simulate the observed behavior even after substantial deviation of many model parameters from their expected values. Traditionally, nonlinearities have been relatively unimportant because the system was "overdesigned" and rarely stressed to its operating limits. That situation is not likely to persist.

Another topic worthy of attention is uncertainty in power system operations and reliability. At present, probabilistic methods are not used much in operating the grid. For example, probabilistic methods are not used for assessing the proximity of the present operating condition to unstable operating regimes or for conducting on-line adaptive risk management. In a competitive market, efforts to increase equipment use and life would become even more intense, which would affect the probability of component failure and potentially increase the risk of cascading outages.

Goals and Challenges

The goals and challenges in the area of scale and complexity are as follows:

- Develop a more complete understanding of all the threats and failure modes that can occur in a power system as a result of increased system complexity.
- Develop the tools necessary to mitigate the effects and to understand and prevent problems in complex systems.

If successful, this research would reduce infrastructure vulnerability by addressing the core of one of the more fundamental vulnerabilities of a large interconnected system. It is important that designers, operators, and policy makers understand the issues brought about by complexity. A thorough understanding of these issues would result in:

- Development of policies, procedures, and standards that simplify rather than increase complexity.
- Designs that reduce adverse effects, leading to systems that are inherently more robust and less likely to fail.
- Ability to deal with large-scale systems, which would ultimately reduce costs and improve societal economic welfare.
- A system less vulnerable to deliberate attacks or intrusions, which would reduce the possibility of highly disruptive behavior.
- A reduction in the number of outages and system events, which is timely because disruptive events are expected to increase as a result of deregulation and the pressures to operate more economically. The recent clamor from the outages in Auckland and the western United States in the past two years is an example.

In short, this work is important not only because it will lead to a more reliable grid, but also because it will be capable of promoting efficient competition and improving overall societal welfare.

The main strategy recommended for attaining these goals is an organized research effort that addresses the issues of complexity in general, with specific applications to complexity in power systems. The effort should encompass the following project categories:

- Conduct research on understanding complexity as a discipline of its own. A general understanding is needed of complexity and what it does to systems; principles by which one can deal with complexity in real time; a generic taxonomy of complexity issues; and how dynamic effects, uncertainty, size, interconnectivity, and other factors contribute to the multidimensionality of complexity.
- Perform research on the human aspects of complexity, i.e., general principles and experimental results on how humans cope with complex situations, both when given time and under real-time conditions.
- Perform research on the tools needed to address, understand, and conquer complexity. Tools to monitor power markets and grid operations for evidence of manipulation are also needed.
- Apply the principles of complexity theory to develop tools that address the specific needs of a power transmission system. Other dimensions of complexity in power grids include safety, nonsimultaneity of results, uncertainties due to weather, and more.

Rationale for the Research and Desired Results

When large nonlinear systems are assembled, many patterns of behavior are poorly understood, which can lead to areas of erratic behavior and resulting failures. Modes of operation that do not exist in simple systems can be implemented as systems become complex.

The electric power grid is becoming more susceptible to disruption for financial gain. It is possible to create problems deliberately and then hide behind complexity. The topic of sophisticated, deliberate attacks on the power grid has not been fully explored. Furthermore, unsophisticated attacks on complex systems should not be ignored, because the more sophisticated the lock, the more susceptible it may be to primitive attack. It is important to understand all vulnerabilities.

The inability to determine or comprehend the overall status of the grid in real time is a problem. This aspect of complexity involves the abilities of humans to assimilate and process information about unfamiliar situations. Recently, many problems (including more than one blackout) have been attributed, at least in part, to the inability of an operator to obtain a sufficiently comprehensive "picture" of what is happening.

Timeframe and Resource Requirements

Research on timeframes and resource requirements is more fundamental, but no less important, than some of the other topics. The budgetary and possible project recommendation in this area is organized into several possible project categories:

- An immediate intense three-year effort aimed at understanding how deregulation may (or may not) increase system complexity, along with an understanding of important new issues that result from deregulated operation. Most important is an understanding of the interactions between networks and markets, which should include market power considerations and dynamic effects.
- A five-year effort with strong input from theoreticians and others with a goal to improve our understanding of complex systems in general. This effort would require approximately $2 million per year.[5]
- A five-year effort to understand human interfaces and how humans deal with scale and complexity when under pressure. This effort would require approximately $3 million per year, including some funding for human factors experimental work.
- A five-year effort to understand the complexities in the power grid itself, looking for situations where complexity can lead to fundamental changes in the behavior of the system. This effort can be integrated with efforts aimed at understanding the present and future grid. Suggested budgets would have to be coordinated.
- A five-year effort, coordinated with other groups, to develop computational capabilities for dealing with uncertainty. Suggested budgets would depend on other efforts.
- An effort specifically targeted at understanding uncertainty and all the ways in which uncertainty makes a system vulnerable, along with ways for mitigating the effects of uncertainties. This effort would require approximately $4 million per year.

3.1.3 Vulnerability Assessment

Description

The EPS is being restructured to a market-based environment. It is likely that centralized planning and coordination, as practiced by utilities in a regulated environment, will change. To remain competitive in the future, utilities need to control costs, so they may need to operate with lower safety margins. Traditional safety margins, such as higher generation and transmission reserve capacities, typically built into electric systems in a

5 Some reviewers believed this cost estimate should be increased substantially.

regulated environment, may not be as large after restructuring. Consequently, alternative safety margins may be needed to prevent an increase in the vulnerability of the electric grid or a decrease in its ability to respond to, and recover from, threats.

To date, a comprehensive evaluation has not been performed of the vulnerabilities/threats to the EPS in a restructured environment and with resulting consequences or impacts. Although vulnerability and threat issues have been identified and some consequences have been quantified, a comprehensive evaluation, including significant technical analysis, has not been conducted. Such an evaluation would examine vulnerabilities to sabotage, acts of terrorism, system complexities, and acts of nature.

A careful study of the potential future architecture and structure of the electric industry is particularly timely and important. Incentives for utilities to invest in reliability measures (particularly R&D) are unclear, and investment has dropped precipitously in recent years. In the emerging, competitive market, it is not clear that anyone has responsibility for developing new approaches and technologies for enhancing reliability, particularly if implementation is required at the system level.

Competitive markets are particularly responsive to changes in the environment in which they operate and are very efficient at moving to a new equilibrium point. However, they are generally poor at anticipating major low-probability shifts in the underpinnings of that market. Understanding how such changes can influence grid reliability is important because it can direct R&D to help ensure that a prudent array of technologies and policies is available.

This evaluation would provide useful information on a national or large regional scale for assuring a reliable electric power system. It would also analyze systems under extreme or highly unusual conditions that do not arise during normal business activities. This R&D is not intended to replace or interfere with risk management evaluations performed at the individual utility level.

The purpose of this analysis is to identify system vulnerabilities and strategies to prevent large-scale outages and mitigate consequences from them. It will also identify ways to encourage utilities to make the necessary investments, such as increased generating and transmission reserve capacities, in a deregulated environment to achieve national security goals. The federal rules separating production and delivery create an environment in which tight integration of planning is less likely. The government's role in offering incentives to encourage utilities to make these investments in a competitive marketplace will be examined. Possible incentives the government can offer are cost sharing, tax breaks (unlikely, but possible), policy/regulatory changes, technical support, etc.

Goals and Challenges

The goals and challenges associated with evaluating current and future EPSs include the following:

- Identifying and evaluating strategies for preventing regional outage incidents and mitigating consequences.
- Identifying and evaluating strategies for recovering from incidents.
- Assessing the reliability and maintainability of key EPS components and their relation to the system as a whole.
- Assessing the value of new technologies that could improve the reliability of the power system.
- Assessing local and overall benefits and costs of changes to the system as restructuring transforms it.
- Evaluating the vulnerability of the system to disruptions in fuel supply and assessing the need for alternative fuel or fuel switching generation technologies that could enhance system reliability.
- Identifying and evaluating the effects of alternative electricity restructuring scenarios on the transmission and distribution systems.
- Identifying and evaluating incentives, such as cost sharing, tax breaks, policy/regulatory changes, and technical support, to encourage utilities to invest in technologies and procedures to protect critical components of the electric grid and achieve national security goals.

Rationale for the Research and Desired Results

A comprehensive assessment of the vulnerabilities or threats to the EPS and the resultant consequences or impacts at national, regional, and company levels is needed to aid in decision making concerning research, capital investments, and changes in regulatory requirements and operational practices. A framework and methods are needed for conducting these assessments. Some of the methods can be developed as part of other research recommended in this report, but additional analysis techniques are required as well.

The analysis would also identify and evaluate options to address grid vulnerabilities. Furthermore, because of deregulation in the electric utility sector, government incentives that encourage utilities to invest in the EPS to help achieve national security goals would be identified and evaluated. This system evaluation could develop into a top-level analysis that guides other tasks.

Timeframe and Resource Requirements

The overall objective of these assessment is to improve risk management decisions. To meet this objective requires the following actions:

- Developing systematic and consistent estimates of the vulnerabilities and threats.
- Quantifying the potential consequences or impacts.
- Evaluating the effects of actions to prevent, mitigate, and manage incidents and to aid in recovery.
- Evaluating the need for government incentives to encourage utilities to invest in the electric grid to address vulnerabilities.
- Estimating the uncertainty and the effect on electricity prices for all of the above analyses.
- Developing decision frameworks to incorporate the above information and assist in risk management decisions.

The research required for this topic would be an ongoing effort to develop and improve modeling and analysis capabilities for evaluating regional or national electric power systems. Required funding is estimated to be $35 million through 2010.

3.1.4 Information Assurance and Cyber Security

Description

Electric utilities depend significantly on information and telecommunications systems. Historically, many utilities have installed and maintained their own dedicated communication systems. Often, they had separate computer networks for administrative and operational systems. Operational systems (e.g., supervisory control and data acquisition, SCADA, and energy management systems [EMSs]) have typically been segregated and closely monitored; interconnection with other computer networks has traditionally not been allowed. Utilities typically invested in redundant telecommunications systems to ensure reliable information systems for operation. In general, utilities have not experienced information attacks. However, deregulation provides motivation for financial gain and changes in the sophistication of cyber threats, as well as development of information warfare as an international threat, increase the need to ensure appropriate measures are used for information assurance. Unfortunately, utilities, though long used to dealing with natural disasters or random physical assaults on facilities, are not prepared to deal with cyber threats, particularly from structured adversaries (few infrastructures are).

Electric utilities, in particular, depend on large amounts of real-time information typically associated with their SCADA systems. Current SCADA systems use open protocols (such as the Inter-Control Center Communications Protocol [ICCP]) and a large variety of other protocols (both open and closed) for SCADA communications. Trends to use open systems and protocols, as well as intelligent (computer) electronic devices at field equipment sites (and in equipment itself) increase the potential for inappropriate access. However, the undetected interception and modification of SCADA signals would typically require extensive knowledge of the domain. Currently, encryption is not used in electric utility SCADA systems (or in essentially any other operational elements) nor is authentication commonly used. Information security typically has relied on obscure protocols and the need for considerable domain knowledge.

In addition, a new age of directed energy weapons (such as high-energy radio frequency [HERF]) is entering service and can, quite literally, be built with readily available parts and designs available over the Internet. Few evaluations of the effects of these weapons on electrical equipment have been performed. Research and development therefore focused on seven areas:

- Threat assessment and risk management tools specific to the electric power industry;
- Large, geographically disperse information systems;
- High-security SCADA network systems;
- Efficient, adaptable encryption;
- Robust authentication and authorization;
- Network intrusion detection for high bandwidth communications; and
- Evaluation of the sensitivity of electric power equipment and facilities to directed energy weapons.

There is a significant need to pursue additional efforts in institutional topics related to raising awareness and operations security in each of these seven areas described in greater detail below.

Threat Assessment and Risk Management. The electric power industry is unique in its size; it was constructed as an amalgamation of many diverse and independent stakeholders and relied on legacy systems. These characteristics, together with the current environment of deregulation and centralized control, are creating a situation in which EPS operators and planners are making decisions based on regulatory and economic constraints without access to knowledge of the vulnerability these decisions may pose to the infrastructure. Information systems are a vital part of the operations for the power grid. In the past, the industry accommodated risks according to generally accepted threats and vulnerabilities. Unprecedented institutional change, accompanied by continuing technical change, leaves many in the power industry without an effective basis for making risk management decisions concerning information assurance (and perhaps other security issues).

Significant research is needed to develop threat assessment and risk management tools to help designers safely move the electric power industry into a more interconnected, market-based system. As the industry begins to understand the basic principles of these areas, applied research, technology development, and validation work will be required to adapt existing technologies to this specific domain.

Large Systems Analysis. The electric power grid is a very large, geographically dispersed system. With the move toward deregulation, the interconnectedness and interdependence of widely separated subsystems increase. To ensure the stability of this system in the face of faults, cyber attack, or coordinated physical/cyber assault, the entire system must be characterized and well understood. This information is critical to designing a fault-tolerant, robust power grid.

The EPS combines physical (power generation, transmission lines, etc.), logical (control circuits, automated breaker tripping, etc.), and information systems. Research is needed to understand this complex system, including distributed information assets and coordination and security of such a widely dispersed network of information assets. Models and simulation systems, which currently represent subsections of the grid, must be expanded to keep pace with deregulation and deployment of new technology.

In this area, both basic and applied research activities are needed. As models and tools are developed, a proof-of-principle and validation stage would be required. The outcome of this research effort should be new models, simulation techniques, integrated attack models, and planning/design tools. The tangible outcomes would include a better understanding of this complex system; a heightened awareness of the interdependencies; and a more efficient, reliable, and robust national power grid.

High-security SCADA Systems. SCADA systems handle the measurement and status information to allow decision making at the control center; manage control signals that actually set the operating parameters for generation; open and close breakers in the distribution system; return status information to the EMS; and allow for remote monitoring of equipment. The SCADA network transmits command and control information to remote subsystems. Often, the remote system does not verify the authenticity or validity of the control signal; the command is simply carried out. In the nation's EPS, the importance of providing secure communications for SCADA cannot be overemphasized.

Research into high-security SCADA architectures should be primarily applied with a strong validation phase. The result of this research will be varied and will include design guidelines and tools, models, test and evaluation tools, and possibly new protocols, encryption deployment, and authentication and authorization systems.

Efficient, Adaptable Encryption. Because utilities manage vast amounts of temporally sensitive information and at times must execute control functions in milliseconds, they have been reluctant to use techniques that might either increase potential latency in the data reception or unnecessarily complicate communications. The frequent use of vendor-specific protocols also has prevented the industry from adopting methods such as encryption, which can have high overhead requirements in terms of signal processing. Utilities do not want to use methods that slow operational communications (particularly when they are trying to increase their use of existing assets). However, there may be significant benefits from developing encryption technologies that could be used with minimal downside effects on operations. In the absence of obscure protocols (now being phased out), encryption may be one of the few ways to increase barriers to interception and/or intervention in communication of temporally sensitive information. The real challenge is to develop a cryptographic system that meets the industry's requirements.

Robust Authentication and Authorization. In the context of general information assurance, authentication is the process of confirming the identify of an individual or a system. For this discussion, authentication is the binding of a command or action to the entity or person issuing the command. In other words, authentication is the mapping of electronic actions to the person or system initiating those actions. Authorization is the process of establishing whether an authenticated entity has permission (authority) to carry out a specific action.

Research—basic and applied—is needed to develop and deploy strong authentication and authorization controls to both the SCADA and information networks deployed in the electric power industry. Because of the criticality of the systems involved, authentication and authorization must be hardened to tolerate faults and must not provide choke points for denial of service (or other) attacks. In an EPS, a mistaken denial of timely access can be almost as damaging as allowing unauthorized access.

Intrusion Detection. Detecting probes, penetrations, and attacks on an information system is critical for system security. Probes and attacks must be detected quickly to trigger a response, and penetrations must be detected quickly to initiate mitigation and recovery efforts. Intrusion detection must be efficient and accurate. The price for signaling a false alarm in a real-time control system could be quite high. Because of the high bandwidth and wide variety of communication types and protocols, intrusion detection is a very difficult task for the electric power industry. In addition, mitigation and recovery measures must be consistent with the necessary functionality and reliability of the EPS mission; that is, provide a reliable source of electricity.

Ongoing research in intrusion detection, mitigation, and recovery could be used as a springboard for work specific to the electric power industry. Applied research, technology development, and validation are required (more fundamental research may be necessary to address specific needs related to real-time system operations).

Directed Energy Weapons Countermeasures. Plans for building HERF weapons sufficiently powerful to disable an automobile or a computer from a distance are easily available. The vulnerability of the electric power grid to both random and coordinated HERF attacks must be assessed. If the grid is found to be vulnerable, research into ways to protect both the information systems and critical electric system elements (breakers, transformers, reclosers) should be initiated.

Research to assess the threat and viability of HERF weapons against the EPS infrastructure is a logical first step. The outcome would be a general, high-level assessment of vulnerability that outlines protective measures. This initial work would lead to focused R&D and testing of various facilities and equipment. Guidelines for facility design and security would be developed. More robust technology approaches to shield the system from such attacks could be developed if warranted. Mitigation and recovery plans must be augmented to include a response to this type of attack. (This research also should accommodate the expected increase in the viability and power of these weapons.)

Goals and Challenges

Threat Assessment and Risk Management. Providing a thorough assessment of potential threats and an accurate, detailed model of the EPS that can be used for system design, attack scenarios (leading to policy and operational decisions), and simulations is the primary goal for threat and risk management. With the information from this assessment, risk management tools can be used to help management and system designers make well informed, rational decisions concerning policy and implementation of infrastructure systems.

The vast size and complexity of the system, coupled with the short response time available from real-time control subsystems provide significant challenges. The continuous evolution of technology and threats also poses a problem. With such a large and dynamic environment, model development and validation will be a continuous task.

Large Systems Analysis. An improved understanding of the intricacies and interrelationships among the many diverse subsystems that make up the electric power grid is the primary goal for the research effort for large systems. New models and simulations of the connectivity, logical and physical communication paths, and protocols of the overall system would embody this understanding.

Understanding and modeling such a large system are difficult tasks. Many communication mechanisms, protocols, and legacy systems are woven into the system. The verification and validation of the models pose another significant hurdle. As stated above, the continuous evolution of technology is a significant challenge and requires a long-term research effort.

High-security SCADA Systems. The primary goal of providing secure, hardened SCADA networks is to protect this critical link from internal and external attack. Currently, most SCADA systems are protected by their obscurity and the need for domain-specific knowledge to pose a credible threat. An insider has the knowledge and expertise needed to mount an attack. The addition of encryption, authentication, authorization, and/or other measures to protect this critical link is a great challenge.

Changing the SCADA network would be disruptive and would require the interaction and support of a wide vendor community. Because standards-based solutions typically develop slowly, it would be difficult to migrate to a secure SCADA system within a timeframe sufficiently short to mitigate the risk of attack.

Efficient, Adaptable Encryption. A proposed new research area is in the field of adaptable encryption. The principal goal is to develop technologies that reduce the chance of compromising information transmitted over the EPS, without placing additional constraints or increasing the risks of lowering the performance of the existing communication network. Encryption systems that could respond to threats (e.g., dynamically increase security by using a stronger algorithm or longer key) and constraints (e.g., lower encryption overhead, switch to a decreased level of security, prevent cascade failure) would provide a powerful tool for designers of large distributed systems.

Encryption R&D would focus on methods to ensure signal security and fidelity without introducing latency or risk of signal degradation. Researchers would explore encryption techniques and the potential development of high-performance signal processing microprocessors that would handle encryption; evaluate protocols, particularly emerging protocols; and adopt methods to ensure signal security. Finally, they would collaborate with vendors for major software and hardware for SCADA, EMS, and control systems. Working with vendors would include conducting joint R&D efforts and performing field trials of new approaches for encryption for power system operations.

Robust Authentication and Authorization. Standardized, robust, and efficient authentication and authorization, which can be easily deployed to many applications, legacy systems, and communication protocols, are the primary goals of research in authentication and authorization. Developing, testing, and deploying such a flexible scheme are enormous challenges.

Intrusion Detection. Developing algorithms and other methods for detecting threats and attacks, even previously unknown attacks, while limiting the number of false alarms, is a daunting task. It is more difficult because of the size and complexity of the system, the numerous unique subsystems, and the short window of opportunity to mitigate a detected threat in the real-time environment.

Directed Energy Weapons. The goal of this research is to understand the threat posed by HERF weapons and then develop and implement preventive measures throughout the EPS. Difficulties in implementing such measures include the cost to design, build, and test such weapons in a reasonable environment. Also, it may not be feasible to implement preventive measures in some existing facilities.

Rationale for the Research and Desired Results

Threat Assessment and Risk Management. Currently, the information systems needed for large-scale EPSs do not have threat assessment and risk management tools. The lack of such tools makes it difficult to assess or manage an existing risk. With continuing deregulation and concentration of decision making, the risk continues to increase.

Large Systems Analysis. As the electric power industry becomes more and more interconnected, understanding these large, complex information systems is crucial for providing reasonable security. Without a solid understanding, even if research provides the necessary models and tools, the future growth of deregulation will continue to add vulnerabilities to this critical infrastructure.

High-security SCADA Systems. Currently, many SCADA networks on the grid are vulnerable to attacks from insiders and sophisticated adversaries. As deregulation continues and the use of shared communication channels increases, the risk of compromising SCADA networks increases. Research in this area is needed to mitigate the threat posed by the current trend of interweaving multiple, diverse systems over shared communication systems.

Efficient, Adaptable Encryption. Encryption can play a large part in mitigating vulnerabilities of the information infrastructure within the electric power industry. Encrypting information and control signals significantly increases the level of effort an adversary would expend in trying to obtain unauthorized knowledge of system behavior or seize control of power system operations (or portions thereof).

Robust Authentication and Authorization. Authentication and authorization schemes are effective measures for controlling risk in a high-threat environment. These measures are especially effective in regions where general access control is required, but they are also effective when multiple levels of security or authorization are required. Combined with encryption, the development and deployment of authentication and authorization measures for the power grid could substantially reduce some critical vulnerabilities.

Intrusion Detection. Detecting attacks is critical for providing a robust environment. This capability must be developed and enhanced to protect the power grid information infrastructure. It can be safely assumed that the power grid will continue to be a highly visible target and that probes and attacks will continue to increase. In this environment, intrusion detection, and the accompanying policy and procedure for mitigation, is crucial. Similarly, development of technologies and methodologies that enable appropriate and timely response to detected probes or intrusions is vital. Examples of response topics worthy of further research might include increased partitioning of the network and selective routing of traffic. Coordination among multiple parties collectively responsible for system operation creates additional challenges and research topics. Basically, what is needed is to develop an appropriate, timely response, which clearly is a daunting challenge.

Directed Energy Weapons. As the availability of HERF weapons increases, their threat to the power grid increases. Because there is no known means for preventing a determined adversary from using these weapons, the risk must be mitigated through acquired knowledge (research), planning, development of mitigation technologies and preventive actions (implementation of mitigation technologies), and development of coordinated response plans.

Timeframe and Resource Requirements

Because the EPS is complex and our nation relies on it for our well being, the development and demonstration of systemic technologies are typically long and frequently expensive processes. The electric industry is the most capitalized in the nation, with equipment lives often measured in decades. Therefore, options must be developed so that information security technology and measures can be adopted to minimize risk.

Many of these activities are interdependent. Assessing threats and risks, understanding large systems, and developing secure SCADA systems are linked as base-level, architectural activities. Understanding large systems and developing credible threat and consequence models are a logical first step for evolving risk management procedures. Secure SCADA is an important part of the overall "large system." The numerous diverse systems, companies, and priorities will make the initial work in these areas difficult.

Developing, implementing, and deploying encryption will (most likely) be an evolving activity. It is difficult to retrofit encryption into legacy systems without introducing overhead and general system disruption. Because these conditions are not well tolerated in the power industry, the initial focus should be on developing robust, flexible and scalable encryption for deployment on new systems. Existing systems, which are both critical and vulnerable, should be identified and protected as soon as possible. This task implies a link to the projects on threat assessment and intrusion detection.

Research in encryption should be linked to the authentication and authorization project. Because portions of the authentication and authorization protocols will undoubtedly require encrypted channels, these activities should be carried out in parallel.

Research on intrusion detection should initially focus on deployed systems. A longer-term goal should be to engineer intrusion detection into the design of future deployments.

Research into high-energy weapons and their effect on this critical infrastructure should be tied closely to both the threat and risk assessment project and to persons concerned with physical security.

Table B.2 provides estimates of the timeframe and resource requirements for developing information assurance technologies for application in the electric power industry.

3.1.5 Emergency Response and Recovery Information Technologies

Description

Electric power grids in the United States rely heavily on a complex, interconnected network control system and are expected to do so in the foreseeable future. This system is widely dispersed and highly vulnerable to computer-based intrusions and attacks. Effective ways to identify, respond to, and recover from attacks on the information systems that underpin this interconnected network are not well understood. Utilities are experienced in responding to and recovering from disruptions in their physical system, such as those caused by hurricanes, floods, and other natural disasters. Developing emergency response and recovery protocols and procedures for information technology systems within electric power grids is an area requiring future R&D.

This effort would involve both basic and applied research. One way to institute emergency preparedness from a national security point of view would involve the concept of a minimum essential information infrastructure (MEII). The MEII concept would identify the minimum portion of the electric power grid information infrastructure necessary to ensure the grid's continued functioning even in the face of a sophisticated strategic cyber attack.

Table B.2 Estimates of Timeframe and Cost for Information Assurance and Cyber Security

Topical Area	Timeframe (yr)	Cost[a]
Threat Assessment and Risk Management	3-5	25
Large Systems Analysis	5-10	45
High-security SCADA Systems	5-10	80
Efficient, Adaptable Encryption	3-10	75
Robust Authentication and Authorization	3-10	75
Intrusion Detection	3-10	75
Directed Energy Weapons	3-10	60

[a] Costs are estimated in millions of U.S. dollars.

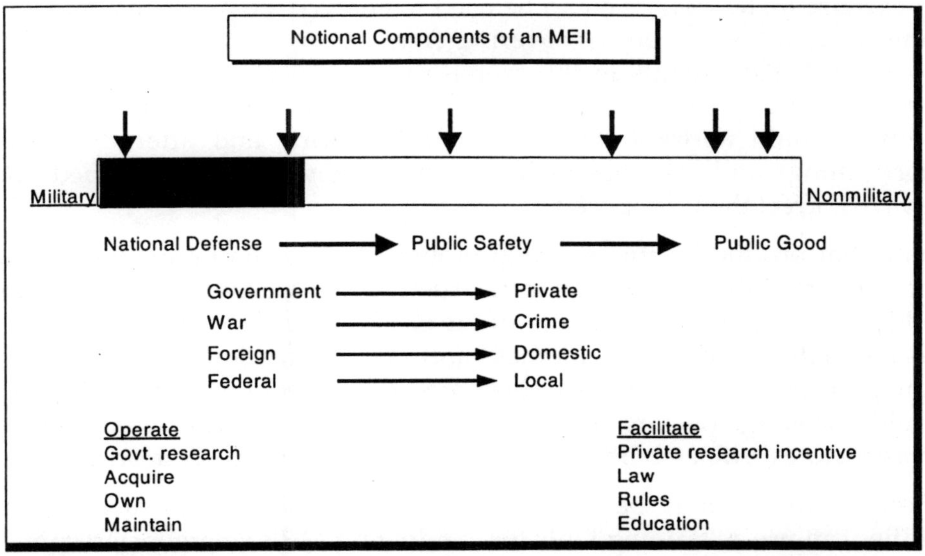

Figure B.2 Spectrum of National Security Preparedness and Government Roles for the Electric Power System Infrastructure (adapted from Molander et al. 1996)

Figure B.2 shows the spectrum of different kinds of preparedness across the electric grid information infrastructure.[6] The traditional military preparedness (left) and the nonmilitary (right) means of preparedness are shown. Moving from left to right the events resembling war tend to look more like crime; foreign threats look more like domestic threats; government responsibilities move to private issues; and within government, the level changes from federal to local.

It is not feasible to protect the entire electric grid information infrastructure from attack. In Figure B.2, the vertical arrows along the top of the spectrum represent "point defenses," defined by selecting those parts of the infrastructure most critical to military and civilian operations and then defending them in appropriate and affordable ways. For example, an arrow on the far left could indicate a portion of the grid information infrastructure critical to military operations that would be placed on dedicated fiber-optic cables. An arrow on the far right could be a tax incentive that would encourage utilities to cooperate with U.S. government-led protection processes and to develop reconstitution capabilities. Point defenses between the far left and far right can be implemented by some combination of laws, regulations, and tax incentives.

An exercise methodology could be used to analyze the problems in identifying, responding to, and recovering from cyber attacks on the electric power grid. Participants in the exercise would be presented with hypothetical future crises and asked to develop appropriate responses. Responses would address issues that occur during and after the crisis. Shortcomings and weaknesses in the response would be identified and ways to correct them proposed.

The initial product of this research would identify the minimal essential components of the information infrastructure that are critical to the continued functioning or reconstitution of the electrical grid. Another product of this research would be development and implementation of a set of rules, regulations, and tax incentives, sponsored by the federal government, that would encourage owners and operators of the electric grid to reduce their infrastructure's vulnerability and/or ensure rapid recovery from an attack.

Another product may be developing computer simulation models that utilities can use as training tools for conducting MEII emergency response exercises for utility system personnel. Periodic exercises would help ensure that utility personnel are familiar with their MEII emergency response plans. Exercises can also be used to fine-tune the plan as changes occur in

---

6 Molander, et al., 1996, *Strategic Information Warfare: A New Face of Warfare*, RAND MR-661-OSD. This document is available at (http://www.rand.org/publications/MR/MR661/MR661.pdf).

the electric power grid and in information technologies. This approach is similar to using utility control room simulation to train operators on routine and emergency operations of the grid (as opposed to the information system).

Another product could be designation of a "red team" chartered to conduct and evaluate attack exercises on hardware and software. Benefits would include increased realism, focus, and urgency for the program at large; reality checks on priorities; feedback that would help decision makers adjust research milestones; additional stakeholders; and increased potential support.

Goals and Challenges

Achieving some of the goals and challenges of this research may be especially difficult. Given the diversity and subtlety of attacks within the information infrastructure, it will be necessary to detect and differentiate among mistake, accident, deployment of software agents designed for espionage, and predeployment of software weapons. Even after the essential elements of the electric grid's information infrastructure have been identified, it may be necessary to develop technologies to protect them.

The fact that the private sector controls or owns major portions of the electric power grid may present a significant challenge. However, studies can be conducted to determine an optimal combination of government policies, procedures, regulations, and tax incentives needed to encourage owners and operators of the grid to reduce vulnerability and ensure rapid recovery from cyber attacks. The private nature of the business, combined with the public image requirements in a competitive environment, often keeps utilities from disclosing attacks, particularly successful ones.

To ensure that owners and operators of the grid maintain a high level of preparedness, it will be necessary to develop a program to exercise electric system personnel on a periodic basis. Exercises would test coordination between the public and private sectors. Computer simulation models could be developed and used as training tools to conduct exercises for utility system operators. The capability to share and implement lessons learned during the exercises should also be developed.

Additional challenges to the research could arise from deregulation of the electric utility sector. Competing companies may be reluctant to share critical, essential, or sensitive information. Procedures will need to be developed so that utilities do not compromise their competitive positions by cooperating in certain activities.

Finally, perception of excessive government interference needs to be addressed. The government's role in national security preparedness must be balanced against public perceptions of the loss of civil liberties and the commercial sector's concern about unwarranted limits on its practices and markets.

Rationale for the Research and Desired Results

This research is important because it could help mitigate an urgent infrastructure threat/vulnerability. Because it is not possible to completely eliminate a vulnerability, it is necessary to develop contingency plans to minimize the effects of an attack or disruption. Procedures and protocols for identifying, responding to, and recovering from cyber threats to the electric grid are areas that have not received enough attention. The interconnected nature of the grid and the impending transfer of large blocks of power over several grids makes it more important than ever to ensure that utilities coordinate their efforts in emergency response and recovery. Therefore, the risks of not having this framework available in the timeframe of interest are potentially significant.

Timeframe and Resource Requirements

In the near term (i.e., before 2000), the MEII concept could be developed. Critical components in the information infrastructure of electric grids could be identified and ways to protect them explored. Protocols and policies to implement the concept, as well as computer simulation models to use in the exercise process, need to be developed. By 2005, exercises would be conducted on a periodic basis and the process refined as necessary. A capability to share and implement lessons learned from the exercises would be developed and applied. By 2010, the exercise process would be fully mature. However, as changes occur in the structure of the electric grid and in information technologies, the process would be refined to address those changes. The estimated level of resources required to develop and implement the MEII concept to full maturity is about $10 million.

This research is not limited to the electric sector. Oil and gas pipelines are highly interconnected networks and also vulnerable to attacks on their imbedded information infrastructure. Consequently, this research area is very applicable to these networks. Depending on the experience with implementing the MEII concept in the electric sector, development of the concept for the oil and gas pipeline network could begin after 2000.

3.1.6 Transmission and Distribution Technologies

Description

The transmission and distribution (T&D) components of the electric infrastructure deliver power to meet customer loads. The integrated network is frequently divided into high- (greater than 100 kV) and low-voltage (less than 100 kV) systems. Increasing the capacity and capability of existing T&D systems improves system reliability by increasing margins to system thermal and stability limits. Technologies that relieve congestion will improve reliability under the demanding conditions of a competitive power market.

The construction of new power lines to expand transmission capacity has slowed in recent years by more than one-third, in part because of public concerns about the aesthetics of transmission towers and lingering concerns over the health risks of electromagnetic field exposure. Because of the difficulty in finding acceptable sites for new transmission lines, utilities are looking for ways to increase capacity. One way is to increase the rating of existing lines or add (repack) lines in existing corridors.

Flexible AC Transmission System (FACTS) technologies now being developed and tested are replacing electromechanical controllers, which are too slow to govern the flow of current in real time, resulting in loop flows and bottlenecks. FACTS controllers can increase or decrease power flow on particular lines to alleviate system congestion. In addition, FACTS controllers can enhance system reliability by counteracting transient disturbances almost instantly by allowing lines to be loaded closer to their thermal limits. Two generations of FACTS controllers are currently in service, and a third generation is nearing demonstration. Further R&D is required to adapt these devices to specific uses and to reduce their costs to practical levels before they can be adopted nationwide. FACTS technology will eventually be deployed nationwide, because it is an essential component in a true open power market with acceptable levels of reliability. Accelerated support could cut the costs of FACTS devices by one-quarter and speed their deployment.

Recent studies suggest that with the new FACTS technologies, remote interactions that involve controls in one end of the system can, at times, have a profound effect on distant regions of the system. Clearly, these concerns need further analysis because the threat is twofold:

- It is possible to have adversely affect the grid from long distances.
- Any need for coordinated control over long distances without means for backup control if the system is disrupted is likely to be counterproductive during emergency conditions.

Wide bandgap semiconductors (WBSs)—primarily nonsilicon materials such as diamond thin films, Group III nitrides, and silicon carbide—have the potential to dramatically reduce the cost of power electronics controls for the intelligent network. The WBS could result in an "integrated circuit of power electronics" by replacing complex, multi-thyristor switching devices with a single, multifunction controller. Ultimately, WBSs could greatly reduce the costs of FACTS and custom power systems and speed their deployment.

With further development, the WBS has potential for lower cost, greater reliability, higher current density, and reduced size. The nation that leads in WBS commercialization will gain a major advantage worldwide. Currently, American manufacturers significantly lag behind their Japanese and European competitors. Forming a nationwide consortium could substantially speed U.S. development of this technology, which would allow the United States to become more competitive.

Hierarchical control of FACTS, which requires more highly integrated, centrally coordinated control by system operators, is needed to integrate the actions of multiple FACTS devices as they come into widespread use. This hierarchical control will raise the power transfer limits of transmission systems over wider areas, eventually extending from coast to coast. Utilities and power pools also need the capability to understand disturbances that develop in neighboring regions to ensure that they do not spread and that stability is maintained throughout the continental grid.

Implementing hierarchical control requires real-time communications and monitoring capabilities, as well as on-line system analysis. Although work has begun on these capabilities, their completion and implementation throughout the North American grid is expected to take at least two decades of intensive effort.

Underground T&D cable systems are a vital part of many networks, and utilities are increasingly using these systems to deal with problematic overhead lines. Underground transmission provides an alternative in large population centers. It has supplied critical downtown loads in large cities for decades, and now is increasingly being used in suburban and rural areas. However, underground transmission has historically been a costly alternative—ranging from 2 to 20 times the cost of an overhead line, depending on operating voltage and installation environment. In addition, the industry is moving toward cables with cross-linked polyethylene (XLPE) insulation to avoid the environmental risk of leakage of the dielectric fluids used in traditional cable systems. Concerns about the reliability of the XLPE systems at higher voltages abound.

There is a need to develop direct-current (DC) transmission; the biggest hurdle to this development is AC/DC converters. Also, vendors are primarily located in Europe.

Many existing underground transmission systems are aging, leading to concerns about reliability and the cost of maintaining system performance. Load growth in urban centers, where most of the underground transmission systems are installed, is increasing at a rate of 4% to 5% per year. Installing new systems is difficult and costly, and reliability requirements are increasing. In this environment, utilities and system operators need a way to increase the capacity of existing circuits while improving reliability and service life. Research is needed to find ways to reduce the costs of new systems, increase the public's confidence in high-voltage XLPE cable systems, and maximize the use of installed cables.

Custom power involves the use of solid-state power electronics to control distribution systems. While the technology is essentially the same as FACTS, the scale and complexity of the installations are smaller. Within 10-20 years, custom power controllers should provide the interfaces needed for widespread use of distributed generation. These interfaces would perform four critical functions:

- Control the bi-directional flow of power between the distribution network and small generators on the customer's property.
- Provide voltage conditioning to the output of a small generator before it enters the network.
- Correct network stability problems that might arise from the presence of many distributed resources.
- Provide on-site reliability and enhance power quality.

Custom power devices also will be used in distribution automation applications to provide real-time network control and reduce system operating costs. Their use must be researched carefully to characterize system behavior during emergencies.

The first custom power devices are beginning to enter utility service, approximately 5-10 years behind FACTS. They are expected to become commonplace as the price of electronic components continues to decline. The major problem is cost; more intensive R&D is required to achieve the substantial savings needed in a competitive timeframe. This R&D would focus on re-engineering custom power devices for greater efficiency and developing better device control methods. WBS technology, as noted above, could also be applied to custom power applications with appropriate research.

High-temperature superconductors (HTSCs) have developed rapidly (only 10 years from discovery to prototype applications), implying that these devices could profoundly affect the electric power industry over the next two decades. One area of high potential impact is the use of HTSCs in the power delivery infrastructure to meet growing customer demand for more power at higher levels of reliability and lower costs.

An individual HTSC wire can carry as much as 100 times the current of an ordinary conductor, and HTSC cables promise to offer at least double the capacity of existing underground conduits for a given diameter and voltage. They could therefore provide an important upgrade option for satisfying demand growth on heavily loaded distribution systems, while making underground transmission a more economical alternative to overhead lines—reducing electricity rates to consumers by transferring low-cost power over longer distances.

The HTSC cables for distribution systems are expected to be particularly attractive for retrofits in the crowded urban underground network. The increased capacity resulting from using existing duct banks would permit major new commercial and industrial developments to be added, while minimizing the disruption (e.g., tearing up city streets and re-routing traffic). However, unless the mean time between failures is very high, having more customers (load) per distribution circuit may reduce reliability.

High-voltage transformers made with HTSC materials can be designed so that they are one-half the weight of conventional units and have a smaller footprint. In addition, HTSC transformers can reduce power losses and operate more efficiently than their conventional counterparts.

Application of superconductors to equipment such as transformers adds efficiency, but also drastically different characteristics. Integrating this equipment with conventional types may lead to many new problems.

New methods of stationary energy storage are on the horizon. They have the potential to level the hourly demand of power plant facilities and provide new ways to increase the reliability of power delivery. Environmentally sustainable hydrogen production (from solar, wind, and nuclear sources) is the most dramatic possibility, for use both in fuel cells and in direct clean combustion. Other promising future storage options include large-scale ultracapacitors, advanced flywheel systems, and superconducting magnets.

Rapid-response energy storage can greatly expand the effectiveness of custom power devices needed for improving retail service. One candidate is the superconducting magnetic energy storage (SMES) system. A project to build a 20-MW SMES capable of providing ride-through for outages of a few seconds using current technology would cost approximately $30 million. Further development of HTSCs may eventually change this picture because HTSCs require much less expensive refrigeration. However, HTSC technology is not yet ready for SMES use. Continued HTSC development, particularly in superconducting materials development and wire fabrication, is crucial to long-term practical SMES use, as it is to other valuable future technologies, such as large generators and motors, power transmission lines, and magnetically levitated high-speed transportation.

Flywheel energy storage (FES) devices also show good potential because they are highly efficient, transportable, operationally robust, and require relatively little maintenance. Small FES devices using superconducting bearings have been developed at the laboratory scale. Larger, higher-performance, more economical, and field-tested devices are needed.

Ultracapacitors of the near future may increase energy storage capacity of conventional capacitors by millions. In addition, ultracapacitors can release their energy 10 to 100 times faster than batteries. Applications may include hybrid electric transportation, power quality and outage ride-through assurance, manufacture of advanced materials, and communication devices. Specific research is needed in miniaturization, large-scale manufacturing methods, and cost reduction.

Goals and Challenges

The challenges for improving the T&D systems fall into three broad categories: materials, devices, and systems. Materials advancements are at the core of two critical enabling technologies—HTSC and high-power electronics.

Superconducting cables have been fabricated in 300-m lengths, but additional improvements in fabrication processes are needed to achieve lengths in the range of several kilometers, which is both a reasonable increase in scale from present capability and a useful length for commercial application in utility distribution systems. Significantly, the near-term challenge for HTSC is not to increase the transition temperature, but to reduce the cost of fabrication and to improve the performance of cryogenic systems and thermal insulation at less cost.

Advanced semiconductors for power electronic devices facilitate fast control of power flows at lower costs so that the technology can actually be deployed. Fast control increases reliability by increasing the steady-state transfer capacity of the system; flows are routed on lines with available capacity. Fast control allows the system to respond rapidly enough to maintain stability under contingencies conditions.

Other goals and challenges include:

- Reduced cost and improved reliability for instrumentation and control;
- Proof of principle and validation of the reliability of large, "smart" systems;
- Siting and environmental impacts of new transmission capacity;
- Large-scale simulation to assure that the complex distribution system is reliable;
- Hardening the T&D system against sabotage and physical threats; and
- Long-term reliability of thermal insulation.

Rationale for the Research and Desired Results

Improvements in T&D equipment affect all aspects of power system planning and operations and indirectly improve system security and reliability. Increased transmission margins significantly lessen the likelihood of reaching critical system limitations, thereby avoiding cascading system outages.

Additional operating flexibility helps systems to recover from disturbances. Larger operating margins provide system operators with alternative methods for resolving emergency conditions, thus increasing system reliability.

Advances in HTSCs and semiconductors for power electronics will contribute to advances in T&D components and system design. Measures that will maximize the use of existing transmission corridors, through either compact tower designs, or underground transmission, will lead to more secure system operation.

Rapid-response storage devices at suitable locations can mitigate the effects of severe events by providing emergency power and preventing cascading outages.

Timeframe and Resource Requirements

This topic involves many potential R&D projects and demonstration facilities (e.g., 20-MW SMES at an estimated cost of $30 million). Substantial progress is needed in each of the several research areas listed above. Although industry contributes substantial funds to the general area of T&D technologies (e.g., FES), there is an important federal role in pursuing R&D that is especially relevant for infrastructure assurance (e.g., SMES) and longer-term, high-risk R&D. The R&D funding needed through 2010 is more than $500 million.

3.1.7 On-line Security Assessment

Description

Electric power system operators need to operate the system safely within allowable tolerances on line loadings, voltage levels, and frequency under varying conditions. Computations that attempt to assess whether the operating system is safe are called "security assessments." On-line security assessments use near real-time data to predict system performance under assumed or anticipated system disturbances and identify preventive measures to maintain the system in a safe operating state. OSAs can also be used in system restoration planning.

Utilities must be able to conduct OSAs so that they can cope effectively with power system contingencies, especially multiple simultaneous faults. OSAs include power flow (feasibility) computations over many contingencies, optimal power flow-based redispatch, and on-line transient analysis.

The following components are needed to perform an OSA:

- *Accurate models of the system.* The August 1996 western outage revealed that system models had not been adequately calibrated or tested for the unusual circumstances and event sequence that led to the outage.

Model calibration is expensive and needs to be improved. Research on network "equivalencing" is also needed.

- *On-line analytical tools.* On-line analysis is in its infancy. The first generation of software can now provide operators with near real-time information on system conditions. Analytical tools are needed to reduce the time required for analysis and recommendations.
- *Accurate, timely, synchronized information on the system state.* In many areas of the country, information about the state of the system is not readily available from remote sites. Although the Wide Area Measurement System (WAMS) shows promise in remedying this problem, very accurate synchronization of state information (within a fraction of a cycle) is needed to identify incipient stability problems. Timing signals from Global Positioning System (GPS) satellites can be used to provide this synchronization.
- *Communication system to collect, store, and transmit system state data.* Advances in the rate of data collection from a geographically dispersed sensor network are needed as a prerequisite to detailed real-time calculations.
- *Real-time database systems.* Current systems are difficult to modify because of ad-hoc, proprietary designs. The system should include telemetry data, state estimates, and computation results.
- *State estimation software.* Improved state estimation software is needed to resolve differences among measurements and to predict future states. Distributed and parallel computation methods are needed to exploit major technologies for building high-performance computational systems.
- *Algorithms and facilities for performing the security assessment computations.* Perhaps the most difficult challenge in implementing OSA is the development of improved algorithms for accurate, timely calculations. Fault scenario screening tools, parallel or distributed computing facilities, improved algorithms for solving large sparse matrices, and incremental algorithms that do not require recomputation for added faults are candidates for research initiatives.
- *Integrated security assessment system.* The security assessment system must be highly reliable and immune to faults. Issues relating to the security of the system involve trade-offs between a large centralized facility (housing all data and processing systems) and distributed computing and data storage facilities. Various options need to be evaluated, including cost/benefit studies. Probabilistic risk assessment tools should prove valuable in these evaluations.

Goals and Challenges

On-line security analysis systems need substantial improvements in performance to meet the functional requirements for preventing and reducing the effect of power grid disturbances. Current systems require about 15 minutes (approximately 1,000 seconds) to analyze a complex power grid. However, detecting system faults and taking corrective action require state calculations every few cycles, 10,000 times faster than current capabilities. Another requirement calls for processing orders of magnitude more input data, which implies extremely large improvements in processor speed and probably massively parallel and/or distributed architectures. It may be advisable to investigate probabilistic and agent-based computational methods for analyzing large systems, rather than rely on the traditional deterministic approach.

A second challenge relates to input data requirements. Most transmission and distribution systems have rudimentary instrumentation systems, often based on analog sensors, characterized by low data rates, and infrequently calibrated. OSA requires digital sensors, data buses, and "smart" sensors capable of self-calibration and fault diagnosis. Instrumentation and control systems developed for other industries can be adapted to the needs of the power grid, but the power industry faces a significant challenge because of the sheer numbers of geographically dispersed sensors required.

Rationale for the Research and Desired Results

OSA will be most useful in preventing or mitigating damage from cascading faults. The 1996 western outages were caused by cascading faults. A single fault created a disturbance that propagated through a large system, which ultimately resulted in an outage that affected millions. If a suitable OSA system fed by detailed power grid data had been in place at the time of the initial disturbance, the cascading outage probably would have been prevented and damage would have been limited to the vicinity of the initiating event.

Developing suitable OSA systems also will allow analysis of the signature of various system disturbances. For example, it should be possible to differentiate natural or accidental initiating events (e.g., overloads during peak demand periods, transmission bottlenecks, system instabilities) from deliberate acts (actuating breakers at substations, shooting at transmission lines).

However, current OSA systems are not capable of monitoring, controlling, and simulating large power grid systems. Sensors and communications systems need to be developed for handling large parallel data streams. Algorithms for analyzing these data and for recommending changes to the operation of the system also need to be developed to prevent or mitigate disturbances.

One alternative to using algorithms may be coordinated dispersed controls. Substantial R&D is required, but this approach could reduce data communication requirements.

In the near future, the reliability of the grid also will be tested by the increasing demands for access to transmission resources in an open power market. The demand for transmission resources will affect the grid, but it is difficult to predict in what ways. However, the operating state of the system may be somewhat different than it is now. OSA will be useful in predicting stress on the grid caused by the open power market. Furthermore, advance information on upcoming transactions and demands for transmission resources will provide useful input for the OSA. The OSA can use these data for computing system stability and thus help grid operators anticipate future demands on the system. This "look-ahead" capability implies additional enhancements of OSA algorithms to analyze both short- and long-term time dependencies.

Timeframe and Resource Requirements

In the next few years, a 1,000-fold increase in speed with subcycle state information can be achieved. By 2005, accurate models and tools for the national grid can be devised. By 2010, new tools and techniques for OSA will be developed. Funding requirements through 2010 are estimated to be $50 million.

3.1.8 Dispersed Generation and Backup Infrastructures

Description

Renewable-resource Generation. Advanced renewable electric energy sources (solar, wind, hydro, and biomass) have the potential for significantly increasing the diversity and flexibility of electric generation, conserving fuel resources that reduce the carbon intensity of generating electricity, and reducing dependence on a single-source fuel supply. The advantages of this diversity are increased competition among generation alternatives, resulting in cost savings for electric energy and a greater degree of choice for the consumer. This flexibility will make the overall system more resilient and able to cope with naturally occurring disruptions.

As concerns mount about urban pollution and global warming, these renewable technologies grow more attractive. Both solar and wind technologies are now at an economic disadvantage for generating bulk power compared with fossil fuel. Moreover, the current wholesale power market in the United States is characterized by very low marginal prices and a glut of fossil and nuclear generation, which does not favor the introduction of new generation resources. In the next decade, the market must adjust for decommissioning of nuclear plants and retirement of old coal-burning plants. Renewable generation in developing countries, however, may be more attractive in the near term and could become a major export opportunity.

Renewable resources are sustainable because their availability is unlimited, at least from a global perspective, in quantity or time, and because they have little effect on the planet's ecosystems. Renewables are also suitable for distributed generation. Thus, they offer the potential for making the power system more resilient and reliable by locating electricity generation near the point of use. However, renewables will not become more than a niche generation alternative without technical advances to improve performance and reduce costs.

Solar Photovoltaic Power. Steady improvements in the technology of converting sunlight directly into electricity have led to the production of viable "off-grid" power systems. With a small solar system in place, a remote village in a developing nation could have refrigeration, communication, a light source, and some pumping capability.

Currently, these systems have far-reaching applications in the developed world. Cellular telephone installations, signal repeater stations, water pumps, isolated homes, and weather stations in remote locations are routinely powered by solar energy systems. More than 100 MW of solar electric installations operate worldwide. The solar electric industry is on the verge of mass production of portable power generation units suitable for installation as self-sustaining, affordable electric supply systems in developing nations or in remote locations in the United States.

The technology of solar electric conversion must improve substantially before it becomes an economically viable alternative to grid power in developed countries. The conversion rate from solar energy to electricity is about 7% new. Research indicates that the conversion rate could double or triple within the next few years.

For example, with flat-plate photovoltaic solar energy conversion technology, an energy conversion efficiency of 15% is possible for direct or indirect sunlight. Overall life-cycle delivered electricity costs are competitive with fossil and nuclear central station power. However, several key knowledge gaps exist. Additional development is needed for triple-layer photovoltaic cell materials and manufacturing processes. Long-term stability at 15% efficiency needs to be assured to meet cost targets. For amorphous silicon photovoltaic technology, a competing approach, costs are potentially very low, but additional development of manufacturing processes is required.

Wind Power. Wind energy is available in many locations worldwide. The newest, most technologically advanced wind installations can produce power at rates comparable to new fossil generation. However, new wind power installations in the United States must compete with existing fossil, nuclear, or hydro power plants, which produce energy at extremely low prices.

Given the nature of today's wholesale U.S. electric power market, which is characterized by very low marginal prices and a glut of fossil and nuclear generation, the construction of large new wind power stations in the United States in the near future seems only a remote possibility unless driven by carbon-reduction needs. "Green" pricing and renewable portfolio standards offer potential for expansion of wind power and other renewables. Wind installations in developing countries, however, may be more attractive and could become a major export opportunity as well as an environmental gain.

Biomass. Burning plant matter (wood chips, sugar cane bagasse [remains of sugar cane after the milling process]) has contributed to electricity production for many years. Biomass combustion reduces emissions compared with coal-fired plants and essentially emits no CO2. Research into biomass electricity production in the United States currently is small and focuses on co-firing biomass fuels with coal in conventional power plants and on growing genetically engineered crops that could be used as fuel for power plants or for other products (fiber, food). Additional research is needed to develop better systems for biomass combustion and to explore gasification and other applications for the use of biomass.

Distributed Generation. Distributed generation technologies, including fuel cells, photovoltaics, microturbines, diesel engines, and energy storage devices can provide another path for diversifying electricity generation. Distributed generation also increases flexibility for users of energy. They can insulate themselves from grid reliability problems; use gas and electricity interchangeably, depending on the relative prices of gas and grid-supplied electricity; improve efficiency; and reduce costs. Depending on the technology, distributed generation systems can operate on such diverse fuels as biogas, methanol, and hydrogen.

Fuel cells are a key technology for achieving fuel diversity, particularly in distributed generation. Investigations range from fundamental research on materials to increasing unit efficiency to field demonstrations of early units. Phosphoric acid fuel cells are already commercialized and operating at 75 sites worldwide, achieving efficiencies of 35% to 45% and an overall availability of 95%. Continued development is addressing technical, operating, and economic issues to make this option cost-effective. Commercial molten carbonate fuel cells—which can accommodate such unconventional fuels as landfill gas, digester gas, and biomass fuels—should be commercially available by 2002, as work in progress addresses technical issues and reduces balance-of-plant costs. Other promising fuel cell technologies—solid-oxide fuel cells and polymer electrolyte membrane fuel cells—are also being pursued.

Goals and Challenges

Large-scale integration and simulation are needed for distributed generation systems. There is a need to understand how to control a large number of dynamically interacting distributed resources. Also, integration is needed for massive numbers of instrumentation and control systems.

Researchers need to find methods to reduce costs and improve reliability of small-scale power generation systems. Another important challenge is the ability for the systems to run unattended for long periods of time.

For advanced backup power systems, improved control systems applied to existing backup generators are needed. Also needed are policy changes to allow backup systems to power the distribution system in emergencies.

Rationale for the Research and Desired Results

The improved diversity and flexibility of electrical generation are major benefits of renewable sources; there also are benefits to infrastructure assurance. The environmental and sustainability benefits are likely to be even more important in the coming years. Finally, distributed generation can reduce the likelihood of regional blackouts from large-scale grid problems.

Timeframe and Resource Requirements

This topic has a number of worthy R&D areas at different levels of development. The electrical industry and the federal government are investing substantial funds in related R&D. Federal support that emphasizes the infrastructure assurance aspects of these research areas is needed. Estimated additional funding needed through 2010 is $100 million.

Improved energy storage devices (rapid response systems were described in Section 3.1.6, Transmission and Distribution Technologies) could also contribute to system reliability through distributed siting. Options include flywheels, batteries, and superconducting systems.

3.2 Oil and Natural Gas Systems

3.2.1 Critical Consequence Analysis

Description

The U.S. natural gas pipeline transmission network is the interconnected sum of a large number of privately owned and operated gas pipeline networks. While each pipeline company has full knowledge of its assets and the operations of its own network (intakes, deliveries, flows on pipeline links), no one—private company or governmental agency—has a clear, detailed picture of the operations of the whole system, nor does any outside company know how the various subnetworks feed into each other and are balanced over time. Because of this interconnectedness, disruptions in the physical system of one company may have far-reaching consequences, such as a lasting interruption of gas supply to a major metropolitan area or a major electric power generating plant, or no consequences at all because the structure and capacity of the overall network frequently allow for alternate gas supplies to be easily rerouted to these consumption nodes. Developing a thorough understanding of the possible consequences of physical failures, as well as strategies for optimally coping with them, is in need of future R&D.

This effort involves elements of basic research (mathematical modeling of complex networks) and applied research (data analysis and model computer implementation). The proposed research centers on the development, calibration, and computer implementation of gas network simulation and/or optimization models. Researches would develop a detailed network representation of the U.S. system, including all interstate and intrastate pipelines, to the distribution city gates and beyond. Each delivery point could be characterized by a curtailment impact index—the higher the index, the more catastrophic the impact of one unit of curtailment.

These models would be used ideally to test the vulnerability of the network under different incident scenarios (one or several links, compressors, storage fields, or interconnections are out of service). The source of the incident can be either a physical or cyber action. The model would then attempt to reroute the available gas while minimizing the total impact of the curtailment. If rerouting is successful and the total impact is nil, the nodes/links assumed to be inoperative can be considered noncritical. Alternatively, if deliveries to a major metropolitan area must be curtailed, the nodes/links are critical and should be given a high priority in any risk management approach. The models could be used to test numerous incident scenarios, from which researchers could derive an ordered list of critical system components (links, compressors, storage fields, interconnections).

The products of this research include (1) information on critical network components and on the consequences of their failure; (2) a system of computerized models (software) that could be implemented on powerful PCs, workstations, or mainframes; and (3) a set of rules or procedures for mitigating the negative effects of incidents once they have occurred.

Goals and Challenges

The overall goals of this project are to identify critical components in the U.S. gas transmission network, assess the consequences of any dysfunctions, and propose strategies for mitigation. These goals would be achieved with the help of computerized models. A fundamental difficulty in this research is to design sufficiently detailed models that provide useful answers to various questions, while remaining manageable from a computational and data input viewpoint. The size of these models may prove to be a serious challenge. Simplifications (e.g., network aggregation) may be necessary, but they would have to be tested carefully so that they do not decrease the overall usefulness of the models. To build the models, publicly available information at the federal level (FERC, DOE, DOE's Energy Information Administration [EIA], U.S. Department of Transportation [DOT]) would have to be complemented by data from state governments (e.g., public utility commissions) and by data from pipeline companies, particularly intrastate pipelines, and major local distribution companies. These companies may be reluctant to share the necessary data (e.g., gas flows) because of competitive pressures; appropriate procedures would have to be developed to protect these data while establishing cooperation with these companies.

Rationale for the Research and Desired Results

This research is important for the following reasons:

- A network representation of the U.S. gas system is the only way to understand, in an operational fashion, how the system works.
- Models are essential for vulnerability assessment, particularly for identifying and ranking the weak components of the system and determining where risk management resources should be allocated.
- Models can be natural tools for mitigating the negative effects of incidents and for planning recovery activities (e.g., prioritizing recovery actions).
- Models would also allow for interfacing with the natural gas infrastructure and the power infrastructure, particularly at the level of gas-consuming power plants.

Timeframe and Resource Requirements

This R&D project is classified as most important. The issues involved are physical threats, complexity, and interdependencies. The time needed to complete the project is about four years. Resources of $3 million are needed.

Three major activities have been identified for "Critical Consequences Analysis" that would span the four-year duration of the project:

- *Basic model design.* This activity would be completed in Year 1. The mathematical structure of the model(s) would be designed, and decisions would be made regarding the level of model detail or aggregation and the type of necessary input data.

- *Model development and implementation.* This activity would be completed during Years 2 and 3. Activities would include processing and analyzing the input data obtained from public and private sources, programming the model, debugging it, and testing it to ensure that it is a reliable representation of the U.S. gas transmission network. This testing may lead to model adjustments.
- *Consequence analyses.* This activity would be completed in Year 4. Numerous incident/failure scenarios would be developed and input into the model(s). The model(s) would be run and the resulting curtailment impacts analyzed. This analysis would lead to the development of an ordered list of critical network components (e.g., supply sources, storage fields, compressors, pipeline links, and interconnections).

3.2.2 Decision Support Systems

Description

This purpose of this research is to develop and implement risk management and decision support tools to allow gas and oil industry decision makers to prioritize resources, thus minimizing risk and effectively responding to incidents.

Predictive Risk Management. Mitigation of risks to both processing (e.g., gas processing plants or oil refineries) and piping systems is an important element of private-sector management of such physical facilities. As a result, gas and oil production, transportation, and delivery are relatively low-risk activities. Nonetheless, past pipeline failures caused by third-party damage or mechanical failure have been costly, and industry activity in risk management is increasing. Furthermore, the increasing system complexity and interdependencies, described elsewhere in this report, exacerbate the potential impacts of incidents. These changes occur at a time when energy industry deregulation calls for overall reductions in production and delivery costs.

Response and Reporting Decision Analysis. Following recent oil and gas pipeline ruptures, the industry joined with the federal government to improve risk management tools. DOT is currently funding a demonstration to determine the safety and economic advantages of risk management processes. Despite this important progress, the development of risk management tools and decision support models is in its infancy. Use of decision models (e.g., Pipeview™ or Pipeline Maintenance Optimization System) is very limited. Spatial analysis tools, such as the Integrated Spatial Analysis Techniques, funded by the Gas Research Institute, are under development. However, these systems focus entirely on the physical risks to the oil and gas pipeline industries. These technologies need to be developed and applied both upstream to production and downstream to distribution and expanded to include both cyber and physical threats.

Incident reporting and response are other areas of increasing concern to industry and government decision makers. The gas and oil industry currently uses sophisticated procedures for emergency response. However, the increasing complexities and interdependencies in the evolving energy business also illustrate the need for development of decision analysis tools.

Another important consideration in the development of decision analysis tools for prediction, mitigation, response, and reporting is the continuing development and application of new sensors for monitoring and inspection. As these technologies (Section 3.2.4) evolve, decision analysis tools need to be continually upgraded to take advantage of improvements in data input.

Goals and Challenges

Predictive Risk Management. Risk management models are needed that allow integration of real-time operational control data (e.g., processing plant/refinery process controls, pipeline SCADA) with detailed physical history data (e.g., construction type, past inspection information, maps, component types, repair history, environmental history). These models are needed for each sector of the industry—production, processing, transportation, storage, and distribution. Development of an enterprise-wide model requires careful consideration after sector models have proved to be effective.

The overall goal of risk management is to increase security and safety while minimizing operating costs. Specific goals for predictive risk management models include the following:

- Provide a comprehensive description of the physical and cyber properties of the industry segment using spatial (e.g., geographical information system, GPS) methods.
- Incorporate an interpretive capability, including historical operational, inspection, data transfer, and electronic commerce information in decision analysis.
- Include a predictive capability to allow optimized resource allocation to maintenance, repair, inspection, capital improvement, or computer system/software upgrade activities.
- Provide real-time recognition of high-risk conditions (physical or cyber) caused by natural system deterioration (e.g., corrosion, cracks, sensor failure), operator error (or intentional action), or third-party intrusion.
- Incorporate an element to resist tampering.

Response and Reporting Decision Analysis. Decision analysis tools should also be developed to permit each industry segment to minimize response time and cost and to provide real-time reporting to appropriate organizations. These capabilities would help industry detect and potentially thwart coordinated or interdependent incidents. Because the existence of such decision analysis tools could actually increase risks (and the systems could become the targets of terrorists or disgruntled insiders), they must be developed with integral security considerations.

The overall goals for developing these decision analysis tools are to minimize damage, disruption, and cost of incidents of any kind on the gas and oil energy production and delivery system and to allow immediate response by national security and law enforcement agencies to terrorist or other illegal attack on the infrastructure. Specific goals include the following:

- Provide real-time interpretation of system monitoring sensors.
- Ensure full integration with risk management models and all automated operating data.
- Incorporate accurate modeling of the system interconnections and interdependencies.
- Include an automated ability to order rapid acquisition of additional information such as satellite photos, the news media, and rapid response industry crews.
- Integrate communications with emergency response, law enforcement, and national security agencies.
- Include the capability to determine trends in incidents over time.
- Incorporate an element to resist tampering.

Rationale for the Research and Desired Results

Predictive risk management is an effective method for effectively allocating limited industry and government agency funds to minimize risks. Existing processes in the oil and gas industry, while effective in the past, have entered a period of increasing threat, while operating budgets are increasingly under pressure. Physical threats are generally known to the industry segments, but complexity and interdependencies are increasing their potential impact. Currently, most incidents that result in physical damage are managed as singular events, and response abilities and time vary greatly. Cyber attacks and incidents represent a new threat to the industry. Currently, protection from such incidents is provided by standard computer system "firewall" technology. The current approaches no longer adequately protect this critical infrastructure from the growing potential threat.

Finally, some important scientific advances have occurred in monitoring, sensing, and detecting critical conditions. Many of these advances are beginning to enter the gas and oil industries. However, the decision analysis tools to use the new data effectively and to integrate existing data with new sources have not been developed. Development of such tools can be justified on both economic and security grounds.

Timeframe and Resource Requirements

Predictive Risk Management. As noted, predictive risk management models are needed for each sector of the gas and oil industries. At a minimum, models are needed for gas and oil production; oil refineries, gas processing plants, liquid pipelines, high-pressure gas transmission pipelines, underground gas storage facilities, receiving/storage facilities for petroleum liquids, LNG terminals and storage facilities, petroleum products distribution, and medium- and low-pressure gas distribution networks. Development efforts on these models can be parallel or prioritized following completion of the vulnerability and physical protection assessments described in Sections 3.2.1 and 3.2.3. DOT-funded efforts to develop partial risk management models are underway for liquids and high-pressure gas transmission sectors. These efforts should be continued and expanded to include cyber threats. After all sector models have been developed, an assessment should be made as to the need for, benefits from, and costs of an enterprise-wide risk management model.

Activities for each sector model include the following:

- Assess all available historical data on system cyber and physical components.
- Assess available operating data and its time availability (e.g., monthly, daily, real time).
- Assess available monitoring and inspection data and their time of availability.
- Assess available environmental data (e.g., weather, earthquake) and their time of availability.
- Develop a spatially/geographically based software platform to depict historical and current physical, operating, and inspection/monitoring data.
- Develop expert system models capable of interpreting time change sequences in data, comparing historical with current data, and evaluating environmental data to provide decision-making outputs, including operational changes and maintenance/repair schedules; efforts during this stage of activity will also highlight the need for improved data or information and identify needed capital improvements.

- Demonstrate models over a sufficient time to show that improved safety and security have been achieved at minimum cost.

Response and Reporting Decision Analysis. As in risk management, response and reporting decision analysis tools should be developed for each industry sector either in parallel or by priority. While response and reporting models can be developed without a comprehensive risk management model, the results will be greatly enhanced if both models are developed and fully integrated. Full achievement of the goals stated above requires such integration.

Activities for each sector model include the following:

- Assess available disruption/incident/tampering detection/identification data and their time characteristics.
- Characterize likely damage or disruption.
- Describe response alternatives.
- Delineate all reporting and communications requirements and channels.
- Study human interface elements of the overall response and reporting system.
- Develop an expert system model capable of (1) evaluating available system data and comparing those data in real time with probable conditions during disruption, and (2) providing response outputs (requests for additional information, warnings, or automatic communications as appropriate) necessary to meet the goals stated above.
- Test and evaluate the model, including simulation of potential incidents.
- Deploy and demonstrate the model and its integration with human elements of the industry sector.
- Develop an incident tracking and trending model.

Decision analysis tools for predictive risk management and response/reporting can be developed, tested, and deployed for each industry sector in three to five years at an estimated cost of \$3 million to \$8 million, depending on the complexity of the industry sector. If both risk management and response/reporting models are developed in parallel for the 10 sectors listed below, the effort could be completed in five years at an estimated total cost of approximately \$120 million. An alternative approach would be to develop the five highest priority sector models first, followed by the lower priority sectors. As discussed above, sectors would be prioritized following the completion of the vulnerability and physical protection assessments (Sections 3.2.1. and 3.2.3). Taking this path, completion would require 10 years at approximately the same total cost. The roadmap described below is based on taking this development path.

Finally, after individual sector models are completed, it would be appropriate to assess the need for enterprise-wide models. This resource estimate does not include the cost of such an assessment or of the model development efforts.

The industry sectors and a preliminary assessment of decision analysis model complexity are given in Table B.3.

A roadmap of input for decision analysis models has been developed for the five most important industries. The roadmap identifies goals and groups them by the year targeted for achievement: 2000, 2005, and 2010. They are listed in the subsections below.

Table B.3 Assessment of the Complexity of Decision Analysis Models by Industry Sector

Industry Sector	Complexity
Gas and oil production	Low
Oil refineries	Medium
Gas processing plants	Low
Liquids pipelines	Medium
High-pressure gas transmission pipelines	High
Underground gas storage facilities	Low
Receiving and storage facilities for petroleum liquids	Medium
LNG terminals and storage facilities	Medium
Petroleum products distribution	Low
Medium- and low-pressure gas distribution networks	High

Roadmap Target: Achieve by ~2000

For the five most important industry sectors, initiate work on the following tasks:

- Assess all available historical, operating, monitoring/detection, and environmental data capabilities.
- Develop a spatially/geographically based software platform to depict historical and current physical, operating, and inspection/monitoring data.
- Assess available disruption/incident/tampering detection/identification data and its time characteristics.
- Characterize likely damage or disruption conditions.
- Describe response alternatives.

- Delineate all reporting and communications requirements and channels.

Roadmap Target: Achieve by ~2005

For the five most important industry sectors, initiate work on the following tasks:

- Develop expert system models capable of interpreting time change sequences in data, comparing historical with current data, and evaluating environmental data to provide decision-making outputs, including operational changes and maintenance/repair schedules; efforts during this stage of activity will highlight the need for improved data or information and identify needed capital improvements.
- Study human interface elements of the overall response and reporting system.
- Develop an expert system model capable of evaluating available system data, making real-time comparisons with probable disruption conditions, and providing response outputs—requests for additional information, warnings, or automatic communications as appropriate—to meet the goals stated above.
- Test and evaluate the response model, including simulation of likely incidents.
- Develop an incident tracking and trending model.
- Complete the assessment and characterization activities listed for achievement by 2000 for the highest priority sectors.

Roadmap Target: Achieve by ~2010

For the five most important industry sectors, complete the following task:

- Demonstrate and verify both predictive risk management and response/reporting decision analysis tools.

For the five very important industry sectors, initiate work in the following areas:

- Develop export system models capable of interpreting time change sequences in data, comparing historical with current data, and evaluating environmental data to provide decision-making outputs, including operational changes and maintenance/repair schedules; efforts during this stage of activity will highlight the need for improved data or information and identify need capital improvements.
- Study human interface elements of the overall response and reporting system.
- Develop an expert system model capable of evaluating available system data, making real-time comparisons with probable disruption condi-

tions, and providing response outputs—requests for additional information, warnings, or automatic communications as appropriate—to meet the goals stated above.

- Test and evaluate the response model, including simulation of likely incidents.
- Develop an incident tracking and trending model.

3.2.3 Physical Protection Assessment

Description

This research topic will result in a comprehensive assessment of the physical assets of the gas and oil industry, the points of physical exposure, current protection methods, and strategies for future protection. The assessment will cover 10 industry sectors:

- Gas and oil production
- Oil refineries
- Gas processing plants
- Liquids pipelines
- High-pressure gas transmission pipelines
- Underground gas storage facilities
- Receiving and storage facilities for petroleum liquids
- LNG terminals and storage facilities
- Petroleum products distribution
- Medium- and low-pressure gas distribution networks

Goals and Challenges

The goal of this activity is to complete a comprehensive report that achieves the following:

- Statistically based numerical counts of the components of the oil and gas industry physical system (e.g., onshore and offshore wells, gathering lines, dehydrators, compressors, processing plants, receiving terminals, storage facilities, city gates, valves, regulators);
- Specific identification of areas of high concentration of physical facilities (e.g., processing plants, refineries, oil/LNG receiving terminals, pipeline "hubs");
- Characterization of current protection methods used by the industry; and
- Determination of advanced protection methods and an analysis of the costs and benefits for the application of these methods.

Rationale for the Research and Desired Results

No comprehensive study of the physical assets of the gas and oil industry has been compiled. Government (DOE/EIA and U.S. Department of the Interior) data requirements and industry databases provide a partial, but incomplete, picture of industry assets. No analysis of current and potential advanced protection methods is available.

Timeframe and Resource Requirements

The following tasks are required to assess the physical assets of the gas and oil industry. A roadmap of input for these assessments has been developed. The roadmap identifies goals and groups them by the year targeted for achievement. The goals are listed below. The resource requirements in the near term are estimated to be $5 million.

Roadmap Target: Achieve by ~2000

- Conduct surveys and statistical analyses to fill the gaps and to upgrade existing data.
- Collect existing data from government and industry sources; determine whether the data are adequate and identify existing gaps.
- Analyze the data to determine the points of concentration and vulnerabilities of the physical facilities.

Roadmap Target: Achieve by ~2005

- Survey the industry to determine the protection methods currently being used for areas identified as highest concentration and vulnerability.
- Conduct a technology assessment of physical protection methods.
- Develop strategies for use of advanced protection methods in the oil and gas industry.
- Analyze the costs of and benefits from using enhanced, advanced methods.

An additional task to be completed by 2005 is to publish the study.

3.2.4 Multisensor and Warning Technologies

Central to the protection of any infrastructure is the implementation of an integrated, corroborative system of overlapping technologies designed to warn against intruders at any of the critical facilities and control nodes along that system. The proposed integrated Multisensor and Warning Technologies (MSWT) system would further facilitate analysis of data to provide information that can be used to anticipate attacks and identify perpetrators.

The most critical of such facilities and control nodes in the gas industry include:

- Interstate pipelines,
- Compressor stations,
- City-gate stations,
- Odorant injection sites,
- District regulator sites,
- Any pressure or flow control site,
- Gas control centers,
- Remote metering sites,
- SCADA control centers,
- Any SCADA-driven controls, and
- Any site that intersects with other vulnerable infrastructures.

Description

Industry and government research and operating personnel would evaluate leading technologies for immediate development and commercialization. Initially, they would focus on tamper detection and failure warning technologies for remote locations, including acoustics, electronic signals, biological and chemical toxin sensors, video-imaging, satellite oversight with GPS systems, remote methane detection, expert system predictive methodology, and SCADA communications and control standards.

Goals and Challenges

The most important element of this analysis is determining whether the identified tamper detection and failure technologies are both scientifically sound and operationally practicable. The leading technologies in each of these areas would be analyzed to determine whether the industry was likely to view them as commercially justifiable in terms of the benefits they could bring in today's highly competitive world. Those technologies that are most beneficial from a commercial viewpoint would have a preliminary advantage over technologies viewed as noncommercially productive.

Rationale for the Research and Desired Results

The approach described above is necessary because industry will be reluctant to spend money to guard against potential emergencies, unless it can see a payback on an ongoing basis from a business perspective. When properly implemented, through the combined resources of government and industry, this strategy will result in a profoundly more robust infrastructure, more accessible to open-access commerce and trading, yet far less accessible to sabotage or terrorism.

Scientists, engineers, and industry operating personnel will review the selected technologies. They will establish the best way to link the strongest technologies into one integrated intrusion warning system. This system will communicate attempted intrusion at any site along the infrastructural system and then automatically verify the attempt by querying another independent technology. For example, if an acoustic sensor placed along a pipeline were to detect a variation in the sound of gas flow through the pipeline that was not explained by electronically monitored valve settings, it would automatically call for backup verification of leakage or sabotage from a satellite with remote methane detection capability or an electronically driven pattern-recognition system.

Software and hardware additions to existing commercial products that must be added to make the warning system fully functional will be developed in partnership with government oversight and relevant technologies developed within both government and industry laboratories.

The system must also be designed to immediately deliver a real-time warning to the gas control centers and emergency response centers of the involved gas companies. In addition, the system must warn the control centers of intersecting infrastructures such as electric power control centers, so that they can take appropriate mitigative actions. It is crucial that at least two intrusion warning technology systems are in place at each site so that the two technologies can validate each other's findings in real time. This dual-technology approach greatly reduces the ability of a saboteur to "spoof" one technology or another, which would result in incorrect response measures.

In addition, the intrusion protection system must be interpretive and integrated. In this sense, interpretive means that results from the sensor outputs will be examined to determine whether they fall into temporal or geographic sequences of events that indicate an actual threat. At the site level of a physical assault, for example, a sequence of events consisting of a video image of a person climbing a fence, followed by detection of a door being opened, followed by a change in a set-point would be assigned a much higher threat potential than a single door opening. The warning, in other words, would be increased based on interpretations that the sequence of events in the example accords with a pattern expected for site penetration. The same sequence analysis would be performed and fine-tuned to protect against cyber assault. The system will be interpretive in that it will collect security data in a central repository for further analysis. Both the cyber and physical detection systems must also be designed to collect information about the individual attempting the intrusion.

In partnership with all sectors of the gas industry, including manufacturers and vendors, the next step is to implement the MSWT physical and cyber intrusion warning system on an operating basis. The partnership of gas industry executives and technical staff is essential to assure that the system is initiated over as large an area of the country as possible, as efficiently and cost-effectively as possible.

The operating expertise and the substantial market power of industry are the most powerful market-building tools here. Large regional gas companies operating in each of four regions of the country will be selected to establish themselves as standard-setting and manufacturing/distribution centers for the technologies considered to be most effective for system implementation. These companies will be selected on the basis of market power, integrity of personnel and operations (as determined by an ongoing record of outstanding industry performance), and willingness and capability to manufacture the required hardware and software on a mass basis.

The companies selected will be able to recapture their partnership costs and gain significant profit through sales of the required hardware and software to themselves, their subsidiaries, and the smaller gas companies in their service territory who wish to share in the economic and security advantages of participating in the intrusion warning system. This significant manufacturing and vending opportunity will strongly encourage all involved to place their considerable marketing power and expertise behind the project, thus expanding the market at a rapid rate to include the entire country within a short time.

This plan will reduce government spending, while, at the same time, garnering strong industry support for this crucially important project.

Timeframe and Resource Requirements

It is proposed that a 10-year program be put in place beginning in 1999. The purpose of the program would be to fully plan and evaluate, design the hardware and software for, and then implement an infrastructure-wide intrusion warning system that covers all these critical points and others within the infrastructure. The plan is envisioned to take place in three carefully defined phases, each running a set number of years with carefully designed end-points and deliverables that lead into the next phase.

The near-term deliverable, as outlined above, is an extended report on technologies analyzed, architecture recommended for system design, and analysis of technological gaps that remain in the system. The last will require additional hardware and software development and an explanation as to why those additions are required. The report will be distributed to relevant government and industry review parties and be released as a formal guideline objective. The starting and completion dates for Phase 1 are September 1998 and August 2000. The approximate cost is estimated to be $20 million over two years.

Phase 2 involves a comprehensive description and roadmap of an accepted infrastructure intrusion warning system based on multiple verifying technologies. It may be necessary to add software and hardware to make the independent technology systems capable of reliable and hardened communications at all times, once the full system has been implemented. Starting and completion dates for this phase are September 2000 and August 2005. The estimated cost of Phase 2 is $40 million over five years.

Phase 3 is commercial deployment or implementation. The commercially available physical and cyber intrusion detection system will be deployed or implemented across one or more major regions of the country in cooperation with the largest gas companies. Full market expansion forces will be at work throughout the nation. An industry/government investigative committee will continue to oversee potential vulnerabilities of new operating facility designs and analyze them to determine whether additional sensors or other warning technologies should be incorporated. The starting and completion dates for Phase 3 are September 1998 and August 2010. The estimated cost is $100 million.

3.2.5 Emergency Response Capability Enhancement

Description

Natural gas and oil companies have emergency response plans to use in times of crises. Each company's plans are unique and typically are not shared among industry and government. However, help is provided informally during crises, as companies contact other companies for assistance. Historically, the gas and oil industries have been tested with various emergencies and have responded well. However, these industries are downsizing, while additional threats, such as cyber threats, are surfacing. Little formal assistance within the industry or within the federal government is available. A formal emergency response plan could provide additional assistance to these industries as needed.

This topic focuses on what can be done to change our natural gas emergency response procedures. Potential changes include identifying formal communication channels during crises, establishing protocols for these communication channels, identifying what industry and government assistance should be provided, and deciding what best practices should be implemented in this area. Also included is an R&D technology plan to assist industry during crises; specifically, increased development in technologies such as portable compressor stations, portable gas supplies (e.g., compressed natural gas [CNG] trailers), quicker pipeline repair techniques, and city-gate station repair, which could play an important part in mitigating the impacts from these emergencies. Federal ownership of gas supplies in storage or development of new storage capacity are other options. Also, changes in policy and regulations would be needed to create a formal national response plan.

Goals and Challenges

The major goal for examining emergency response is to allow industry to be better positioned to respond to crises, from either natural or man-made disasters. Minor disruption of gas and oil supplies can cause economic hardship to businesses and individuals; it even threatens life itself, as many people require gas or oil to provide heat during winter months.

Challenges to this research topic arise in several areas. Deregulation pushes companies to focus more on profits and less on emergency procedures. Companies are sometimes hesitant to work with other companies for fear of divulging proprietary information. Anti-trust laws also discourage company discussions. Each gas and oil system is unique, which makes it more difficult to determine what can be done at a national level. A large representation of companies would be needed to ensure that a range of vulnerabilities is addressed.

Industry is reluctant to involve the government for fear of increased regulation. It will take time to develop the necessary communication channels between industry and government. It is important, however, to involve the government. The government must create a level playing field so that all companies participate to a certain minimum level. This level should be developed jointly, with heavy industry involvement. The government also has vast resources of expertise that could be tapped to assist companies in emergencies.

Rationale for the Research and Desired Results

The natural gas and oil industries face emergencies from natural disasters, physical sabotage, and cyber attacks. These occurrences have the potential to disrupt service of gas and oil supplies for extended periods. Minimizing the time needed to restore service is paramount in lessening damage from these disruptions. These industries have an excellent track record during crises; however, new constraints and threats are being introduced.

Companies must operate their systems at higher capacity, with less staff, and with reduced operational budgets. Much equipment is available during crises, but budgets prevent companies from maintaining all the equipment needed. A possible solution is to have an industry pool of resources combined with a government pool of resources. An industry/government partnership would examine both the need for equipment/staff during crises and the need for potential measures that could help mitigate these crises.

The government has many resources that can be used during emergencies: stockpiles of necessary equipment, such as pipe, valves, and compressors, as well as portable equipment, such as portable compressor stations, pumping stations, and CNG trailers that hook into gas pipelines. For oil, the Strategic Petroleum Reserve is one mechanism currently in place to mitigate the effects from a disruption in the oil supply. For gas, government ownership of gas supplies in storage could be considered, as could development of additional storage capacity.

An industry/government partnership could help determine where R&D dollars should be spent in this area. Together, both entities could identify and prioritize vulnerabilities. From that list, they could begin to map an R&D plan that could be a template for cooperation toward mitigating the impacts from these vulnerabilities.

Timeframe and Resource Requirements

In the near term (end of 2000), the industry/government partnership would be established. The partnership would begin to identify roles and any technology gaps for R&D projects. Between 2000 and 2005, R&D dollars could be allocated, with some technology implementations starting during this period. By 2010, technologies and best practices would be widely implemented within the industry. It is estimated that this near-term (end of 2000) effort would cost $2 million. The costs for efforts between 2000 and 2005 are estimated at $50 million, and the costs for efforts between 2005 and 2010 are estimated at $100 million.

3.2.6 Cyber Protection Enhancement

Description

SCADA systems contain all information and control elements, including flow control devices that can be remotely or automatically triggered via microelectronic signal. Systems are as robust or as weak as their weakest remote-accessed element. The record-keeping capabilities and physical control capabilities of such systems are increasingly being integrated.

The natural gas industry's electronic commerce and SCADA systems are increasingly being linked to each other and are therefore becoming more vulnerable to cyber intrusion. The speed with which such vulnerability increases is driven by the economics of competition under open access, where all companies must operate their SCADA systems by means of widely published standards of communication. These standards, and the access they provide outsiders into corporate computer centers, increases the probability of malicious access not only to financial and other operating records, but also to SCADA-driven controls.

The industry must develop a viable method to economically enhance the security of these systems, reversing the trend toward greater vulnerability.

Goals and Challenges

The degree of linkage between commerce trading requests and direct SCADA physical control centers that fulfill those requests is likely to accelerate rapidly because such direct interaction enhances the speed with which a transaction can be processed. As a result, more transactions can be processed per day, which leads to a greater flow of dollars into the company. The speed of linkage must be improved, while maintaining the integrity of the system.

Industry is tending toward bringing the standards for commerce and SCADA communications closer together. While this trend enhances the ease of transactions, it also adds to vulnerabilities because outsiders can more easily access (and cause damage to) multiple sites and even multiple companies across the nation simultaneously.

The gas industry is not yet fully aware of this increasing vulnerability. As a result, the industry has become increasingly susceptible not only to major financial sabotage, but also to the manipulation of physical controls through cyber intrusion. This vulnerability creates the potential for significant physical damage to industry facilities and urban centers through the remote intervention of outside parties who are familiar with industry operations and communications codes.

If these trends continue unabated, without protective measures such as encryption being taken to safeguard the integrity of the cyber system driving these transactions, it is easy to envision a scenario of grave proportions. Outsiders could stage an attack and simultaneously take control of the SCADA systems, which control pressures at critical sites in numerous urban centers and military installations. Such an attack could lead to a cascade of failing pressure and a major disruption that would cut across electric power, financial, governmental, and other infrastructures at a critical time.

Rationale for the Research and Desired Results

An industry-government partnership is critical for success in creating and implementing appropriate encryption and other safety standards that will enhance the speed and security of commercial transactions, while significantly strengthening the infrastructure and making it less vulnerable to cyber attack. Cooperation between industry and government scientists and engineers greatly enhances trust and acceptance, and assures the effectiveness of the operating units as they are put into the market. This partnership should include such groups as the standards-setting committee that is working toward an open architecture with communication standards.

The objective is to create an open architecture that has the necessary flexibility to allow for the unique needs of multiple system users and vendors, yet one that will still provide full protection against a large-scale cyber assault. These systems and codes can be designed to allow quick access to the electronic commerce gateways required for ease of open-access trade, yet block the interior encodings that drive the physical components of the SCADA system. This capability could be developed in a three-phase cooperative effort.

In Phase 1, the partnership entity would design and identify appropriate encryption algorithms that would make it extremely difficult for any outside party to access the industry computer data banks beyond those that record commercial transactions. A search of COTS and government off-the-shelf (GOTS) products would be performed initially to leverage off of existing research.

Phase 2 would incorporate these encryption systems and other devices onto computer chips that can be attached to all commercial-transaction units as well as all SCADA-driven control units. These chips would verify the integrity of messages sent to those units. Ongoing communications, laboratory work, and product verification are required for each manufacturer's SCADA system, along with separately configured SCADA components for each manufacturer to assure full compatibility and communications capability with the rest of the systems on the market. The manufacturing design of each component must be further investigated under field and laboratory conditions to ensure that adding encryption chips or other electronic protective devices does not interfere with the unit's operational quality. Without such attention to detail, one or more operating controls or critical data nodes within the SCADA system would go unprotected. Because any comprehensive SCADA system is only as strong as its weakest link, that unprotected link could allow an intruder to enter the overall system.

Because the design mechanism for each of these controls is unique from one SCADA element to another, coordinated industry participation is essential and must include operating experience, the leading manufacturers and vendors in the gas industry and the large transmission and distribution companies themselves to assure that each chip is properly attached in a functional mode.

The goal for Phase 3 is to have an Enhanced Cyber Protection System for SCADA and electronic commerce running in major regions of the country. To accomplish this task requires taking the standards and prototypes developed in Phases 1 and 2 to the largest regional gas companies in each section of the country. These companies would act as proponents of the system and manufacturers/vendors of system components.

The industry-government partnership would also promulgate a set of security protection standards that all future SCADA units and components would be required to meet. These standards would ensure that despite the unique features devised by individual vendors in the future to enhance continued commercial advances, the units would remain protected against cyber assault.

Close work with industry participants is required in this phase to help them recognize the opportunities and profits to be made by accepting and adhering to these standards. Not only will the acceptance of these standards guard the industry against cyber assault, but it will also standardize signals that provide a gateway to the entrance of each manufacturer's system components. In this way, companies can guard against the possibility of incurring huge overall system replacement costs they might have incurred if their chosen SCADA component manufacturer goes out of business and cannot replace units or expand existing system coverage.

Timeframe and Resource Requirements

Phase 1 will result in a comprehensive report on the design of the above-mentioned encryption and corporate-address identification standards that can be used for commerce and SCADA control systems, as verified by government oversight. These standards are further to be accepted as realistic, practicable, and useful by the industry as evidenced through industry committee acceptance and the beginning of work toward implementation of the suggested system. The start-up and completion dates are September 1998 and August 2000, respectively. The estimated cost is $1 million.

In Phase 2, researchers will review current hardware and software security measures, along with operationally practicable chips, for proper encryption and protection methodologies for all existing major data and physical control units that form a significant share in SCADA system and electronic commerce. In addition, a prototype will be manufactured. The start-up and completion dates are September 2000 and August 2010, respectively. The estimated cost is $100 million.

In Phase 3 the new technology and standards will be deployed. These are to be fully accepted by industry by September 2010, with commercial implementation of the EPS underway at that time. The start-up and completion dates for this phase are September 2000 and August 2010, respectively. The estimated cost over the full scope of the task is $100 million.

3.3 Joint Topics

3.3.1 Evaluation of Policy Effects

Description

Many potential vulnerabilities of a system can be averted by having appropriate public policies in place. However, some policies can have a very detrimental effect on the vulnerability of the grid. Because it is important to understand these relationships, the following tasks should be performed:

- Study any cause-and-effect relationship between the degree of vulnerability of a system and laws, directives, operating policies, and standards.
- Understand the effect of financial incentive and/or tax policies on security.
- Develop the means for accurately assessing vulnerability so that policies that address vulnerability issues are more specific.

Conversely, it is reasonable to assume that appropriate policies can reduce system vulnerability.

It is important to understand the relationship between financial incentives and creation of robust, reliable, disaster-resistant energy infrastructures. Without the proper incentives, implementation of measures to provide such infrastructures will be limited and haphazard. The very substantial financial investments required to develop these infrastructures and long asset lifetimes also argue for careful attention to this topic. Because establishing such incentive structures is often an issue of contention, and because reliability of complex infrastructures is difficult and challenging, it is imperative that this topic be given considerable attention in a collaborative and cooperative industry and government program.

Goals and Challenges

Goals and challenges for policy implications on security include the following:

- Understand all the connections between a policy and its effect on system vulnerability.
- Understand any trade-offs between system security and cost. Develop policies that improve the economic welfare but also consider system security.
- Develop policies that provide adequate economic incentives or regulatory mechanisms to ensure prudent construction and operation of energy transmission facilities.

Rationale for the Research and Desired Results

Energy infrastructures are complex and largely privately owned, but system failures can have widespread implications for the nation as a whole. An appropriate public policy must balance the needs of private enterprise against those of individual consumers and the nation.

Relying exclusively on private efforts to address vulnerability problems can result in promotion of self-serving policies and the adoption of specific technologies that are not in the best interest of society. Relying exclusively on government efforts can stifle creativity. Balance and cooperation are needed.

Appropriate policies can lead to situations where less vulnerable systems are the natural consequence of normal business practices. The converse is also true.

Implementing appropriate policies provides the opportunity to internalize environmental and other externalities. An understanding between environmental policies and network vulnerabilities is important.

Relating policies to good objective engineering criteria is essential. Several elements of an electric power grid make it quite unique and may require creative new types of policies and laws.

Narrow vested interests on the part of specific groups (regulators, conventional utilities, power marketers, and others) can lead to policies for system construction and operation that are detrimental to the system, and under some conditions, lead to large-scale disruptions. In particular, it is essential to all parties who have influence into these policies to recognize that the power system of the future is less constrained by state or company boundaries than it is by the physics of the grid.

Public policy can have serious long-term consequences. Once a policy has encouraged the construction and deployment of a given technology, we are generally bound to live by that technology for many years. Thus, it is important that public policy be directed appropriately.

Another key role for public policy is to address environmental factors. It is important that public policy recognize any effects on the environment.

Timeframe and Resource Requirements

A strategy for attaining the research goals includes creation and fostering of efforts intended to train individuals with broad backgrounds, who can understand both the technological aspects of a problem as well as associated policy issues.

Research intended to ascertain the economic impact of any regulation, policy, or standard before and after it is enacted is important. The implications of such a decision on the welfare of specific interested parties and the interests of society at large are important.

Furthermore, an independent investigation of alternative industry and system structures should be performed. This investigation should include research on means to make the power system less brittle and less complex. It is essential that such an investigation be conducted by reasonably independent groups from a variety of viewpoints, rather than merely as a direct extrapolation of present practice. This exercise will take place regardless of any research activities undertaken. What is needed is an investigation of fundamentally different policies that may lead in different directions for a more efficient evolution of the industry, but that would have been overlooked by individuals whose main concern is the next round of decisions or the next quarter's performance.

The budgetary and project recommendations in this area are organized into several categories:

- Investigate the effect of numerous proposed or conceivably proposed policies on the vulnerability and security of the system. An effort on the order of $1 million per year for three years would be appropriate.
- Explore the implications of operating the grid as a single, integrated grid to which participants connect (the highway system analogy) compared with operating privately owned grid structures. Do so by performing comprehensive studies of various alternatives. The estimated cost is $3 million per year for three years.
- Study the implications of allowing independent standard-setting bodies to establish guidelines and standards for system design and/or operation. The other alternative is to allow industry groups with specific interests to be in charge of these matters. This category is very timely and highly urgent, and it is recommended that $1 million per year be allotted for these studies for two years.
- Encourage the creation of educational programs that lead to graduates who are knowledgeable in both technical and public policy issues. Appropriate grants to selected universities to foster this type of activity would be welcome. A suggested level of funding is for eight institutions at $250,000 each (on average), for a total of $2 million per year for five years.
- To lead to a more informed set of decisions, engage in investigations of the social costs associated with various possible outages and other vulnerabilities of the grid, including fuel supply and other nongrid disruptions. Suggested spending is $1 million per year for five years.
- An understanding of power market issues in electric transmission is far from resolved. A three-year, $2 million per year effort is suggested to address vulnerabilities that can result from power market concentra-

tion, including perhaps new theoretical and experimental work on power market issues.

3.3.2 Institutional Barriers

Description

This research topic focuses on institutional issues that are potential impediments to the successful implementation of the Commission's strategic and technical objectives. A number of these issues have surfaced in activities following the release of the Commission's report. For example, the need to establish a joint industry-government partnership became apparent during an Information Assurance Wargame held at the Army War College in February 1998. The initial research activities are predominately analytical and directed at characterizing the issues and options.

This research affects a spectrum of Commission activities, particularly the process of implementation. Accordingly, it is based more on the disciplines of policy and operations research than on technological disciplines.

The result of this research and analysis is a series of plans that recognize and address the potential strategic, policy, and structural constraints facing an initiative that embraces national coordination and alignment to a common set of priorities. The plans may include operating charters in which teams are either involved or proposed.

Goals and Challenges

The Partnering Model. Development of partnerships is based on joint pursuit of a specific concept or model of how the partnership is structured, and the respective roles, responsibilities, equities, and resource requirements. A shared vision of the model is critical, yet rarely exists at the initiation of discussions. Excellent examples of these comments already are evident within the Commission initiative.

This research area supports the development of these partnerships. It is concurrent with the partnering process and plays a supporting role, and in some instances, may serve a host function in the process. The partnering model should be established by government-industry teams from the respective infrastructure areas. There will be multiple teams, each with its own model, because the industries are not homogeneous with regard to need or culture.

A significant challenge will be to obtain the appropriate representation on the teams to achieve successful partnering. The specific goals of the team must be defined. The focus should be on characterizing the needs and implementing the appropriate infrastructure to support each industry. A host, or supporting function, for each team, preferably familiar with the respective industries, will be necessary to implement the teams' directions.

Basic Tools. The partnering concept depends on mutual industry and government agreement on key issues such as the threat to the infrastructure and the need to address it. An implicit assumption is the dedication of resources. At the present time, however, the effort is primarily driven by the government's concern with regard to national security. Industry is, for the most part, resigned (if not content), with the status quo. Therefore, communication and implementation "products" must be developed to foster recognition of the threat and means to address it.

For example, one objective is to foster enhanced cyber threat security in firewalls and SCADA systems. Therefore, success depends on:

- Individual companies concurring with the premise that the threat is significant and imminent, and
- Availability of firewalls superior to those that the companies are using.

This effort presents a host of barriers because the threat has not been adequately characterized, and there are no recognized uniform standards, or even metrics, to rank the security effectiveness of various firewall products.

The product needs to consist of (1) a package of specific examples that characterize the threat sufficiently to enable consideration of new defenses or at least evaluation of the existing defense, and (2) development of standards and test protocols that enable comparative evaluation of various security mechanisms.

Leveraging Existing Infrastructure. The enormity of the task outlined in the Commission's report is apparent. Not only must the essential message be communicated and embraced by infrastructure operating units and their respective government agencies, but plans, resources, and actions must ensue. The diversity of needs adds to the challenge.

Each of the critical infrastructure industries has organizations that serve the industry in various capacities, from R&D management to lobbying and marketing. Understanding the roles of these organizations and leveraging their existing networking and understanding of their industry are advantageous from a time- and cost-effectiveness standpoint. Strategic alliances may be formed that can help to bridge the formidable cultural gap between government imperatives and industry priorities.

There is an added complexity of focusing on domestic infrastructure within multinational companies that increasingly minimize the implications of national boundaries. Particularly in the oil industry, it is important to recognize that additional security that emphasizes U.S. domestic boundaries can impede normal business operations, which are not constrained by these boundaries.

Rationale for the Research and Desired Results

The requirements for heightened security of the national critical infrastructures are very broad and cut across industrial, governmental, policy, technological, and financial issues. Therefore, conflicting priorities that arise must be resolved before the Commission plan can be successfully implemented.

Take, for example, crosscutting policy/financial issues. The backbone of the Commission recommendations is based on a "partnering" between industry and government, which requires resource investments from each. It is not clear, however, where the line is drawn to distinguish between national security priorities that should be supported by the government, and corporate governance that should be supported corporately. This fact influences the respective resource investments.

Furthermore, some of the governmental agencies earmarked for partnering also have a regulatory function. Industry has a traditional perspective that regulators "live to regulate" and to expand their authority. To establish a partnering relationship, it is necessary to clearly identify the nature and objectives of the relationship. Alternatively, other structural approaches to the partnering arrangement can be examined.

Such issues are subtle, yet effective barriers to achieving a successful merger of objectives between organizations of any type. Understanding and addressing such issues is a prerequisite to success. Within the context of the Commission initiative, three areas of potential actions are apparent: (1) the partnering model, (2) basic tools, and (3) leveraging existing infrastructure.

Timeframe and Resource Requirements

The Partnering Model. The plans for establishing a partnership would begin by forming a gas, oil, and electric team by April 1999, with final plans in place by December 2000 and implementation by 2002. The budget is estimated to be $900,000 per year for 1999 and 2000. This amount covers leadership and coordination, fact finding, analysis, and logistical support.

Basic Tools. The tools needed for the initial planning phase would be in place by December 1999, with subsequent plans in the following three years. The deliverables depend on the product or tool. The budget is estimated to be $2 million for 1999 and $5 million per year for 2000 through 2004. These funds would be used for analytical support for this phase.

Leveraging Existing Infrastructure Support. The budget for infrastructure support of outreach and operations activities is estimated to be $500,000 to $900,000 per year per industry for five years. The outyear budgets depend on the operating structure within the industries to maintain the support and networking needs, such as the Federal Bureau of Investigation security center.

3.3.3 Infrastructure Interdependencies

Description

The Executive Order that created the Commission determined that certain national infrastructures are so vital that their incapacity or destruction would have a debilitating impact on the defense or economic security of the United States. These infrastructures include electric power, gas and oil production and storage, banking and finance, telecommunications, transportation, water supply, emergency services, and government services.

Procedures related to normal operations, response to an incident, and recovery for any one of these infrastructures typically assume that services from other infrastructures would be available for support. The electric power infrastructure is critically important for operating other infrastructures. Each infrastructure depends to varying degrees on electric power for systems and facilities, as well as emergency backup power. For example, power outages affect virtually every mode of transportation, including subways, elevators, and street traffic (no traffic lights or gasoline pumps). Another important example is the dependence of computers and computing systems on electric power.

On the other hand, the energy infrastructures depend strongly on computers and computing systems for operations and communication. The energy infrastructures also depend on the oil and gas production and storage infrastructure and on the transportation infrastructure for delivery of fuel, including coal, which supplies more than one-half of all electric generation. The energy infrastructures also depend on the other critical infrastructures for financial services and transactions, water supply, and emergency and government services.

Another type of interdependency that may become more prevalent in the future is two infrastructures sharing the same component, such as an energy utility sharing the same cable with a telecommunication utility. This new interdependency will be driven by the needs of the deregulated electric utility sector to control costs by deploying both supply-side information technologies and demand-side energy information services. These information services will enable utilities (1) to provide higher-quality services at lower cost with lower environmental impact and (2) to give their customers better control over their power usage. The excess capacity on these lines could be sold or leased to information services providers.

Other examples of interdependencies that need further examination include:

- The impact of decreases in electric power quality on communications and computing;
- Widespread use of electric vehicles on transportation and electric power;
- Remote control mechanisms and communication for improved gas distribution network performance when electric power is not available;
- Small, reliable, efficient gas-driven generators to reduce dependence on electric power for gas delivery and utilization;
- Energy conservation devices on electric power network security and telecommunications; and
- Increasing dependence of the electric sector on natural gas.

A high priority identified in the Commission's report, *Critical Foundations,* was to conduct R&D in this area:

> Advanced methods and tools for vulnerability assessment and systems analysis are needed to identify critical nodes within infrastructures, examine interdependencies, and help understand the behavior of these complex systems. Modeling and simulation tools and test beds for studying infrastructure-related problems are essential for understanding the interdependent infrastructures.

Goals and Challenges

Identification of the existing vulnerabilities and the technical impacts of interdependencies for the energy systems is a challenging first step. Improved understanding of the potential impacts of interdependencies is needed to describe and justify the requirements for modeling and simulation R&D.

Quantifying impacts of the vulnerabilities on the energy system will also be a challenging step and may need to consist of a number of measures. One measure would be the potential loss in dollars to the local or national economy caused by a disruption in the energy system. Another measure would be the time or resources required to mitigate a disruption in the energy system. As the analysis progresses, other measures that need to be considered may be identified.

After quantifying the impacts, a ranking methodology should be developed so that all quantified measures can be considered appropriately. This ranking can then be used to determine those interdependency issues that need attention first. However, some measures may not be easily quantified but may have important impacts. These impacts should not be ignored in the final ranking.

Recent deregulation of some infrastructures and imminent deregulation in others will create new interdependencies in the future (e.g., the telecommunications and electric utility infrastructures). Consequently, another challenge of this research area will be to forecast new interdependencies that may develop and to assess their potential impacts. Because technology can change rapidly, analysis of new interdependencies will be a dynamic process.

Interdependency tools need to address large-scale interdependency issues that affect more than one infrastructure from a technical, economic, and national security perspective. Traditional modeling and simulation tools, while capable of addressing a subset of these issues for a portion of a single infrastructure, are not computationally capable of addressing the complexities and uncertainties associated with these issues on a national level. In particular, the number of infrastructure dependencies and dynamic feedback loops that need to be considered is prohibitively large (i.e., computationally intractable). New computational algorithms and supercomputing capabilities have the potential for efficiently and effectively addressing these modeling and simulation shortfalls. With enhanced computational capabilities, it would be possible to comprehensively address, for the first time, infrastructure dependencies and real-time interactions within a technical, economic, and security framework.

Rationale for the Research and Desired Results

A system description and basis are needed for evaluations of options for prevention, mitigation, response, and recovery. Evaluations should include a comparison of the benefits and costs of introducing the options. The existing framework is too infrastructure-specific and, in most cases, represents only a portion of the infrastructure, let alone any specific dependencies on other infrastructures and the consequences of losing services from those infrastructures.

This research topic would not only improve understanding of interdependencies, but also provide a basis for evaluating the options to address vulnerabilities created or enhanced by the interdependencies. Also, because of rapidly changing technologies, forecasting future interdependencies and projecting their impacts will be important. These forecasts and projections will allow preventive or mitigative measures to be identified early in the process and "built into" the interdependency. This will be a more effective and less expensive way of dealing with the interdependency.

Timeframe and Resource Requirements

Interdependency research topics include the following:

- Methods to relate the technical complexities to business disruptions and economic losses, thereby allowing prevention and mitigation options to be presented and analyzed in a business framework. This task is achievable by 2000 with resource requirements estimated to be less than $1 million.

- In-depth analyses that identify and quantify the technical impacts of the many interdependencies of the energy system infrastructures. This task is achievable by 2000 with estimated resource requirements of approximately $1 million. This effort should be updated periodically to address new developments and changing interdependencies.
- Identification and analysis of options to reduce the effects of interdependency, expressed in the business framework developed earlier. This task would be ongoing and would also benefit from the subsequent modeling and simulation work. Some results would be available by 2000; however, it may be between 2000 and 2005 before thorough analyses can take advantage of the prior work on this topic. The estimated cost is $3 million, with a modest annual updating requirement.
- Examination of the requirements for advanced computational modeling and simulation tools to address large-scale interdependency issues that affect more than one infrastructure from a technical, economic, and national security perspective. This task is also achievable by 2000 with estimated resources of approximately $1 million.
- Development of modeling and simulation tools and their application to improve strategies for reducing the impacts of interdependencies. This task would be ongoing and would result in continual improvement of tools and analysis of options to reduce interdependency-related vulnerabilities. Preliminary results of this effort may be available by 2005, but actual results may not be available until between 2005 and 2010. The estimated cost for this effort over the entire 1999-2015 period is $25 million.

3.4 Summary of Research Topics

Table B.4 summarizes the research topics described in this report. The table addresses the type of research, rationale, research products, goals and challenges, threats and vulnerabilities addressed, and priority category recommended by the Energy Infrastructure Assurance R&D Team. All R&D topics identified in this report are considered well worthy of federal support. If the Energy Infrastructure R&D Team had authority for research funding, all topics identified would be likely to receive some support, even if budget constraints were relatively severe.

Three priority categories are shown in Table B.4: most important, very important, and important. Topics not worthy of serious consideration are not included. In judging the relative priority, the following interrelated factors were considered:

- The extent to which the R&D, if successful, would reduce infrastructure vulnerability, mitigate the impacts, or speed the recovery after a disruption;
- The magnitude of potential consequences that would be prevented or mitigated; and
- The importance of the R&D for national security, the economy, and the social well-being of the United States.

Although the contributors to this report have suggested relative priorities, further study is warranted for many reasons; among them, the short time available for preparation of this report and the several R&D topics that contain a wide variety of research topics at various stages of progress.

Table B.4 Summary of Research Topics

No.	R&D Topic: Title (Type[a])	Rationale	Product	Goals and Challenges	Threats and Vulnerabilities	Priority Category
1	Real-time Control Mechanisms					Most important
1.1	Instrumentaion and Monitoring for Distributed Control (A, ATD)	Enable greater use of existing electrical system.	Hardware and software	G: Share information in real time. C: Develop common data model, sensors and timing, high-bandwidth communication, information exchange.	Physical, cyber, complexity, interdependencies	
1.2	Analysis and Computing for Large-scale Systems (B, A, ATD)	Prevent and recover from large system outages; implement control countermeasures against malicious attack.	Software	G: Measurement-based methods. Detect attempts to disrupt a competitor's position. C: Develop stability indices. Handle uncertainty.	Physical, cyber, complexity, interdependencies.	
1.3	Advanced Control Methods (B, POP)	Increase options to prevent or manage outages.	Software, mathematical theory	G: Control large-scale systems. C: Hierarchical control architecture, robust control theory advancements, control methods that use incomplete information.	Physical, cyber, complexity, interdependencies	

R&D Topic						
No.	Title (Type[a])	Rationale	Product	Goals and Challenges	Threats and Vulnerabilities	Priority Category
1.4	Decision Support Tools (B, A, ATD, POP)	Diagnose problems and sort important information during emergencies.	Hardware and software	G: Develop enabling tool. C: Artificial intelligence, autonomous agents.	Physical, cyber, complexity, interdependencies	
2	Analysis of Scale and Complexity (B, A, ATD, POP)	Mitigate urgent threat or vulnerability; recognize the potentially large consequences of not addressing this threat; common mode failures.	Assessment reports; identify and evaluate incentives	G: Understand complex systems. C: Work after utility deregulation occurs. Develop national security goals for electric grid. Develop incentives to encourage utilities to make necessary investments.	Physical, cyber, complexity, interdependencies	Most important
3	Vulnerability Assessment (B, A)	Assess vulnerabilities and impacts needed to aid decisions regarding research and capital investment.	System vulnerability information, quantification of impacts, method for evaluating options	G: Provide credible information about the performance of the electric power system. C: Assemble methods, tools, and research participants.	Physical, cyber, complexity, interdependencies	Most important
4	Information Assurance and Cyber Security					Very important

No.	R&D Topic: Title (Type[a])	Rationale	Product	Goals and Challenges	Threats and Vulnerabilities	Priority Category
4.1	Threat Assessment and Risk Management (A, ATD)	Tools do not exist.	Tools to help designers of interconnected, market-based system	G: Develop accurate model of electrical system. C: Address vast size and complexity of system and short response time.	Physical, cyber, complexity, interdependencies	
4.2	Large Systems Analysis (B, A, ATD, POP)	Understand large, complex systems.	New models, simulation techniques, integrated attack models, design tools	G: Improve understanding of electrical system. C: Address variety of protocols and legacy systems, validation, technology evolution.	Physical, cyber, complexity, interdependencies	
4.3	High-security SCADA Systems (A)	Changing industry means increased risk to SCADA systems.	Design guidelines, tools, new protocols	G: Protect communications system from attack. C: Add encryption, authentication, and authorization.	Physical, cyber, complexity, interdependencies	
4.4	Efficient, Adaptable Encryption (B, A)	Makes intervention by adversary much more difficult.	New encryption technologies	G: Reduce chance of system compromise. C: Ensure no significant delays and no signal degradation.	Physical, cyber, complexity, interdependencies	

	R&D Topic					
No.	Title (Type[a])	Rationale	Product	Goals and Challenges	Threats and Vulnerabilities	Priority Category
4.5	Robust Authentication and Authorization (B, A, ATD)	Reduce critical vulnerabilities.	Controls to SCADA and information networks	G: Develop standardized, efficient, easily deployed systems. C: Develop and implement controls.	Physical, cyber, complexity, interdependencies	
4.6	Intrusion Detection (B, A, ATD)	Critical for system protection and response.	Improved detection techniques	G: Ensure efficient algorithm with limited number of false alarms. C: Resolve issues of size and complexity of the system and short timeframe.	Physical, cyber, complexity, interdependencies	
4.7	Directed Energy Weapons Countermeasures (B, A)	Need better understanding of prevention, mitigation, and response.	Improved understanding of threat and responses	G: Understand threat and implement preventive measures. C: Prepare costs to design, build, and test such weapons.	Physical, cyber, complexity, interdependencies	
5	Emergency Response and Recovery Information Technologies (B, A)	Mitigate urgent threat or vulnerability; cyber threats in electric grid are not well understood; potentially large consequences from not addressing this threat.	Protocols, policies, laws, computer simulation models, exercises, lessons learned	G: Detect attacks. C: Detect, discriminate, and develop technology; deregulate utilities.	Physical, cyber, interdependencies	Very important

No.	R&D Topic: Title (Type[a])	Rationale	Product	Goals and Challenges	Threats and Vulnerabilities	Priority Category
6	Transmission and Distribution Technologies				Physical, cyber, complexity, interdependencies	Very important
6.1	Advanced Power Electronic Systems (ATD)	Reduced likelihood of cascading outages.	Hardware: improved FACTS, UPFC, SMES systems	G: Reduce costs and improve reliability. C: Develop hierarchical control systems.	Physical, cyber, complexity, inter-dependencies	
6.2	Instrumentation and Control (ATD, POP)	Improve operation and information; provide more options at crisis times; improve system reliability.	Hardware and software: improved two-way communications for load monitoring and control	G: Reduce costs and improve reliability. C: Proof of principle of reliability of large, "smart" systems.	Physical, cyber, complexity, interdependencies	
6.3	Upgrade Transmission System (ATD)	Improve margins to reduce likelihood of outages.	Hardware: increased capacity of above-ground transmission corridors	G: Enhance transmission capability. C: Conduct siting and determine environmental impact of new transmission capacity.	Physical, cyber, complexity, interdependencies	
6.4	Upgrade Distribution System (ATD)	Improve margins to reduce likelihood of local outages.	Hardware and software: technologies for reliable, smart, multidirectional distribution; application of solid-state power electronics to distribution	G: Enhance distribution capability. C: Develop large-scale simulation to assure reliability of complex system, harden system against sabotage and physical threats.	Physical, cyber, complexity, interdependencies	

No.	R&D Topic: Title (Type[a])	Rationale	Product	Goals and Challenges	Threats and Vulnerabilities	Priority Category
6.5	Superconducting Transmission and Distribution (ATD, POP)	Improve efficiency and have a more secure system operation.	Hardware: demonstrations of distribution systems that use several km of HTSC cable	G: Enhance delivery capability C: Develop manufacturing techniques for long cables and thermal insulation with long-term reliability. Reduce cost. Complexity of system may make it vulnerable to sabotage.	Physical, cyber, complexity, interdependencies	
7	On-line Security Assessment					Important
7.1	Incremental Algorithms (ATD)	Enable rapid calculations needed for on-line assessment	Software: tools for perturbed problems (power flow, optimal power flow, eigen problems, coupled algebraic/ordinary differential equation problems)	G: Attain low-cost, fast-running problem solvers without sacrificing accuracy. C: Recognize and deal with complexity. Complete research in a short time.	Physical, cyber, complexity, interdependencies	
7.2	Geographic Decomposition Techniques (B, A, ATD)	Extend theoretical and numerical algorithms; improve performance for real-time control.	Software: tools for geographic decomposition in nonsymmetric complex cases	G: Increase speed of analysis to permit real-time control. C: Extend complex techniques to address real and reactive power components.	Physical, cyber, complexity, interdependencies	

	R&D Topic					
No.	Title (Type[a])	Rationale	Product	Goals and Challenges	Threats and Vulnerabilities	Priority Category
7.3	Database Replication Techniques (B, A)	Specify large numbers of slightly different types of problems.	Software: methods for maintaining and replicating databases; advances in simulation query languages	G: Increase the size of databases and the ease of updating in real-time analyses. C: Resolve complex computational questions.	Physical, cyber, complexity, interdependencies	
8	Dispersed Generation and Backup Infrastructures					Important
8.1	Distributed Generation Systems (ATD, POP)	System more likely to withstand large-scale grid disturbances.	Hardware: demonstrations of distributed generation systems integrated with storage and controlled with custom power systems	G: Improve system reliability. C: Implement large-scale integration and simulation. Integrate massive amounts of advanced information and communications systems.	Physical, cyber, complexity, interdependencies	
8.2	Small-scale Power Generation Systems (ATD, POP)	Have a diverse supply; improve reliability.	Hardware: microturbines, fuel cells, and photovoltaic systems	G: Reduce costs and improve reliability, including the ability of systems to run unattended for long periods. C: Determine economics. Implement systems.	Physical, cyber, complexity, interdependencies	

No.	R&D Topic Title (Type[a])	Rationale	Product	Goals and Challenges	Threats and Vulnerabilities	Priority Category
8.3	Advanced Backup Power Systems (ATD, POP)	System reliability needs to be improved to reduce the likelihood of large outages.	Hardware and software: integration of backup power systems into distributed generation networks to improve security	G: Improve system reliability. C: Apply control systems to existing backup generators, change policy to allow backup systems to power the distribution system in case of emergencies.	Physical, cyber, complexity, interdependencies	
9	Critical Consequence Analysis (B, A)	Modeling is needed for simulating complex systems.	Computerized model, model output identifying critical components	G: Identify critical components C: Collect data and determine model size.	Physical, cyber, complexity, interdependencies	Most important
10	Decision Support Systems (B, A, ATD, POP)	Decision analysis is effective in determining where best to allocate funds to mitigate risk.	Assessment reports, tool development	G: Identify risks and where money should be best spent to mitigate risk. C: Develop products to mitigate risk.	Physical, cyber, complexity, interdependencies	Most important
11	Physical Protection Assessment (B, A)	No comprehensive study has been completed in this area to date.	Report that will identify physical protection measures	G: Characterize current protection methods and determine advanced protection methods. C: Gain industry support.	Physical	Most important

No.	R&D Topic: Title (Type[a])	Rationale	Product	Goals and Challenges	Threats and Vulnerabilities	Priority Category
12	Multisensor and Warning Technologies (B, A, ATD, POP)	Sensor and warning technologies can help mitigate vulnerabilities.	Technology reports, methodologies, product development	G: Implement industry-wide adoption of sensor and warning systems. C: Develop cost-effective standardized systems; ensure industry adopts technology.	Physical, cyber, complexity, interdependencies	Very important
13	Emergency Response Capability Enhancement (A)	No formal emergency channels currently exist.	Best-practices report, policy changes, work groups	G: Develop a formal national emergency plan and identify roles. C: Develop a partnership between industry and government.	Physical, cyber, complexity, interdependencies	Important
14	Cyber Protection Enhancement (B, A, ATD, POP)	No automated standards for system controls and electronic commerce systems. Systems lack standardized protocols and security measures.	Technology reviews, hardware and software development	G: Secure electronic commerce and SCADA capabilities. C: Develop cost-effective standardized systems, ensure adoption of technology by industry.	Physical, cyber, complexity, interdependencies	Most important
15	Evaluation of Policy Effects (B, A)	Assure best interests of society, reduce system vulnerabilities	Appropriate policies for security	G: Understand connections between policy and system vulnerability impacts. C: Develop policies that use economic forces to improve security.	Complexity, interdependencies	Very important

	R&D Topic					
No.	Title (Type[a])	Rationale	Product	Goals and Challenges	Threats and Vulnerabilities	Priority Category
16	Institutional Barriers (A)	Very broad infrastructure security cuts across government and industry; establish priorities and roles.	Development of partnerships, assessment of security tools, development of best practices	G: Prepare national infrastructure plan that addresses concerns, priorities, and roles. C: Cooperate, develop partnerships, and establish roles.	Physical, cyber, complexity, interdependencies	Most important
17	Infrastructure Interdependencies (B, A, ATD)	Determine how critical infrastructures depend upon each other for proper operation; develop mitigation strategies.	Reports analyzing current/future interdependencies/ mitigation strategies; analysis tools	G: Improve understanding. C: Identify vulnerabilities and technical impacts, quantify/rank vulnerabilities and impacts, develop advanced modeling and simulation tools, identify mitigation strategies.	Physical, cyber, complexity, interdependencies	Most important

[a] B = basic; A = applied; ATD = advanced technology development; and POP = proof fo principle and validation.

Table B.5 provides estimates of the timeframes and funding requirements by research topic. The total estimated funding required over the 1999-2015 period is $2.4 billion.

Table B.5 Summary of Funding Requirements by Research Topic

	R&D Research Topic		
No.	**Description**	**Timeframe (yr)**	**Funding Requirement[a]**
1	Real-time control mechanisms		
1.1	Instrumentation and monitoring for distributed control	3–15	130
1.2	Analysis and computing for large-scale systems	3–10	100
1.3	Advanced control methods	3–10	88
1.4	Decision support tools	5–15	85
	Sum of 1.1–1.4,	3–15	**Subtotal, 403**
2	Analysis of scale and complexity	3–5	75
3	Vulnerability assessment	1–12	35
4	Information assurance and cyber security		
4.1	Threat assessment and risk management	3–5	25
4.2	Large systems analysis	5–10	45
4.3	High-security SCADA systems	5–10	80
4.4	Efficient, adaptable encryption	3–10	75
4.5	Robust authentication and authorization	3–10	75
4.6	Intrusion detection	3–10	75
4.7	Directed energy weapons countermeasures	3–10	60
	Sum of 4.1–4.7,	3–10	**Subtotal, 435**
5	Emergency response and recovery information technologies	3–12	10
6	Transmission and distribution technologies	1–15	>500
7	On-line security assessment	1–15	50
8	Dispersed generation and backup infrastructures	1–15	100
9	Critical consequence analysis	1–4	3
10	Decision support systems	10	120

	R&D Research Topic		
No.	Description	Timeframe (yr)	Funding Requirement[a]
11	Physical protection assessment	1–3	5
12	Multisensor and warning technologies	1–10	160
13	Emergency response capability enhancement	1–5	152
14	Cyber protection enhancement	1–12	201
15	Evaluation of policy effects	1–5	35
16	Institutional barriers	1–6	74
17	Infrastructure interdependencies	1–15	31

[a] Funding requirements are estimated cumulative amounts in millions of U.S. dollars over the timeframe shown. Some topics, such as transmission and distribution technologies, will have substantial contributions from industry. At a minimum, a modest federal role, emphasizing infrastructure assurance considerations, is needed.

Section 4
R&D Topic Roadmaps

This section outlines the R&D topic roadmaps, which describe the research pathway, including the timeframe and sequence of activities required to achieve the specified goals. The roadmap is communicated most simply in a table (Table B.6) that identifies the elements of the R&D topics over time. The R&D topics are listed in the same order as they appeared in Section 3.

Table B.6 Summary of the Energy R&D Roadmap

R&D Topic				
No.	Title	Achieved by ~2000	Achieved by ~2005	Achieved by ~2010
1	Real-time Control Mechanisms			
1.1	Instrumentation and Monitoring for Distributed Control	Implement common data model and identify measurement requirements.	Develop advanced sensors, measurement timing standards, and data compression tools. Establish high bandwidth communication channels.	Establish wide area monitoring, data storage and retrieval, and adaptive monitoring methods.

R&D Topic				
No.	Title	Achieved by ~2000	Achieved by ~2005	Achieved by ~2010
1.2	Analysis and Computing for Large-scale Systems	Implement on-line security assessment tools.	Establish stability indices. Develop measurement-based analysis tools and parameters for integrating measurement and model-based tools.	Establish uncertainty theory and implement integrated analytical approach.
1.3	Advanced Control Methods	Assess current state of robust control theory and decentralized control theory.	Advance theoretical basis for robust and decentralized control.	Develop proof of principle and validation on integrated large-scale system control theory.
1.4	Decision Support Tools	Develop new visualization techniques and operator interfaces for increased data volume.	Implement first-generation reasoning tools. Develop tools to assist operators in handling many transactions.	Develop autonomous agents and implement multiconstraint optimization tools.
2	Analysis of Scale and Complexity	Study restructuring effects on complexity. Develop theoretical understanding of complex systems and applied understanding of the evolving complexity of the power grid.	Develop an understanding of human interfaces and how humans handle scale and complexity. Understand effects of uncertainties on vulnerability and develop mitigation methods.	
3	Vulnerability Assessment	Complete systematic and current estimates of vulnerabilities and threats. Estimate impacts of outages. Define modeling requirements. Characterize restructuring effects.	Develop or enhance models. Analyze restructuring impacts. Evaluate infrastructure assurance options.	Develop improved procedures and evaluate more options.

R&D Topic				
No.	**Title**	**Achieved by ~2000**	**Achieved by ~2005**	**Achieved by ~2010**
4	Information Assurance and Cyber Security			
4.1	Threat Assessment and Risk Management	Conduct systematic, industry-wide threat assessment and vulnerability mapping. Develop base risk management tools.	Develop standardized, industry-wide threat model. Integrate risk management tools into design tools. Ensure consistent models are used to define threat environments and assess risk. Integrate models into design and validation tools.	
4.2	Large Systems Analysis	Develop basic models and simulations and basic design tools.	Develop integrated models and near real-time prediction, model-based control.	Validate the entire power grid. Incorporate models into design. Develop simulation and validation tools.
4.3	High-security SCADA Systems	Develop a baseline understanding of existing systems and current industry practices. Develop design guidelines.	Develop and validate proof of concept. Standardize efforts for deployment of new SCADA networks.	Produce and adopt standard SCADA design guidelines.
4.4	Efficient, Adaptable Encryption	Develop a baseline understanding of requirements for major system areas. Evaluate encryption technologies.	Deploy encryption technologies throughout the power industry.	Deploy dynamic and high-bandwidth encryption.
4.5	Robust Authentication and Authorization	Map the requirements for authentication and authorization of existing systems. Define general-purpose, scalable mechanisms. Begin working with standards.	Work with the electric power industry and product manufacturers to adopt standardized mechanisms.	Implement standardized authentication and authorization models on all new systems added to the grid.

R&D Topic				
No.	Title	Achieved by ~2000	Achieved by ~2005	Achieved by ~2010
4.6	Intrusion Detection	Develop understanding of threats and current vulnerabilities. Deploy threat detection to both the communication and control infrastructure of the grid.	Develop and deploy efficient, dynamic intrusion detection tools.	Link intrusion detection into central threat center for grid-wide system monitoring. Deploy automated response capability.
4.7	Directed Energy Weapons Countermeasures	Develop understanding of the current state of high-energy weapons. Construct and test devices. Develop test bed. Prepare design guidelines for protection.	Integrate information learned into overall design tools.	Conduct further research into directed energy weapons.
5	Emergency Response and Recovery Information Technologies	Develop concept. Identify critical components and protection and mitigation strategies. Begin developing exercise process and computer simulation models.	Conduct exercises on a periodic basis. Develop and apply lessons learned from exercises. Begin developing concept for oil and natural gas pipeline networks.	Refine process as changes warrant. Begin conducting exercises for oil and gas pipeline networks.
6	Transmission and Distribution Technologies	Examine specific infrastructure assurance contributions for several R&D topics. Improve siting and environmental impact process for new transmission lines.	Develop hardware and software. Complete proof of principle for smart instrumentation and control systems. Make progress in advanced power electronics systems.	Achieve significant progress in superconducting technologies. Implement advanced power electronics systems.

R&D Topic				
No.	Title	Achieved by ~2000	Achieved by ~2005	Achieved by ~2010
7	On-line Security Assessment	Examine incremental algorithms for system perturbations Obtain 1,000-fold increase in speed with subcycle state information. Develop database replication techniques.	Reduce cost and running times. Develop accurate tools and models for the national grid. Develop tools for geographic decomposition in nonsymmetric complex cases.	Develop and implement improved and new tools. Reduce cost and running times.
8	Dispersed Generation and Backup Infrastructures	Analyze infrastructure assurance benefits of dispersed generation. Prioritize options.	Demonstrate and integrate distributed generation systems with storage. Demonstrate and control with custom power systems. Develop improved backup system.	Continue reducing costs and improving reliability of technology options. Improve ability for systems to run unattended for long periods.
9	Critical Consequence Analysis	Complete and implement basic design of model.	Develop incident/failure scenarios and consequence analysis, including curtailment impacts, by using the model.	
10	Decision Support Systems	Assess data and tools. Assign decision analysis requirements with priorities.	Develop expert system tools. Make models for highest priority items. Assess secondary priority items.	Continue to develop high-priority items. Develop expert system tools and models for secondary priority items.
11	Physical Protection Assessment	Collect historic reports and data. Survey industry to determine highest vulnerabilities. Assess technology. Develop and implement strategies.		

R&D Topic				
No.	Title	Achieved by ~2000	Achieved by ~2005	Achieved by ~2010
12	Multisensor and Warning Technologies	Assess current technologies. Design needed technologies. Establish industry-government partnership.	Roadmap national technologies. Develop software and hardware.	Implement technology pilot program. Commercially develop technologies. Set up an oversight committee.
13	Emergency Response Capability Enhancement	Develop industry-government partnership. Establish roles for government and industry. Identify technology gaps.	Develop roles. Develop a national emergency plan. Begin technology implementations.	Ensure that technologies and best practices are widely implemented in industry.
14	Cyber Protection Enhancement	Identify encryption algorithms and standards.	Complete technology review and selection. Manufacture chips.	Implement enhanced protection system for SCADA and electronic commerce. Obtain acceptance of approved standards by industry.
15	Evaluation of Policy Effects	Determine the effect of numerous proposed policies on vulnerability and security of energy systems. Explore grid operation implications.	Establish college programs that deal with technical and public policy aspects of infrastructure assurance.	
16	Institutional Barriers	Develop partnerships.	Develop tools and roles and establish priorities.	Maintain support and networking needs, such as the FBI security center.

R&D Topic				
No.	Title	Achieved by ~2000	Achieved by ~2005	Achieved by ~2010
17	Infrastructure Interdependencies	Relate technical complexities to business disruptions and economic losses. Complete in-depth analysis of technical impacts. Examine requirements for advanced computational modeling and simulation tools.	Identify and analyze options to reduce interdependency impacts. Develop analysis tools.	Obtain results of analyzing options to reduce interdependency-related vulnerabilities.

CHAPTER 5

PRELIMINARY RESEARCH AND DEVELOPMENT

ROADMAP FOR PROTECTING AND ASSURING THE INFORMATION AND COMMUNICATIONS INFRASTRUCTURE[1]

1 This document is one component of a longer report entitled *Preliminary Research and Development Roadmap for Protecting and Assuring Critical National Infrastructures* (Transition Office of the President's Commission on Critical Infrastructure Protection and the Critical Infrastructure Assurance Office. Washington, D.C. July 1998).

Contents

Section 1 Introduction

1.1 Scope of the Infrastructure

1.2 Characterization of the Infrastructure

1.2.1 Rapid Evolutionary Growth and Change

1.2.2 Interdependencies

1.2.3 Regulatory State

1.3 Issues and Trends

1.3.1 Managing the Internet

1.3.2 Establishing a Legal Basis for Cyberspace

1.3.3 Developing Critical Technologies Offshore

1.3.4 Collecting Data and Ensuring Privacy, Dissemination, and Protection

Section 2 Threats and Vulnerabilities

Section 3 R&D Topics and Activities

3.1 Risks, Threats, and Vulnerabilities

3.1.1 Vulnerability Detection and Analysis

3.1.2 Valuation of Information

3.1.3 Risk Analysis

3.1.4 Characterization and Notification of Threats

3.2 Intrusion and Incident Detection, Response, and Recovery

3.2.1 Intrusion and Incident Detection and Warning

3.2.2 Response, Recovery, and Reconstitution

3.3 Engineering High-confidence Infrastructures

3.3.1 Security Architectures

3.3.2 Assurance Technologies

3.3.3 Advanced Concepts and Theory

3.3.4 Management of Information Protection

3.3.5 Characterization of Minimum Infrastructure for Essential Services

3.3.6 Encryption Technology

3.4 Modeling and Simulation Tools

Section 4 R&D Topic Roadmaps

4.1 Roadmap for Development

4.2 Suggested Pilot Projects

4.2.1 Development of an Experimental Test Bed

4.2.2 Lexicon and Procedures for Defining and Reporting Data

Section 5 Complexities

5.1 System Administrator and User Trust

5.2 Threats and Vulnerabilities from an International Perspective

5.3 Readily Available Advanced Attack Tools

5.4 Security Priority

Section 6 Other Important Issues

6.1 Education Curricula and University Funding

6.2 Continuous Training for System Administration

6.3 Growth and Consolidation in the Security Industry

6.4 Legal Issues

6.5 Information Sharing

6.6 Industry/Government Partnership

6.7 International Issues

6.8 Year 2000 Software Update Initiative

6.9 Cryptography

Section 7 References

Tables

C.1 Summary of R&D Topics for Information and Communications

C.2 Summary of Information and Communications R&D Roadmap

C.3 Summary of Estimated Research Investments for Enhancing the Protection of the ICI

Section 1
Introduction

The U.S. information and communications infrastructure (ICI) is integral to our nation's security and economic competitiveness. Experts agree that this infrastructure is fragile and cannot defend or heal itself adequately. Without continual vigilance and renewed efforts to bolster security, the ICI would degrade or fail in the event of an attack or disaster.

This report expands on the 1997 study performed as part of the work by the President's Commission on Critical Infrastructure Protection. In their report, the Commission recommended a series of research and development (R&D) topics and their priorities to provide a greater level of assurance for critical infrastructures they had identified. The Commission studied eight critical infrastructures: banking and finance, electric power, emergency services, government services, information and communications, oil and gas production and storage, transportation, and water supply.

This effort expands on the ICI baseline report. It provides a technology R&D[2] "roadmap" that suggests a research agenda to develop methods required to improve protection of the ICI. This effort is the product of a working group composed of representatives from national laboratories, government agencies, industry, and academia.

1.1 Scope of the Infrastructure

The ICI consists of three primary layers. The first layer (physical layer) is an underlying "link" that moves data from point to point (e.g., satellites, copper wire, optical fibers, wireless transmissions). The second layer is a network and transport layer that deals with addressing, routing, and data transport services. The third layer consists of the computing systems and applications that generate, manipulate, store, display, or control the ICI, for example, by using information and facilitating human collaboration and creative activities. The combination of these three layers provides a full spectrum of communication, computation, control, information, and human collaboration systems that is critical to all aspects of society.

The ICI is closely coupled to the other infrastructures studied by the Commission. Because of the strong interdependencies among the ICI and the other infrastructures, a break in the ICI can affect other infrastructures, such as banking and finance. In addition, the ICI depends on other infrastructures, such as the electric power infrastructure.

For their link layer, most wide-area data networks use "public-switched networks," the system of control centers, communication lines, and circuit

2 Throughout this report, the words "research" and "development" are used synonymously.

switches maintained and operated by the telecommunications industry. Internet technology differs from the public-switched network primarily because all communication is accomplished by breaking the data streams that provide the services mentioned above into "packets" that are independently routed through an inter-network. The Internet protocol routing element of the ICI has a different set of vulnerabilities than the switched network, which also requires research in routing security.

1.2 Characterization of the Infrastructure

1.2.1 Rapid Evolutionary Growth and Change

The ICI systems have undergone dramatic changes in the last decade. Once dominated by AT&T, the communications industry is now represented by numerous players in both the local and long distance markets. In addition to providing communications services, many of these companies are beginning to offer other services, such as Internet connectivity.

In the area of communications, wire-based telephony is rapidly being supplemented by wireless systems. The introduction of affordable satellite telephone systems means that soon anyone can phone any point in the world. In addition, most U.S. military communications depend largely on commercial systems.

In just a few years, the Internet has evolved from a low-bandwidth network used by the military and the scientific community to a system that literally anyone can access. It is hard to find an organization that does not have an Internet home page, and e-mail rapidly is becoming the preferred form of communication in many organizations.

1.2.2 Interdependencies

The boundaries between the individual elements in the ICI have become less distinct. Every component of every layer in the ICI relies on computer control. Internet communication is being used increasingly to control and manage the components of the layers below the Internet (i.e., the public-switched network, routing infrastructure of the Internet). Many modern computer applications use Internet technology for communication, whether through the global and public Internet, or in private (isolated) corporate Internets (sometimes called "Intranets"). Software is being developed that automatically connects users to the Internet; also, numerous packages are available to assist the user in building Web sites. With this pervasive assimilation of the Internet into the ICI comes the reality that geographic boundaries are becoming less meaningful. With this geographic transparency in the Internet, a cyber attack could come from anywhere. Because of the close interaction among computers and the other infrastructures, all infrastructures are vulnerable to a cyber or a direct physical attack. For example, the viability of remote control systems, such as the electric power system's Supervisory Control and Data Acquisition (SCADA) systems, depends on the ICI.

1.2.3 Regulatory State

Federal regulation of wireline and wireless communication of voice, data, and image signals within the United States is authorized by the Communications Act of 1934 (the Act),[3] as amended by the Telecommunications Act of 1996. The Act established the Federal Communications Commission (FCC), within the U.S. Department of Commerce, as the body to execute and enforce its provisions. The FCC is now an independent agency.

With regard to national infrastructure policy, however, the FCC is neither the sole developer nor the only purveyor. The National Telecommunications and Information Administration (NTIA), created recently within the U.S. Department of Commerce, has, through its Office of Policy Analysis and Development, the role of "principal advisor to the President on telecommunications policies."[4] As one of its primary policy functions, the NTIA was directed by Congress to foster ". . . national safety and security, economic prosperity, and the delivery of critical social services through telecommunications."[5] The NTIA has filed numerous replies concerning matters docketed before the FCC to express the administration's desires with regard to deregulating the industry, in particular the assurance of universal access to telecommunications service at affordable rates (NTIA 1996).

In addition to the federal presence, all 50 states have some form of regulatory body that addresses telecommunications, generally a public utility commission or a subpart thereof. For the most part, state agencies are concerned only with facility siting, equipment siting, and rate-setting matters, but a growing number are addressing access and continuity of service issues (Q.V. 1995-1996). They focus primarily on promoting and accommodating commerce, while ensuring the most democratic distribution of service economically permissible.

1.3 Issues and Trends

The explosive growth of wireless communications characterizes the rapid technological development that has occurred in the ICI. New area codes are being created at a rapid pace, and the U.S. telecommunications industry is beginning to face the issue that demand is outpacing supply with respect to the current 10-digit phone number structure.

---

3 47 USC—*Telegraphs, Telephones, and Radiotelegraphs.*

4 47 USC §901.(b)(6); and U.S. Department of Commerce Word Wide Web Home Page, National Telecommunications and Information Administration, Office of Policy Analysis and Development (http://www.ntia.doc.gov/opadhome/opadhome.html).

5 47 USC §901.(c).

The use of the Internet is expanding faster than society can cope with it. Particularly problematic are the reach and the speed of information transmission via the Internet. With the Internet, information can be disseminated around the world in seconds. Increasingly, telephone service is being provided over the Internet, and this trend significantly affects the reliability and security of Internet technology.

1.3.1 Managing the Internet

In terms of transferring or sharing information, the Internet is difficult to categorize because it combines software and communications protocols. From its beginning as a network developed and supported by the U.S. government, it is today an international communications resource. Some groups believe the Internet should be totally unregulated and that anything posted on it should be free for anyone to use.

1.3.2 Establishing a Legal Basis for Cyberspace

Legal theorists are struggling with how to develop and apply laws for the Internet. Do laws developed for print or broadcast media apply to the Internet? How can electronic documents be protected by copyright and watermarks? A recent Supreme Court ruling, which overturned an attempt to regulate content on the Internet, illustrates that the legal status is quite unclear.

The ability to exchange data and information widely on the Internet also has provided an entry point for computer viruses and other malicious code. Until recently, few laws governed "cyber" attacks against computer systems, and existing laws were not well enforced.

As the Internet becomes a medium for commerce, a number of issues have emerged. For example, the security of Internet electronic transactions is a subject of active debate. Even with the introduction of encryption, the perception is that Internet commerce is less secure than conventional commerce. Another issue is liability; that is, who is responsible if credit card numbers are stolen—the Internet service provider or the Internet commerce provider?

1.3.3 Developing Critical Technologies Offshore

Many critical technologies and security products are developed at non-U.S. locations or by companies that are wholly or partly foreign owned. Moreover, many software development efforts are exported to other countries that have either cheaper labor costs or a greater abundance of available programmers. A concern is that these offshore developments may result in the insertion of software "back doors" or hidden "sleeper" code that could go undetected and be accessed by a hostile agent.

1.3.4 Collecting Data and Ensuring Privacy, Dissemination, and Protection

More data are being collected on individuals and organizations and are being "mined" and warehoused to create profiles for marketing and other purposes. These data are sold, in most cases, without the knowledge of those profiled in the databases. Internet providers also can and do track usage patterns, often without the knowledge or consent of the user. While this practice is perfectly legal, concern is increasing in regard to personal or organizational invasion of privacy.

Section 2
Threats and Vulnerabilities

It is impossible to build a perfectly secure ICI, so the goal is to design and build cost-effective systems with the degree of protection consistent with the needs of users and to emphasize continual improvement. The threats to the ICI can come from a variety of sources, such as deliberate attacks (cyber or physical) by insiders or outsiders, natural disasters, simple accidents, or failures in poorly designed or outmoded equipment. A recent series of hacker attacks against U.S. Department of Defense (DoD) computer systems vividly demonstrates the reality of these threats.

Although the possibility of cyber attack has received increased attention (*Defense News* 1998; *The Washington Post* 1998), the threat to the ICI from physical attack must not be excluded. Satellites and ground-station equipment are highly vulnerable to a physical attack and interference, and, if they should occur, the impact could be felt on a global scale. Many of the recent serious disruptions in the ICI have occurred through physical means, such as cable breaks, other accidents, or natural disaster.

Section 3
R&D Topics and Activities

Thirteen R&D needs in the information and communications infrastructure are prioritized as "most important," "very important," or "important." These needs are further categorized into three primary research areas: (1) risks, threats, and vulnerabilities; (2) intruder and incident detection response, and recovery; and (3) engineering high-confidence infrastructure.[6] In addition to these areas, modeling and simulation tools are needed that cross all of these areas. The topics presented are in addition to any of the basic and applied research being performed in the classified communities. The R&D activities outlined in this report need to leverage, complement, and integrate with the research underway in the various government

6 A significant reference for this section is a report by Mayfield (1998).

agencies and departments, as well as the private sector. These research results may also require protection. Government-funded research should not duplicate or reinvent the progress driven by market forces; rather, it should focus on areas not addressed sufficiently by the private sector, long-term research, and specialized technology required by the government.

It is expected that strong synergistic relationships will form among these areas, with results from one area driving research in others. These research topics are interrelated in a dynamic and nonlinear fashion, which raises the complexity of a research plan. The resulting research will be used to improve the security and protection in legacy and future systems and technologies.

3.1 Risks, Threats, and Vulnerabilities

The objective of this area is to develop the essential information, tools, and procedures for identifying, analyzing, and continuously managing the risks inherent to the ICI and those imposed by outside forces. Risk management is used to analyze the relationships among five critical components:

- Assets—the resources or objects of value to be protected;
- Threats—the sources or causative agents that can harm the system or cause loss;
- Vulnerabilities—the "windows of opportunity" through which a threat can materialize;
- Losses—the direct or transient effects on users of the system, resulting from something possessing or representing value being removed, devalued, denied, or otherwise exploited, such as lost information, degraded computational or communications resources, falsified data, loss of life, or loss of confidence in the system; and
- Safeguards—the physical, administrative, and technical controls designed to provide protection and reduce vulnerability.

Risk management ultimately determines what investments to make to provide a specified level of protection and what cost one may be willing to accept in the form of potential losses and putting in place the necessary contingency plans, procedures, and resources to mitigate the effects of such losses.

The anticipated products from this research area include the collection of data and information for characterizing and analyzing risks, threats, and vulnerabilities; the development of procedures to manage such information; the development of software tools; and the advancement of key theoretical areas. Specific areas that require support for R&D are described in the following subsections.

3.1.1 Vulnerability Detection and Analysis

Description

The first objective for this research is to identify, collect, organize, and disseminate system, network, and infrastructure vulnerability information. The second objective is the development of applied technologies and methodologies to avoid, reduce, or eliminate vulnerabilities during the development of hardware and software products and their integration into systems. This research would result in (1) a lexicon of threat and vulnerability information, (2) methodologies and information databases on vulnerability and attack taxonomies, and (3) technologies and methodologies to analyze vulnerabilities. Short-term results could be expected as information databases are assembled and shared, but a continuing research investment would be required. Specific areas of research are described in the following subsections.

Develop Threat and Vulnerability Lexicon. A lexicon of terms needs to be developed so that data can be precisely defined and collected. This effort should extend the earlier works on information security performed by the National Security Agency Information System Security Organization,[7] the Federal Bureau of Investigation (FBI), and DoD. The requirement for a lexicon spans all of the infrastructures being studied. It is recommended that this task be pursued first, and that a system be considered that is similar to the one used by the FBI for defining and reporting crime statistics. A lexicon, and a subsequent vulnerability and attack taxonomy for both cyber and physical attacks, could be useful for many purposes, such as incident handling, crime statistics reporting, intrusion detection, and vulnerability analysis.

Develop Vulnerability and Attack Taxonomies. Research is required to develop vulnerability and attack classification taxonomies (e.g., distributed coordinated attacks against a single target, a single attack against many targets, and distributed coordinated attacks against multiple targets). This research is required to support the prediction and testing of new vulnerabilities. Ideally, it would enable the development of tools for testing vulnerabilities and methodologies for analyzing programs and systems in a systematic fashion. The problem of classification is subtle because of the interaction of the level of abstraction and the point of view within which the vulnerability occurs. Such research would lead to the development of a database of vulnerabilities useful to other areas of security.

Develop Tools to Analyze Vulnerabilities. Research is required to develop tools and techniques to support the identification of, interdependencies

---

7 See, for example, ISSO's *Unified INFOSEC Glossary*, V 2.0, 1996.

among, and understanding of the vulnerabilities in systems and networks. Examples of tools needed are configuration checkers, functional testers, attack and penetration analyzers, topology mapping software, visualization tools, and modeling and simulation frameworks. Additional research is required to develop a new generation of automated technology that analyzes; provides an alert; or avoids, reduces, or eliminates vulnerabilities during the development or integration of hardware products. These technologies could employ intelligent agents, for example, that would operate on a semi- or fully autonomous basis.

Automate Vulnerability Analysis Technologies. Research is required to support the development of automated technologies to analyze, provide an alert about, avoid, reduce, or eliminate vulnerabilities while developing or integrating hardware and software products.

Study Satellite and Wireless Communications. Satellite and wireless communication systems have unique vulnerabilities that require an end-to-end study. Although these systems share many of the threats and vulnerabilities of wire-based systems, unique aspects for protecting these systems are evident. The physical aspects of security include protecting the ground stations and transmission disks. Satellites are subject to jamming, interception, collision, interference (regarding the signals and the control systems of these satellites), as well as malfunctions, electromagnetic interference, and environmental impacts (e.g., solar flares). The increasing reliance of military communications on commercial satellites requires adequate protection for these systems.

In addition, satellite services, such as the Global Positioning System, provide both location information (on which the transportation infrastructure depends) and essentially a global clock (on which cellular phone services depend). These services are international in scope, and the protection of these assets requires agreements, treaties, and enforcement at an international level.

Goals and Challenges

The goal for this R&D topic is to produce technologies and methodologies to detect and analyze vulnerabilities in integrated systems and networks efficiently and cost-effectively.

The challenge is to have procedures and tools for collecting and disseminating vulnerability data in place at the national level and, it is hoped, at the international level.

Rationale for the Research and Desired Results

The rationale is, that to apply protective measures, one must be able to identify where the vulnerabilities are in the ICI and how they might be exploited by an attacker.

Timeframe and Resource Requirements

The estimated total investment over this time period is $330 million.[8] The proposed commitment is $90 million in 2000, $90 million between 2001 and 2005, and $150 million between 2006 and 2010.

3.1.2 Valuation of Information

Description

Research is required to develop tools and methodologies to assist information owners in determining how to value their holdings and determine what level of protection is appropriate. A means for determining the value of information also would be useful in risk management. the determination of critical assets, and the insurance industry.

In addition, tools and methodologies are required to evaluate the effect of aggregated information. This effort is important especially because by using data-mining techniques, individuals or entities can collect data from multiple sources to develop a "picture" or "report" that otherwise would be considered sensitive or confidential.

Goals and Challenges

The goals and challenges are to provide efficient and easy-to-use tools and procedures for valuing information and determining the appropriate level of protection.

Rationale for the Research and Desired Results

The requirement for these tools is critical because if service is interrupted, the impacts can be distributed widely and are potentially life-threatening. Therefore, a form of triage assessment will be required to determine what information and data assets are given priority in terms of protection and recovery. Because the value of information may be linked to time and context, an assurance level approach may be appropriate. Such an approach makes it possible to use the importance or criticality of information to the system function to determine the level of assurance for the system.

---

8 All years referenced in this document are fiscal years.

Timeframe and Resource Requirements

The timeframe for this activity extends to 2010 and beyond. The total estimated investment over this period is $110 million. The proposed commitment is $30 million in 2000, $30 million between 2001 and 2005, and $50 million between 2006 and 2010.

3.1.3 Risk Analysis

Description

Conventional risk analysis consists of surveying the components of a system or network, as well as the users, to determine the exposure of valued resources to loss, damage, or denial. Such an analysis often is performed manually, although some commercial off-the-shelf tools are available to automate the collection and analysis of the survey information. These analyses are also typically done on a periodic basis, such as annually. Although sound analyses of risk are often performed during these annual security exercises, risk management needs to be performed on a continuous basis, especially if changes are made to the system or network (e.g., changes in equipment, software, or procedures). Automated tools and technologies are required that detect new components in systems and networks and that then can assess the vulnerabilities in the modified system. Metrics need to be developed for evaluating security technologies, in particular, tools to evaluate the cost-benefit of implementing changes in systems. Specific research topics related to the development of automated risk management and cost-benefit tools and metrics are discussed in the following subsections.

Automated Risk Management. Automated tools and techniques are needed to support risk management. The desired tools need to be able to detect automatically when new software or hardware is added to the system or network. These tools would analyze the new component and present an analysis of known or postulated threats that could exploit discovered vulnerabilities in the new software or hardware component, a prediction of the likely exploitation path, and an assessment of the potential consequences. Research is needed in foundational techniques to support the development of such automated tools across systems, networks, and infrastructures.

Risk Management Metrics. Metrics for evaluating security technologies need to be developed. Measures of effectiveness and performance must be defined to enable managers to evaluate and compare security technologies.

Cost-benefit Analysis. Tools and techniques are needed to enable developers and integrators to estimate the investment and performance costs of implementing security technologies and/or procedures. These tools and techniques must be able to incorporate such critical concepts as "trust," the value of information and system resources, timeliness and responsiveness, ease of use, cost of ownership, and potential liabilities. Trade-off algorithms and associated metrics used to balance desired cost-performance attributes appropriately must be developed to provide the foundation for such tools. The development of such algorithms and metrics likely would require extensive experimentation, that is, similar to what has been done in hardware and operating system performance analyses.

Goals and Challenges

The goals and challenges are to provide efficient, easy-to-use tools and methodologies for analyzing and measuring risk in evolving environments and to perform cost-benefit trade-off analyses.

Rationale for the Research and Desired Results

The rationale is as follows: given that risk cannot be completely eliminated, managers and implementers need to be able to reduce risk to acceptable levels and to evaluate the trade-offs between risk reduction and cost.

Timeframe and Resource Requirements

The timeframe for this activity extends to at least 2010. The estimated investment over this period totals $200 million. The proposed commitment is $75 million in 2000, $75 million between 2001 and 2005, and $50 million between 2006 and 2010.

3.1.4 Characterization and Notification of Threats

Description

Threats to the ICI can come essentially from any point in the world. However, the implication of a specific threat varies with the targeted infrastructure element (e.g., individual, corporate, national, international) and the objective of the attack (e.g., mischief, crime, espionage, terrorism, information warfare). This effort is primarily a data collection and analysis, which can effectively leverage existing intelligence databases, with respect to the threats to the ICI. Specifically, data would be collected to assist in characterizing threats in terms of motivation and origin and to develop tools and technology that would profile attackers and pinpoint where the attacks are coming from. Specific research areas under this topic are described in the subsections below.

Characterize Threats by Motivation and Origin. Limited data are available for characterizing threats on the ICI. Research is required to characterize and identify threats in terms of their motivation and origins. This research is required to develop tools and procedures for identifying potential threats in existing and emerging technologies.

Profile Potential Attackers. Data of relevance for determining what constitutes a potential ICI attacker are limited. Research is required to develop profiles of potential attackers that incorporate such factors as motivations, origins, and capabilities. Threat identification and characterization should include attack methods and prerequisites. It is necessary to understand the differences and similarities between threats from system "insiders" (i.e., system administrators, privileged users, flawed applications) and threats from "outsiders" (i.e., hackers, viruses, intruder-inserted malicious code).

Insiders are a very significant part of the threat spectrum; an estimated 75% to 80% of problems are caused by those who are familiar with the vulnerabilities of systems and the locations of critical system data. Advanced tools are required to monitor the usage patterns of insiders and flag access behaviors that fall outside normal patterns. This research would need to be performed for both individual and organized attackers (e.g., groups or countries). It would provide a foundation for developing tools and procedures to help identify potential threats to existing and emerging infrastructures.

Developing profiles of outsiders is especially difficult because of the anonymity that is possible with the Internet. Fundamental research in human behavior and psychology is required to develop approaches to analyze threat potential on the basis of how one accesses and uses ICI elements.

Pinpoint the Origin of Attacks. Pinpointing the source of attack (physical or cyber) is critical in knowing where to apply defensive measures and where to trace back to search for the attacker. (The discussion in Section 3.2.1 is related to identifying the source of cyber attacks.) Funding is required to enable existing infrastructure managers to analyze carrier interconnections and operations to help pinpoint the origin of attacks. These analyses would allow development of cooperative response strategies. Properly applied forensics and data sanitization procedures also would need to be developed to enable necessary data to be collected and appropriately shared for use in isolating and prosecuting attackers. The latter is important because the interconnectedness in networks promotes the loss of accountability and ability to trace sources of attacks.

Funding in this area would yield both short- and long-term benefits. In addition, a continuing research effort would be required as new technologies are developed and introduced into the ICI. The primary benefits from this research would be sharable data and information and the procedures and tools for collecting, analyzing, and disseminating the data and information.

Goals and Challenges

The goal of this effort is to collect, analyze, and distribute timely and accurate data on the threats to the ICI. Tools and technology are needed to analyze the data to profile both insider and outsider attackers, and to trace the attack across interconnecting networks to the point of origin.

Rationale for the Research and Desired Results

The rationale for this topic is to construct defenses against threats to the ICI, and one must first identify and characterize those threats.

Timeframe and Resource Requirements

By 2010, a formal system for collecting, characterizing, and disseminating threat data should be in place at the national and the international level. It is estimated that a total federal investment of about $95 million is required through 2010. The estimated commitment requires $25 million in 2000, $30 million between 2001 and 2005, and $40 million between 2006 and 2010.[9]

3.2 Intrusion and Incident Detection, Response, and Recovery

The objective of this research area is to develop tools and procedures to detect, respond to, and recover from incidents, losses in service, or attacks. Incident detection is different from intrusion detection. With incident detection, someone or something causes an anomaly or problem, while with intrusion detection, someone or something is assumed to be "looking around," gaining unauthorized access to information or preparing to attack with the intent to damage, disrupt, deny, or destroy.

3.2.1 Intrusion and Incident Detection and Warning

Description

Detecting incidents is not necessarily a straightforward activity. The development of intrusion detection systems is still in its infancy. Also, the results of an incident may not necessarily manifest themselves at the time of the incident. For example, data may be corrupted, but the fact that they are corrupted may not be known until they are used. Once an incident has been detected, the elements in a system or network may be compromised, and alternative systems may need to be used to send a warning. Intrusion detection systems also need to be protected from attack, as these systems have vulnerabilities, too.

The objective of this research is to develop tools and procedures to identify and report the precursors to an attack, or an actual attack, on the ICI. Tools need to be developed that are scalable to large systems and networks and that can respond to different attack strategies (Section 3.1.4). In the short term, manual procedures may be required to provide communications between incident handling teams. In the long term, the goal is to develop automated indications and warning systems.

---

9 The funding estimates given for the 2006 to 2010 timeframe probably would change as a result of developments during the 2001 to 2005 period.

The effort would focus on the development of metrics for evaluating false-alarm rates, strategy-based intrusion detection technologies, tools and technologies for use on high-speed networks, scalable intrusion detection systems, and tools to trace intrusions to their sources.

False-alarm Metrics. Existing intrusion detection systems (IDSs) suffer from high false-alarm rates and unknown, but probably very high, false-negative rates. The goal of this R&D is not to determine the values for "acceptable" false-alarm rates, but to develop standardized algorithmic metrics that can evaluate IDSs so implementers can judge the "quality" or "fitness" of an IDS and then compare systems.

Strategy-based Intrusion Detection. Intrusion detection technologies need to be developed on the basis of different analysis strategies. Examples of new approaches include the following:

- Detecting deviations from the expected behavior of a program or service;
- Using data fusion and data mining tools;
- Analyzing patterns of attack (e.g., signature patterns) to detect denial of service;
- Analyzing "anomalous" or uncharacteristic user behavior; and
- Detecting deviations from the policy-based mandates on the functioning and operation of the network.

High-speed Network Intrusion Detection. Intrusion detection technologies need to be developed for use with high-speed networks. When the network speed increases, a simple or minor security attack can cause problems that can be propagated through a system rapidly. However, the key issue is not the rate at which the problem spreads, but rather the difficulty of performing detection activities with the increasingly faster data rates that are becoming available.

Scalable Intrusion Detection. Components of an information and communications network can be numerous and geographically dispersed. Intrusion detection technologies need to be developed that are scalable to systems and networks at a national level, with thousands of potential penetration nodes that could be geographically diverse.

Trace Back. The ability to trace a cyber intrusion rapidly back to its source is critical in stopping attacks. If the trace can be done rapidly and in a stealthy fashion, it may be possible to catch the attacker. Therefore, technologies and procedures are needed to identify, analyze, isolate, and trace back to their sources any actual or suspected intrusions. These tools would need to produce supporting forensic data that could provide credible evidence in courts of law.

Goals and Challenges

The goal is to develop efficient, cost-effective, real-time tools for intrusion and incident detection and warning. These tools are needed at a national level to integrate information from distributed sources; taken together, such information may warn people of an impending attack.

Rationale for the Research and Desired Results

The rationale for this research is that disruptions in the ICI can have far-reaching effects, including the creation of life-threatening situations. Therefore, technologies and tools are required to detect intrusions and incidents and to send out warnings rapidly and efficiently.

Timeframe and Resource Requirements

The timeframe for this activity extends to at least 2010. The total estimated investment over this time period is $330 million. The proposed commitment is $90 million in 2000, $90 million between 2001 and 2005, and $150 million between 2006 and 2010.

3.2.2 Response, Recovery, and Reconstitution

Description

Once an attack or incident has been detected, a system or network is restored to full working order by using a three-phase process. The first phase is response Ñ-deciding what must be done, in what order, and with what resources. The second phase is recovery—repairing the damage and returning to a degraded mode or full operational capability. The last phase is reconstitution – replacing resources that have been completely destroyed or are beyond repair. The objective of this research is to develop methodologies to contain, stop, or eject intruders and to mitigate damage or restore information processing services in the event of attack or disaster. Specifically, the research would focus on developing tools and methodologies to make rapid assessments of damage from an attack or break in the infrastructure, improved technologies to reject and contain intruders, and more timely and effective network recovery or reconstitution.

Response Assessment. Because response must be immediate, there is an urgent need to develop procedures and tools to perform a triage assessment of the extent of damage from an incident or attack. The assessment methodology would probably follow medical approaches and focus on establishing priorities for applying recovery resources. This research would focus on how to determine what infrastructure elements are "dead," or nonrecoverable, and how to eliminate or isolate them without damaging the rest of the system or network. Tools are needed for self-healing, self-correcting, and self-diagnosis on networks and systems. In the short term, manual procedures may be required, but in the long term, automated tools are desired.

Intrusion Rejection. Once an intrusion has been detected, it must be eliminated as a threat. Therefore, procedures and technologies are required to reject, eject, and/or contain intruders at all stages of attacks or threats to the infrastructure, natural or deliberate. In the short term, manual procedures may be required to provide real-time corrective or adaptive response, but in the long term, automated tools are desired.

Network or System Recovery and Reconstitution. Tools and procedures are needed to recover and reconstitute a network or system in the event of a break. Recovery is best carried out hierarchically, starting at the lowest level and attempting to recover to a known state. A level is restored to a consistent state before recovery is attempted at the next higher level. The tools and procedures used to facilitate recovery and reconstitution would have to identify all affected elements (hardware, software, and data/information) and provide the ordering and procedures necessary for recovery in an orderly fashion. To provide information that could be trusted, these systems would have to be isolated or "hardened" to attack.

Goals and Challenges

The goals and challenges are to reduce the times needed for, and increase the effectiveness of, responding, recovering, and reconstituting systems and/or networks if a disruption occurs.

Rationale for the Research and Desired Results

The rationale for this research is that breaks in the ICI can result in serious, and potentially life-threatening, impacts on society, organizations, and individuals. Reduced time and increased effectiveness to respond and recover are critical for restoring the systems and networks.

Timeframe and Resource Requirements

The timeframe for this activity extends to at least 2010. The estimated investment totals $300 million. The proposed commitment is $95 million in 2000, $105 million between 2001 and 2005, and $100 million between 2006 and 2010.

3.3 Engineering High-confidence Infrastructures

So far, research has focused on knowing where threats and vulnerabilities will be and how to respond to them. Now the focus shifts to making the ICI and other dependent infrastructures more resistant to attack. This research focuses on developing the tools and procedures for building the ICI with minimal vulnerabilities. The resulting products would be applicable for retrofitting legacy systems, as well as for applying to emerging technologies.

3.3.1 Security Architectures

Description

The objective of this research is to organize security components and services to provide confidentiality, integrity, and availability for information and communication systems. For example, research conducted under this topic would examine areas such as the following:

- Interoperability among security components,
- Policies for security implementation in emerging technologies,
- Advanced firewall technologies,
- Adaptive systems,
- Packet switching technologies,
- Secure operating systems for the Internet and automated distribution of patches and information related to security upgrades,
- Scalability and optimization of security architectures, and
- Vulnerabilities in remote control systems such as SCADA systems.

Interoperability among Security Components. When networks and systems become interconnected, security features in one system may be in conflict with security features in another. This incompatibility can be especially true if systems, such as communications systems, span national boundaries, and different standards or approaches are used. Therefore, architectures need to be defined with protection protocols and data exchange interfaces to allow interoperation of security components.

Policies for Security Implementation in Emerging Technologies. It is difficult to predict what technologies will be a part of future ICIs. Therefore, it is a pressing need to develop policies for implementing protection measures within emerging technologies and to focus on engineering security into the technologies as early as possible. In addition, a formal notation, or policy language, must be developed to capture policy for reasoning purposes.

Advanced Firewall Technologies. Firewalls are often the first line of defense in computer systems and networks. As attack technologies and strategies become more sophisticated, firewall technology must advance as well. A recent article in a trade magazine indicated that the quality of commercial firewall products is unsatisfactory and that many of the packages can be easily penetrated (*Internet Week* 1998). The proper configuration of firewalls is important, and tools are needed to assist system administrators. Advanced firewalls are beginning to include intrusion detection and encryption technologies.

Adaptive Systems. Advanced systems and networks are needed. These need to be adaptive and capable of reacting dynamically to changes in the security and reliability environment.

Packet-switching Technologies. Research is required to develop a packet-switching technology (also known as "Internet switching architecture") for supporting isolation of one-to-one, one-to-many, and many-to-many communication flows with respect to bandwidth, throughput, rate of data loss, and security (data encryption and origin-destination encryption).

Secure Operating Systems for the Internet. Considerable activity surrounds the development of the "next generation" Internet. Secure and reliable operating systems are needed for the Internet nodes of the present and future systems.

Automated Distribution of Security Patches. Often the weak link in a security system is the inability to distribute and implement security notices and patches fast enough. Therefore, a protocol is needed for automated distribution of security patches and notices that can operate even under potentially degraded circumstances.

Scalable Security Architectures. Scalable and robust security architectures are needed to meet the need for larger environments. Work in this area would leverage off results from the development of attack taxonomies.

Optimized Security Architectures. The performance of systems and networks should not be seriously degraded by security features. Therefore, the need exists to develop security architectures optimized for performance.

Remote Control System Vulnerabilities. Remote control systems (such as SCADA systems) provide distant control for distributed components within the communications industry and other infrastructures. The protection and security of these systems and protocols are critical for all infrastructures. Using real-time process control of systems over the Internet is an R&D issue.

Goals and Challenges

The goals and challenges are to develop tools and methodologies to efficiently, cost-effectively, design and implement new and improved security architectures.

Rationale for the Research and Desired Results

The rationale for the research is that the threat environment for the ICI is rapidly evolving, and new security technologies and concepts must keep pace with them. It is necessary to improve the focus on the fundamental research and proper design of security engineering and technology for architectures, which is introduced early in the development process to assure security in complex, distributed, multicomponent systems in a dynamic environment.

Timeframe and Resource Requirements

The timeframe for this activity extends at least to 2010. The total estimated investment over this period is $525 million. The proposed commitment is $125 million in 2000, $150 million between 2001 and 2005, and $250 million between 2006 and 2010.

3.3.2 Assurance Technologies

Description

The development of assurance technologies is a critical, long-term research area requiring government investment. The commercial sector rarely invests in this area because of the length of time to see a return on their investments. This topic involves the development of tools and techniques for rigorous design, implementation, testing, and formal verification of hardware and software components and their subsequent integration into larger systems. This research topic would focus on how to make assurance a normal component of system development, how to perform efficient product evaluation from a security perspective, how to do system-level assurance evaluations, how to develop statistical process control procedures, and how to use tools and methodologies for identification and authentication.

Making Assurance a Normal Component of System Development. System engineering teams and their engineering processes must be bolstered to make rigorous assurance methods a natural component of hardware and software engineering. Engineers need better design analogies and better integration concepts that support assurance justification. Technologies and methodologies that can provide this need include the following:

- Development of rigorous design languages that allow the formal expression of a concept or behavior;
- Development of formal protocol specifications and methods;
- Modeling and simulation tools; and
- Formal inspection, testing, model-checking, and verification procedures.

Efficient Product Evaluation Policies. The Trusted Product Evaluation Paradigm[10] used by DoD for two decades is no longer realistic. Although

---

10 The Trusted Product Paradigm is built on four fundamental blocks: (1) security policy (access control), (2) accountability (identification and authentication and audit), (3) assurance (operational and life cycle), and (4) documentation. Such trust has been oriented largely toward the operating system and its Trusted Computing Base (DoD 1985).

the intent was to evaluate a product once and then reuse the assurance evidence to certify many different system implementations, the actual results have not proven to be as effective as intended. Most product providers believe that continuing to evaluate a single product is irrelevant today because that product often must be adapted to work as part of a larger system.

System-level Assurance Evaluation. The current product evaluation approach does not give adequate support assurance at the system level. Procedures and tools need to be developed that address the following:

- Determining objectively what a product does in a process that is highly repeatable and relatively impervious to a different interpretation,
- Performing testing to assess security functionality,
- Providing a basis for characterizing security and system behavioral properties,
- Providing an understanding of the security contributions of various components and how to compose them, and
- Providing an understanding of the "weakest link" within the system at the component level.

Development of Statistical Process Control Procedures. Research is needed on applying statistical process control and other quality approaches to software and hardware engineering processes. Methods for effecting and measuring continuous process improvement through both quality and activity cost measures should be developed.

Identification and Authentication. One way to reduce threat is to limit access (physical or cyber) to critical and vulnerable components. As a result, technologies need further development. These technologies include biometrics and other methods for secure identification and authentication.

Goals and Challenges

The goals and challenges are to develop tools and methodologies for efficient, cost-effective, implementation of new and improved assurance technologies. The effectiveness of the research should be demonstrated in large-scale studies using real systems.

Rationale for the Research and Desired Results

The rationale for the research is that breaks and disruptions in the ICI can be extensive and potentially life-threatening. Rigorous assurance methods, engineering, and evaluation strategies need to be developed and incorporated into system designs to assure the appropriate security functionality in multicomponent, integrated systems.

Timeframe and Resource Requirements

The timeframe for this activity extends to at least 2010. The total estimated investment over this period is $375 million. The proposed commitment is $95 million in 2000, $105 million between 2001 and 2005, and $175 million between 2006 and 2010.

3.3.3 Advanced Concepts and Theory

Description

The objectives of this research are to perform fundamental analyses into the complexities of advanced ICI systems and networks and the processes required to produce secure products, especially software. Examples of areas requiring study under this topic include the theory of protection, how to use expert systems for network management; understanding system-level hazards, tools, and methodologies for improving the quality of software; self-describing systems; and the security implications of systems of integrated components.

Theory of Protection. A theoretical basis through fundamental research is needed to protect the communications and information infrastructure. The security and protection implications of advanced communications concepts should also be studied. Analysis of this topic would result in a body of knowledge with a sound basis in academic research in protection technology.

Use of Expert Systems for Network Management. Advanced, expert-system-based software tools need to be developed for managing and administering complex networks. These tools would facilitate visualization and debugging of underperforming or overloaded networks, offer help in reconfiguring the network, and assist in evaluating hypothetical network architectures.

Understanding System-level Hazards. Innovative approaches are needed to improve our ability to understand system-level hazards, as well as to understand the individual and integrative risk contributions introduced by all system components, especially software.

Improving Software Quality. Theoretical work is required to determine ways in which to improve software quality and develop "safe" programs. This work would include the following:

- Development and use of CASE tools,
- Development of quality standards,
- Development of fault- or bug-tolerant software,
- Development of mathematically rigorous and formal methods,
- Use of standard development procedures, and

- Reuse of software.

Self-describing Systems. Research is needed to investigate techniques by which large-scale systems might "describe themselves" to modeling and analysis tools, to provide greater assurance that analysis of such tools is descriptive of large systems as actually constituted.

Systems of Integrated Components. Research is required on systems with many integrated components. This research would embrace such issues as composition of trustworthy systems from less trustworthy components, graceful degradation when breaks occur, and fine-grain damage containment.

Goals and Challenges

The goals and challenges are to develop the advanced concepts, theories, and tools needed to develop efficient and cost-effective security and protection for the ICI.

Rationale for the Research and Desired Results

The rationale for this research is that as technologies evolve and develop, new potential threats and vulnerabilities may emerge that require advanced concepts and theory to detect and protect against them. Further development of system theory and fundamentals is required to provide a comprehensive understanding of complex systems, at a theoretical and applied level, which is achievable through long-term research programs.

Timeframe and Resource Requirements

The timeframe for this activity extends at least to 2010. The total estimated investment over this period is $110 million. The proposed commitment plan is $30 million in 2000, $30 million between 2001 and 2005, and $50 million between 2006 and 2010.

3.3.4 Management of Information Protection

Description

The objective of this research is to develop methodologies and tools for the application and management of information protection in information and communications systems. Specific areas of study include how to protect data that exist on multiple nodes, how to protect information in a multiple-security-level environment, security based on advanced information protection concepts, the security and management implications of long-term information storage, and configuration management.

Protecting Data on Multiple Nodes. Techniques are needed to protect data in individual files as they reside on multiple nodes in a system. Individual repositories are not adequately protected. Thus, these files may need be encrypted, which means that methods are required to manage the keys for encrypting the files. These methods must support flexible, distributed authorization models, rather than manual key distribution.

Protecting information in wireless communication systems includes the confidentiality of location, levels of protection while roaming in the United States and foreign networks abroad, information security, and personal information on users.

Information Protection in a Multiple-security-level Environment. Metrics are needed for evaluating information protection when different tools and measures are combined in the security infrastructure.

Security Based on Advanced Information Protection Concepts. Security architectures must be developed that incorporate advanced information protection concepts, such as information that carries its own use conditions. (That is, the information may contain, for example, the categories of users that can access these data and the conditions under which they may do so.)

Long-term Information Storage. Research is needed to address the protection issues in long-term information protection. Data storage techniques and media have changed dramatically and are expected to continue to change. Stored media deteriorate with time, and recording protocols change. Research is required to ensure that knowledge about storage techniques is preserved so that data can be retrieved even if the method of storage has become obsolete. While this topic is not solely related to security, it is likely to be a significant security issue, especially as storage and encryption technologies continue to advance.

Configuration Management. Research is required to improve methods for managing remote and local configuration. Errors in configuration management frequently lead to significant vulnerabilities that can be exploited. The next generation of wireless services is expected to permit the handset to be reconfigured by downloading appropriate software, and this capability requires appropriate security mechanisms and configuration control.

Goals and Challenges

The goals and challenges are to develop tools and methodologies for protecting information over time and in diverse environments.

Rationale for the Research and Desired Results

Information collection, analysis, and use are key elements in modern society. Damage or disruption to the information bases used by society could have dramatic consequences. The protection of information depends on the environment (e.g., multiple nodes, multiple security levels) and requires different tools and technologies. Research is needed to define and provide protection mechanisms for information in various system and network environments.

Timeframe and Resource Requirements

The timeframe for this activity extends at least to 2010. The total estimated investment over this period is $110 million. The proposed commitment is $10 million in 2000, $50 million between 2001 and 2005, and $50 million between 2006 and 2010.

3.3.5 Characterization of Minimum Infrastructure for Essential Services

Description

The objective of this research is to determine the minimum infrastructure components required to provide essential national, governmental, and military communication and information services. The characterization of these services includes assuring the exchange of information between government agencies and local authorities, maintaining the functionality of emergency management communication systems, and assuring redundant systems in critical areas.

Goals and Challenges

The goals and challenges are to identify the key elements of the ICI that require maximum protection in order to provide essential services.

Rationale for the Research and Desired Results

Loss or disruption of the ICI could result in serious and potentially dangerous consequences with respect to the continued operation of critical government and military services.

Timeframe and Resource Requirements

The timeframe for this activity extends to at least 2010. The total estimated investment over this period is $55 million. The proposed commitment is $15 million in 2000, $15 million between 2001 and 2005, and $25 million between 2006 and 2010.

3.3.6 Encryption Technology

Description

The objective of this research is to develop and evaluate software, firmware, and hardware encryption technologies. Specific areas of study include developing standards for security key management and providing affordable cryptography.

Standards for Security Key Management. Research is needed to develop a nationwide standard for security key management, including key discovery, key registration and dissemination, dynamic revocation, key refresh, and key escrow (as desired). The approach can use public key mechanisms, but the basic keys also should be suitable for symmetric use. The deployment and management of large public key infrastructures and symmetric key management are research issues that need resolution, in that this technology may form the common denominator in our distributed systems.

Affordable Cryptography. Research into applied cryptographic technology for privacy, integrity, authentication, nonrepudiation, etc., is needed. The emphasis should be on low-cost scalability, user-friendliness, and minimal overhead.

Goals and Challenges

The goals and challenges are to develop robust, high-performance, efficient, and cost-effective encryption technologies. Research needs include improved commercially available encryption technologies, high-speed cryptography for the national infrastructure, and cryptography for ultra-high-speed authentication and other applications.

Rationale for the Research and Desired Results

The rationale for this topic is that the potential effects of not being able to provide adequate protection of information are immense. The increased computer power now available to intruders necessitates the development of more robust and secure encryption technologies. However, the effective use of more robust algorithms requires the development of high-performance methods that can encrypt data more securely without inordinate increases in computation time.

Timeframe and Resource Requirements

The timeframe for this activity extends to at least to 2010. The total estimated investment over this period is $525 million. The proposed commitment is $125 million in 2000, $150 million between 2001 and 2005, and $250 million between 2006 and 2010.

3.4 Modeling and Simulation Tools

Description

The requirement for this research affects all three primary areas because modeling and simulation tools are required in each of them. These tools are needed at the national level to assess risk, security, interoperability, and recovery issues. Examples of areas of study include the development of advanced simulation frameworks for testing and evaluation, the modeling of complex systems, and the modeling of system architectures.

Development of Advanced Simulation Frameworks. A general need exists for advanced simulation frameworks to support the analyses required in each area. For example, a need has been expressed to develop tools that can identify and map the vulnerabilities and interdependencies in systems and networks.

Modeling of Complex Systems. Fundamental work on modeling of complex systems is required. Understanding is limited concerning the components in an infrastructure, their performance implications, and their interaction with other components.

Modeling of System Architectures. Rigorous modeling and analysis at the systems architecture level is needed, and this modeling needs to be combined with techniques for tracking compliance of deployed systems with the architectural descriptions on which the analysis results are based. The need for architectural analysis techniques is well understood, and work is under way to adapt (to the infrastructure protection domain) such techniques as probabilistic risk assessment by means of fault-tree analysis.

Perhaps less well recognized is the problem of validating the results of such analyses in the presence of possible (likely) divergences of modeled systems from their architectural models, especially in system evolution. In real industrial systems, this evolution occurs somewhat haphazardly and, for efficiency, sometimes without adequate, centralized control. The development of advanced modeling and simulation tools and environments would provide synthetic test beds for experimental studies of the infrastructure that cannot be performed under actual conditions.

Goals and Challenges

The goals are to develop the modeling and simulation tools necessary to create and evaluate the technologies required to protect the ICI. These models include the effects of specific attack elements and safeguards against those attacks.

Rationale for the Research and Desired Results

Modeling and simulation activity is a cost-effective way to research issues in a virtual environment on a computer without performing experiments on actual systems.

Timeframe and Resource Requirements

The timeframe for this activity extends to at least 2010 and perhaps beyond. The total estimated investment over this period is $535 million. The proposed commitment is $135 million in 2000, $150 million between 2000 and 2005, and $250 million between 2006 and 2010.

Section 4
R&D Topic Roadmaps

Table C.1 provides a summary of the research topics in each of the thrust areas, as well as in the crosscutting topic on modeling and simulation. Included are the type of research that would be performed, a description of the products that could be expected, the goals and challenges in each area, the performance goals and technical challenges, and a prioritization of the topics.

4.1 Roadmap for Development

Table C.2 provides a "roadmap" for the individual research areas and crosscutting modeling and simulation. The roadmap describes the research path to be followed, estimates of what could be expected over the time-frame 2000-2010, and the total estimated investment required. Table C.3 summarizes the recommended investments over all of the areas.

4.2 Suggested Pilot Projects

A number of pilot projects are recommended for demonstrating that enhanced security and protections can be provided in the information and communications infrastructure. Pilot projects would be used explicitly to refine requirements, apply research products in limited test environments (i.e., test beds), and provide valuable feedback to researchers. The recommended pilot projects are described in the following subsections.

4.2.1 Development of an Experimental Test Bed

It is recommended that an experimental test bed be developed for use in evaluating security technologies. This test bed would be government-funded but available to private-sector firms to test security technologies and interoperability issues.

4.2.2 Lexicon and Procedures for Defining and Reporting Data

A common set of definitions should be developed to describe threats, vulnerabilities, and types of attacks. This lexicon would enable researchers to collect data on threats, vulnerabilities, and attacks in a self-consistent manner so trends could be assessed. It is recommended that a system similar to one implemented by the FBI for reporting crime statistics be used.

Table C.1 Summary of R&D Topics for Information and Communications

Research Topic					
No.	Title (Type[a])	Product	Goals and Challenges	Threats and Vulnerabilities	Priority Category[b]
		Risks, Threats, and Vulnerabilities			
1	Vulnerability Detection and Analysis (B, A, ATD)	Information, management procedures, software tools, advances in fundamental theory	Provide efficient and effective tools to detect and analyze vulnerabilities	Physical, cyber, interdependencies	Most important
2	Valuation of Information (B, A)	Management procedures, software tools, advances in fundamental theory	Provide efficient, easy-to-use tools and procedures for valuing information	Physical, cyber, interdependencies	Very important
3	Risk Analysis (B, A)	Management procedures, software tools, advances in fundamental theory	Provide automated and effective tools for analyzing risk in systems	Physical, cyber, interdependencies	Important
4	Characterization and Notification of Threats (B, A)	Information, management procedures, advances in fundamental theory	Provide efficient and effective tools to collect, analyze, and disseminate data on threats	Physical, cyber, interdependencies	Most important
		Incident Detection, Response, and Recovery			
5	Intrusion and Incident Detection and Warning (B, A, ATD)	Information, management procedures, software and hardware technologies, advances in fundamental theory	Develop efficient, cost-effective tools and methodologies for rapid incident detection and warning	Physical, cyber, interdependencies	Most important

Research Topic					
No.	Title (Type[a])	Product	Goals and Challenges	Threats and Vulnerabilities	Priority Category[b]
6	Response, Recovery, and Reconstitution (B, A, ATD)	Software and hardware technologies, management procedures, advances in fundamental theory	Provide rapid and efficient response, recovery, and reconstitution in the event of a break in service	Physical, cyber, interdependencies	Most important
			Engineering High-confidence Infrastructures		
7	Security Architectures (B, A, ATD)	Hardware and software technologies, management procedures, advances in fundamental theory	Develop efficient, cost-effective tools and methodologies, implement new and improved security architectures	Physical, cyber, interdependencies	Most important
8	Assurance Technologies (B, A, ATD)	Hardware and software technologies, management procedures, advances in fundamental theory	Develop efficient, cost-effective tools and methodologies, implement new and improved assurance technologies	Physical, cyber, interdependencies	Most important
9	Advanced Concepts and Theory (B, A, ATD)	Hardware and software technologies, advances in fundamental theory	Develop the advanced concepts and tools needed to provide efficient and cost-effective security and protection	Physical, cyber, interdependencies	Very important
10	Management of Information Protection (B, A, ATD)	Hardware and software technologies, management procedures	Provide tools and methodologies for the effective application and management of information protection	Physical, cyber, interdependencies	Most important

Research Topic					
No.	Title (Type[a])	Product	Goals and Challenges	Threats and Vulnerabilities	Priority Category[b]
11	Characterization of Minimum Infrastructure for Essential Services (A, ATD)	Information, hardware and software technologies, management procedures	Identify the key elements in the ICI that must be given maximum protection to provide essential national, governmental, and military ICI services	Physical, cyber, interdependencies	Very important
12	Encryption Technology (B, A, ATD)	Hardware and software technologies, management procedures	Develop effective and affordable encryption technologies	Physical, cyber, interdependencies	Important
	Modeling and Simulation Tools for Infrastructures Protection				
13	Modeling and Simulation Tools (B, A, ATD)	Software technologies, advances in fundamental theory	Develop tools and methodologies for simulating complex systems and analyzing different system architectural constructs	Physical, cyber, interdependencies	Very important

[a] B = basic; A = applied; ATD = advanced technology development; and POP = proof of principle and validation.

[b] The order of the R&D topics within a priority category (most important, very important, and important) does not imply relative importance.

Table C.2 Summary of Information and Communications R&D Roadmap

R&D Topic No.	Title	Near Term (Resource Estmate[a])	Achieved by ~2005 (ResourceEstimate[a])	Achievedby ~2010 (Resource Estimate[a])
		Risks, Threats, and Vulnerabilities		
1	Vulnerability Detection and Analysis	Develop procedures for collecting, analyzing, and disseminating vulnerability information. ($90 million)	Develop lexicon and database to identify vulnerability information about the infrastructure. Develop metrics and measures to gauge the effectiveness of tools to detect and analyze vulnerabilities, and automate tools to detect vulnerabilities. ($90 million)	Develop coordinated and scalable tools for vulnerability detection and data notification at the national level. Establish international cooperation for collecting and sharing information on vulnerabilities. ($150 million)
2	Valuation of Information	Develop manual tools, techniques, and procedures to assess the value of information. ($30 million)	Develop automated tools to assist information owners in assessing the value of information and determining appropriate levels of protection. ($30 million)	Develop and refine automated tools to assist information owners in assessing the value of information and protection, including information that can be aggregated from multiple sources. ($50 million)
3	Risk Analysis	Develop semiautomated risk analysis tools and formulate techniques and metrics to assess risk. ($75 million)	Develop automated risk analysis tools to dynamically assess risk on systems and networks as components change. ($75 million)	Develop advanced and automated risk analysis tools to incorporate the emergence of new technologies and system components. ($50 million)
4	Characterization and Notification of Threats	Develop procedures for collecting analyzing, and disseminating threat data. ($25 million)	Implement national database of threat and response information. Profile potential attackers. ($30 million)	Develop and distribute coordinated, national-level tools for threat notification. Establish international cooperation for collecting and sharing threat data. ($40 million)

Intrusion and Incident Detection, Response, and Recovery				
5	Intrusion and Incident Detection and Warning	Develop manual tools and procedures to detect incidents and issue warnings. Establish metrics for assessing intrusion detection systems. ($90 million)	Develop automated tools to detect incidents and issue warnings, strategy-based intrusion detection systems, automated trace-back tools, and scalable detection systems. ($90 million)	Develop scalable tools at a national level to detect indications and warnings of an attack. Establish international cooperation and sharing of data on attacks. Create scalable assessment tools to evaluate Internet threats. ($150 million)
6	Response, Recovery, and Reconstitution	Develop manual tools to detect, contain, and eject intruders, and to perform triage for recovery on attacked systems. ($95 million)	Develop automated tools to detect, contain, and eject intruders, and perform triage for recovery on attacked systems. ($105 million)	Continue development of automated tools to improve robustness, efficiency, and timely response in recovery. ($100 million)
Engineering High-confidence Infrastructures				
7	Security Architectures	Establish methodologies for automated distribution of security patches. Prepare security implementation policies. ($125 million)	Develop advanced firewall technologies and active, dynamic network technologies. ($150 million)	Develop scalable, robust security architectures to integrate security components. ($250 million)
8	Assurance Technologies	Establish standards and methods of incorporating assurance into system development and complete product evaluation policies. ($95 million)	Develop tools for efficient product evaluation and system-level evaluations. ($105 million)	Continuously develop and refine methodologies and techniques for incorporating assurance into system development. ($175 million)
9	Advanced Concepts and Theory	Establish standards, techniques, and procedures for software development. ($30 million)	Research and develop ways to use expert systems in network management and to adaptively secure systems. ($30 million)	Develop self-describing secure systems. ($50 million)

10	Management of Information Protection	Research and develop concepts and techniques for protecting data and performing configuration management in local and remote infrastructure components. Define performance metrics for evaluating information protection. ($30 million)	Research information protection concepts that carry use conditions, or metadata, with the information. Establish economic metrics for evaluating information protection. ($30 million)	Continuously develop and refine measurement concepts, tools, and technologies for managing the protection of data in diverse environments. ($50 million)
11	Characterization of Minimum Infrastructure for Essential Services	Define and characterize minimum essential government and military communications, operations and services, and the required infrastructure to support those services. ($15 million)	Establish interagency contingency and coordination plans and address the introduction of redundant systems in critical applications. ($15 million)	Develop plans and deploy additional technologies to ensure redundancy as new technologies emerge and the scope of government services evolves. ($25 million)
12	Encryption Technology	Establish national standards for security key management. ($125 million)	Develop robust, high-performance, cost-effective cryptographic technologies. ($150 million)	Continually advance and refine robust encryption technologies given the significant increases in computing power available. ($250 million)
	Modeling and Simulation Tools for Infrastructure			
13	Modeling and Simulation Tools	Define requirements and initiate modeling and simulation on small network systems. ($135 million)	Develop tools and models for modeling complex systems at the architectural level, and tools and techniques for modeling interdependencies and vulnerabilities in systems. ($150 million)	Develop automated tools for detecting deviations from system specifications at the architectural level and technologies and specifications for self-describing systems. ($250 million)

[a] Resource estimates reflect qualitative, order-of-magnitude judgments. They are intended to be representative of the resources needed for the R&D topics and are based on assump-

tions concerning the scope, the expected level of effort, and the pace of the research. Detailed cost estimates must be prepared in concert with the development of detailed R&D plans.

Table C.3 Summary of Estimated Research Investments for Enhancing the Protection of the ICI (in millions of U.S. dollars)

Area and R&D Topic	Year 2000	~2001 - 2005	~2006 - 2010[a]	Total
Risks, Threats, and Vulnerabilities	70	**375.0**	**290.0**	**735.5**
Characterization and Notification of Threats	5	50	40	95
Vulnerability Detection and Analysis	30	150	150	330
Valuation of Information	10	50	50	110
Risk Analysis	25	125	50	200
Intrusion and Incident Detection, Response, and Recovery	55	**325**	**250**	**630**
Intruder and Incident Detection and Warning	30	150	150	330
Response, Recovery, and Reconstitution	25	175	100	300
Engineering High-confidence Infrastructures	100	**800**	**800**	**1,700**
Security Architectures	25	250	250	525
Assurance Technologies	25	175	175	375
Advanced Concepts and Theory	10	50	50	110
Management of Information Protection	10	50	50	110
Characterization of Infrastructure for Minimum	5	25	25	55
Essential Services				
Encryption Technology	25	250	250	525
Modeling and Simulation Tools for Infrastructure Protection	35	250	250	535
	Totals	260	**1,750**	**1,590**

[a] The Funding estimates given for the 2006 to 2010 timeframe will most likely change as a result of developments from 2001 to 2005.

Section 5
Complexities

The information and communications component of the infrastructure has unique characteristics and complexities not shared by the other infrastructures.

5.1 System Administrator and User Trust

Successful implementation of any security technologies and procedures ultimately depends on the persons who use the tools and procedures. Individual users must be trusted to protect passwords and follow established procedures. Select individuals must be trusted to manage keys and master passwords. Other trusted individuals or groups must be responsible for validating private/public key holders and certifying electronic identities. These individuals also require the proper training and tools to recognize and rectify security shortfalls (e.g., configuration issues) in the systems they control.

5.2 Threats and Vulnerabilities from an International Perspective

Attacks on the ICI can originate from anywhere in the world via computer connections and the Internet. Traditional international boundaries and checkpoints, and their associated protections, no longer apply. Systems become vulnerable from the interconnection of numerous networks, which are only as secure as the weakest link in the chain. Tools and technologies to assess, measure, and model the interconnection of complex components are needed, along with sharing of threat information on an international scale, as discussed earlier.

5.3 Readily Available Advanced Attack Tools

The tools available to hackers are becoming more sophisticated and are available through the World Wide Web. Many tools available for protecting systems also can be used to penetrate systems. The design of security products typically lags behind the technological capability of the hackers to penetrate systems. New laws and stricter enforcement of existing laws are required to increase the level of deterrence.

5.4 Security Priority

Security shortfalls may develop as a result of corporate downsizing, through initiatives to increase profitability in an increasingly competitive market, and through the breakup of large companies into smaller companies with fewer resources to spend on security. As a by-product of downsizing, many firms are outsourcing portions of their business. As a result, external consulting firms can access computer systems to obtain information necessary to perform their tasks. Guidance for influencing corporate policy in the security area is required to maintain the security of systems and information in a changing corporate culture and environment.

Section 6
Other Important Issues

Other issues related to the protection of the ICI exist; although they are not R&D topics, they also affect the degree to which the ICI can be protected.

6.1 Education Curricula and University Funding

Developers need to include protection concepts routinely in the development process, and the place to start is the educational system. There is a requirement for enhanced academic education and for the diversification of research. Too few students are entering the field of communications and information protection, and too few academic institutions have relevant, high-quality research programs. More academic institutions should have curricula and degrees related to communications and information protection; this, in turn, would require support for course development and computing resources for students. Current research topics and objectives are too limited. It is important to foster creativity by ensuring that research groups and individual researchers are consistently funded. Government funding can be leveraged by requiring universities to develop robust curricula, faculty expertise, and their own research programs as the basis for continued funding.

6.2 Continuous Training for System Administration

As systems and technologies change, the administration of the systems will also evolve. Systems administrators require continuous training (as noted in Section 5.1) to keep up with the changes. Advanced, and automated, training systems are required.

6.3 Growth and Consolidation in the Security Industry

The computer security industry is experiencing strong growth. Projections show that the industry could grow from $2 billion in 1997 to almost $7 billion by 2000 (*International Herald Tribune* 1998). The computer and information security industry is experiencing the beginning of consolidation. Small, successful start-up programs are being acquired by larger companies, and the number of companies providing computer and information security is beginning to decrease. Whether the consolidation will lead to better products or to reduced competition and less diversity is question for debate.

6.4 Legal Issues

Legal questions related to liability must be resolved. For example, suppose an attack occurred on the communications and information infrastructure. What responses would be allowable, legal, and acceptable? Who would have legal jurisdiction to investigate or prosecute? This uncertainty over potential liabilities is probably one of the factors that has limited the deployment of security infrastructures. This factor is of particular concern if a party is held liable for the actions or inactions of others.

Many legal issues arise when virtually any individual or group of individuals can visit our country electronically, without the protocol and checks and balances required for a physical visit. One solution to the jurisdiction issue could be to establish virtual borders that would enclose domains where certain rules and laws would apply.

Questions associated with privacy and anonymity also need to be addressed. Currently, data can be aggregated from multiple sources—Social

Security and medical records and from other government files—to find information about individuals and businesses that, in the world of paper files, would be confidential. Furthermore, many modes of communication in our society provide anonymity, and people expect comparable capability from the infrastructure. Governments are currently working to define principles to ensure privacy, but implementation of these principles depends on effective security. The solution to the privacy question is complicated by the need to reconcile the means of protecting privacy with the technologies and policies related to detecting and responding to intrusion. Once legal and privacy issues are resolved, industry should be more willing to devote substantial R&D resources to areas once avoided because of fear of liability or litigation.

6.5 Information Sharing

To design and implement effective countermeasures, and to make competent decisions about the use of resources, the R&D community requires more information about vulnerabilities, threats, and incidents. Enhanced collection and timely dissemination of intelligence information (foreign and domestic) on the nature and extent of threats to the communications and information infrastructure are essential. Security classification and information-handling guidelines must be reassessed to maximize dissemination of threat and vulnerability information so that this information can be widely, though not necessarily openly, available. Many individuals who do not possess security clearances must have timely access to this information. Recently, the FBI established the National Infrastructure Protection Center to investigate cyber crime; this entity is a candidate for functioning as a liaison between multiple government agencies and private-sector firms.

6.6 Industry/Government Partnership

An industry/government partnership is needed to track R&D milestones, which would provide a continuous assessment process to continue the roadmap set forth here. This government outreach program is needed to continue to set research priorities, while tracking and monitoring the research initiatives under way, as well as to leverage and investigate diverse research areas, without duplication, into actual projects and pilots that can significantly improve infrastructure protection and security. A clearinghouse for research across industry and the government is needed. Issues of classified research and proprietary work need to be handled at some abstract level.

6.7 International Issues

The protection of the infrastructure has become an international issue because of the interconnection of networks and the Internet. The United States should initiate cooperation agreements and lead collaboration efforts to develop and enforce infrastructure protection measures. At the same time, care must be taken to develop key security software in the United States.

Currently, many U.S.-produced consumer software products have security technologies produced by contractors in Finland, Australia, Germany, and Russia. U.S. policies and laws, including a reasonable encryption policy, should support domestic production.

6.8 Year 2000 Software Update Initiative

The large volume of legacy code and the time deadline for avoiding potential failures make the year 2000 update initiative a significant challenge for the government and the private sector. The availability of resources to handle the new security initiatives may be considerably constrained in the near term because of the absolute necessity to deal with the year 2000 problem. For example, General Motors has estimated that it would cost between $360 million and $500 million to update its systems, while the Unilever Group has increased its estimate to £300 million (*Financial Times* 1998). An aspect of the year 2000 problem not often discussed is that even if the United States successfully converts all of its important software systems, failures on the international level may result in problems in this country.

6.9 Cryptography

Cryptography policy is an issue that is beyond the scope of this R&D study. However, it is recognized that research into applied cryptographic technology for privacy, integrity, authentication, nonrepudiation, and other critical areas is essential for effective infrastructure assurance. The mathematical algorithms used to encrypt data must be highly resistant to attack and computationally secure. The keys used for encrypting and decrypting data must be distributed properly, protected, and managed. Promising new encryption technologies, such as elliptic curve, could improve both security and economy of operations. In addition, new concepts of key management infrastructure could emerge to provide a variety of alternatives that industry could develop into interoperable products.

Section 7
References

Defense News, 1998, "Clinton Prepares Infowar Response," Vol. 13, No. 11, March 16-22.

Financial Times, 1998, April 4-5, p. 6.

International Herald Tribune, 1998, March.

Internet Week, 1998, "Burned by Your Firewall?" March 30, p. 9.

Mayfield, T., 1998, *Critical Infrastructure Protection: An Academic & Institution Perspective on Research & Development for the Information & Communications Infrastructure*, Institute for Defense Analyses, April 15.

National Telecommunications and Information Agency (NTIA), 1996, *In the Matter of Implementation of the Local Competition Provisions in the Telecommunications Act of 1996*, CC Docket No. 96-98, Reply Comments, U.S. Department of Commerce, Washington, D.C., May 30.

Q.V., 1995-1996, e.g.: 220 ILCS (Illinois) 5/13-102; *Implementing the Telecommunications Act '96*, Washington Utilities and Transportation Commission, summary of Report Findings, November 30, 1996; California Public Utilities Code, Chapter 4, Article 8, Pars. 851-856 (Universal Service); New Jersey Board of Public Utilities, Ratepayer Advocate Recommendations, Section V. *Definition of Universal Service*; and, Public Utility Commission of Texas, Rule ¶23.97, related to interconnection for local exchange service, Report of the Commission, references to universal, nondiscriminatory service as defined by the U.S. Telecommunications Act of 1996; Texas Register (20 TexReg 8777), October 24, 1995.

The Washington Post, 1998, "Panel Urges U.S. to Power Up Cyber Security," March 20.

U.S. Department of Defense (DoD), 1985, TCSEC, DoD 5200.28-STD.

CHAPTER 6

PRELIMINARY RESEARCH AND DEVELOPMENT

ROADMAP FOR PROTECTING AND ASSURING THE TRANSPORTATION INFRASTRUCTURE[1]

---

1 This document is one component of a longer report entitled *Preliminary Research and Development Roadmap for Protecting and Assuring Critical National Infrastructures* (Transition Office of the President's Commission on Critical Infrastructure Protection and the Critical Infrastructure Assurance Office. Washington, D.C. July 1998).

Contents

Section 1 Introduction

1.1 Scope of the Infrastructure

1.2 Characterization of the Infrastructure

1.3 Issues and Trends

Section 2 Threats and Vulnerabilities

Section 3 R&D Topics and Activities

3.1 Identification and Measurement of and Awareness Training for System Vulnerabilities

3.1.1 Vulnerability Analysis of Existing Systems

3.1.2 Simulation Tool Development

3.1.3 Determination of Risk Perception of Transport System Managers

3.1.4 Communication and Inculcation of Sound Risk Management Principles

3.1.5 Capacity Margin Analysis

3.1.6 Emergency Communications

3.2 Development/Adaptation of Monitoring, Detection, Mitigation, and Incident Response Hardware

3.2.1 Real-time Hazard, Threat, and Detection Monitoring

3.2.2 Robotics Development and Adaptation

3.2.3 Improvement of In-use Performance and Replacement Functionality of Transportation Structures

3.2.4 Unified Vehicle/Guideway Systems (Hardening)

3.3 Development/Adaptation of Monitoring, Detection, Mitigation, and Incident Response Software

3.3.1 Asset Management

3.3.2 System Representation Improvement

3.3.3 Intrusion Detection

3.3.4 Cyber Vulnerability Data Warehouse

3.3.5 Threat/Intelligence Database and Network

3.4 Information Assurance, Human Factors, and Institutional Effects in Preparedness and Response

3.4.1 Information Assurance

3.4.2 Software Assurance

3.4.3 Human Factors Analysis

3.4.4 Recovery Training

3.4.5 Computer Emergency Response and Emergency Response and Recovery Assessment Capacity Building

3.4.6 Public/Private Infrastructure Security Responsibility

Section 4 R&D Topic Roadmaps

4.1 Vulnerability Analysis of Existing Systems

4.2 Simulation Tool Development

4.3 Determination of Risk Perception of Transport System Managers

4.4 Communication and Inculcation of Sound Risk Management Principles

4.5 Capacity Margin Analysis

4.6 Emergency Communications

4.7 Real-time Hazard, Threat, and Detection Monitoring

4.8 Robotics Development and Adaptation

4.9 Improvement of In-use Performance and Replacement Functionality of Transportation Structures

4.10 Unified Vehicle/Guideway Systems (Hardening)

4.11 Asset Management

4.12 System Representation Improvement

4.13 Intrusion Detection

4.14 Cyber Vulnerability Data Warehouse

4.15 Threat/Intelligence Database and Network

4.16 Information Assurance

4.17 Software Assurance

4.18 Human Factors Analysis

4.19 Recovery Training

4.20 Computer Emergency Response and Emergency Response and Recovery Assessment Capacity Building

4.21 Public/Private Infrastructure Security Responsibility

4.22 Crosswalks and Milestones

5 Note

Tables

D.1 Summary of Research Topics by Category

D.2 Summary of Transportation R&D Roadmap

Figure

D.1 Topical Interrelationships by Action Area

Section 1
Introduction

This document charts a systematic course or "roadmap" (i.e., from fiscal year [FY] 1998 to about FY 2010),[2] for conducting public and private research and development (R&D) activities needed to enhance security and reduce vulnerabilities of the transportation infrastructure. This roadmap was developed by a study team of knowledgeable representatives from government, industry, academia, and institutes, and the national laboratories. Additional experts and contributors provided comments. These experts are listed in the Appendix.

1.1 Scope of the Infrastructure

The U.S. transportation infrastructure includes surface, air, and waterborne components. Vulnerabilities and security needs are discussed for (1) public and private airborne and surface aviation activity; (2) railway and highway movement and transhipment of goods and people, including intercity passenger and mass transit services; and inland waterborne commerce, maritime navigation, and port and terminal facilities. Other means of transport, such as oil, gas, and water transmission pipelines, are discussed in specific infrastructure assurance documents.

1.2 Characterization of the Infrastructure

The United States depends on transportation for most of our commerce and much of our success as a nation. The domestic transportation system offers a set of options for safe and reliable movement of freight and people. Both public and private entities own and control the components that provide these options. For example, the intercity freight rail system, its terminals, most of its rolling stock and interchange facilities, and its motive power are privately owned. Commercial airports, port facilities, inland and coastal waterways, and the highway and mass transit systems are either publicly owned or directly subject to public authority; the fleets that use these infrastructures (e.g., cars, trucks, buses, planes, ships) are, except for mass transit vehicles, privately owned. The air traffic control system and the navigation and positioning satellite constellation, which provide one or more vital services to most air and surface traffic, are owned and operated by the federal government.

Recognition of the need for safe and reliable transportation has stimulated competition (by both public and private agencies) to meet the demand for widespread, varied carrier capabilities. The transportation system has de-

---

2 All years referenced in this document are fiscal years.

veloped all-encompassing networks and services; that is, excess capacity for transporting freight and people. Although this capacity margin provides a resilient means for dealing with contingencies that can lead to short-term disruptions, it does not guarantee an expeditious, efficient response to catastrophic or major disruptions. For example, operation and control of much of the transportation system increasingly is becoming centralized to save costs and enhance the capability for real-time system monitoring at a single control point.

Centralized control has the potential to increase vulnerability because an attack could be catastrophic if it targeted a control center. Moreover, procedures and tools that permit knowledgeable authorities to deal effectively with security breaches and other localized disruptions by exercising independent judgment (i.e., "distributed processing") may be disappearing on key components of the overall system. Centralized command and control that intensely relies on electronic communications now is open to hostile, or accidental but pernicious, disruptions of, and intrusions into, the electronic message-passing system that enables such control (so-called "cyber events"). These events can disrupt overall operations more easily than a simple, physical attack, although a physical attack could be devastating if coordinated to target key "choke points."

1.3 Issues and Trends

The consistent, but flexible, U.S. transportation system has engendered site-specific specialization and mutual dependence across the entire nation. Unlike the frontier days, regions and communities of the present probably could not sustain themselves for extended periods because of their dependence on safe and reliable transportation and communication.

However, while the need for community, regional, and global connectedness has increased, actual physical links have declined in number and coverage, especially for smaller communities. Many communities have lost both rail freight and common carrier intercity passenger access in the past 40 years. Despite more freedom to enter the carrier market (because of a wave of transportation deregulation legislation), the number of rail, bus, and barge companies in the United States has declined during the 1990s. Only five domestically owned rail carriers of national stature remain.

Whereas railway service has decreased, roadway miles have increased, though at a slower pace than in the 1950s when construction of the Interstate highway system began. Nonetheless, because of the state of roadways and the number of substandard and unsafe bridges, the U.S. primary and secondary highway system is unsatisfactory in light of demands placed upon it. The gap between highway needs and highway performance is the greatest it has been in decades, primarily because of deferred spending and reduced maintenance budgets at the federal level and in most states. The

Intermodal Surface Transportation Efficiency Act of 1991 has started to alleviate this situation by providing resources for road improvements and bridge replacements.

Because tax-supported mechanisms have not supported an increase in transportation capabilities formerly under public authority, including transit operations and major highway construction, the shift toward private commercial interests and joint public-private ventures is expected to continue. Thus, the primary responsibility for security of the affected infrastructures could shift to interests and organizations that may be poorly suited and positioned to handle such responsibility (compared to public security agencies operating under long-established arrangements). This development is especially worrisome because private organizations may not be able to justify increased security because of financial considerations and without public subsidies.

The desire to reduce costs and increase efficiency in the transportation infrastructure has increased our reliance on information technologies as substitutes for capital investment in physical capacity expansion and/or as a principal tool of strategic and system planning. To protect the transportation infrastructure from physical and cyber threats and vulnerabilities, experienced human surveillance is being displaced by automated surveillance. As a result, the security information is only as reliable and timely as the reliability and durability of the technology, which may not incorporate a "learning" component that, with human-provided security, is value added. Because much of the nation's fixed transportation infrastructure is relatively isolated, reliability and durability are critical issues.

Section 2
Threats and Vulnerabilities

Many threats and vulnerabilities are direct consequences of emerging open architectures, which allow extensive information sharing and asset management, centralized control, and infrastructure isolation. The lack of a fully secure and reliable alternative to the space-based navigation system also is problematic. A wide variation in the perceived magnitude of the transportation system's vulnerability exists among key decision makers. In part, this situation may be a result of a potentially large gap between the theory and the practice of operating transportation systems as complete, yet often interdependent, networks, rather than as discrete point-to-point components. Concern has been expressed about the nature of actual security threats (physical and cyber) and management's understanding and ability to prepare for, and deal with, threats before they become catastrophic events. Recent events have shown that terrorists are willing and able to unleash chemical and biological agents in mass transit facilities; moreover, it cannot be ruled out that they are equally willing and able to attack air terminals, undertake large-scale cyber invasions, or wreak concerted destruction on multiple road and rail "choke points." Decision makers need to determine whether terrorists could be intercepted before an attack begins, and, if not, what mechanisms and capabilities could be counted on to detect the attack in a timely fashion and mitigate its consequences. Both physical and cyber threats need to be considered.

Most if not all of the R&D recommendations for assuring and protecting the transportation infrastructure fall into one of five general action areas:

- Awareness training for threats and vulnerabilities,
- Intrusion and attack prevention,
- Incident mitigation,
- Incident management, and
- Functional recovery.

Research is needed to reduce vulnerabilities in the transportation system and to mitigate their consequences. This research falls into one of four broad categories:

- Identification and Measurement of, and Awareness Training for, System Vulnerabilities;
- Development/Adaptation of Monitoring, Detection, Mitigation, and Incident Response Hardware;
- Development/Adaptation of Monitoring, Detection, Mitigation, and Incident Response Software; and
- Information Assurance, Human Factors, and Institutional Effects in Preparedness and Response.

For these activities, the goal is to substantially enhance capabilities within the five general action areas to reduce system vulnerability to an acceptable level, in particular on the vulnerabilities introduced by the following:

- Increasing openness of communication architectures;
- Increasing centralization of command and control functions at an ever-decreasing number of centers for rail network control, urban traffic management, and urban transit management; and
- Increasing importance and size of intermodal trans-shipment facilities, such as ports, rail classification yards, and truck terminals, which makes them more visible and likely targets.

Although some concern has been expressed about the security of air route traffic control centers (ARTCCs), generally "distributed processing" across regional and local control centers, with its flexibility to hand off control, has made these centers somewhat less vulnerable to physical attack. Moreover, the interface limitations of the admittedly antiquated computer systems used in ARTCCs have ironically, at least in the short term, significantly reduced their cyber vulnerability.

The Federal Aviation Administration (FAA), which continues to develop and install security measures for the ARTCC system, has implemented its own security R&D plan in the context of greater decentralization of responsibility. The final report of the White House Commission on Aviation Safety and Security, released in February 1997, contained the kernel of a recommended approach to aviation security R&D. Much of that approach supports and expands upon ongoing FAA research efforts, including explosive/weapons detection, human factors research, airport security, and aircraft protection through materials hardening.

With respect to emerging technologies for air and maritime navigation, the lack of secure redundancy for the positioning capabilities of the Global Positioning System (GPS) satellite constellation is considered to be a possible vulnerability, but no specific remedial actions in R&D have been identified. Supplementary systems (e.g., the Global Navigation Satellite System [GLONASS], LORAN-C, and ground-based radio-frequency [RF] pseudolites) exist and could be maintained, while alternatives to the C/A (coarse acquisition) GPS transmission code, together with anti-jamming and message-encryption technologies, are becoming available.

One of the main goals of security R&D is to maximize the capability for complex systems, such as the physical and information infrastructure of transportation, to achieve a "soft landing" in the event of massive failure of some component. Another goal is to understand the role that human factors play in the prevention and effective remediation of such a failure. In particular, do individuals in critical command and control positions, from top to bottom of a decision chain, generally possess the kind and degree of sensitivity to low-probability events (such as terrorist attacks) necessary to effectively function in response to a detected threat or actual attack? Do they have the necessary knowledge and span of control? Are "person-machine interfaces" in transportation applications evolving to the point that both sides of this interface can be counted upon to perform successfully in critical situations?

Section 3
R&D Topics and Activities

The transportation infrastructure study team identified four general categories for key R&D tasks. The goal was to capture all of the individual and shared recommendations of team members in a systematic manner. Recommendations were compiled from knowledgeable outside individuals contacted by each team member, as well as by the team's collective understanding. These categories are as follows:

- *Identification and Measurement of, and Awareness Training for, System Vulnerabilities.* The overall purpose is to develop a suite of vulnerability assessment and simulation tools that can identify the existence and location of key weaknesses within systems and instruct those who need to know how to correct those weaknesses. Among the outputs of these methodological developments would be measures to quantify the comparative security of centralized and distributed network control schemes. It may be possible to adapt techniques used in military applications, but in the absence of supporting research, the suitability of such techniques is unknown.
- *Development/Adaptation of Monitoring, Detection, Mitigation, and Incident Response Hardware.* The replacement of experienced human monitoring and surveillance activity by automated technologies for monitoring and controlling systems imposes considerable pressure for real-time delivery of accurate, relevant, and reliable data from instruments designed to detect changes in the state of important system components. Similarly, the potential danger to human health and safety of direct intervention in the aftermath of incidents involving chemical/biological ("chem/bio") and other hazardous materials leads to a demand for remotely controlled damage investigation, assessment, and remediation equipment. It is doubtful that such equipment exists in applications readily transferable for specific use by the transportation infrastructure.
- *Development/Adaptation of Monitoring, Detection, Mitigation, and Incident Response Software.* This category echoes the concerns of the previous item, but with more direct reference to cyber attack rather than to physical attack.
- *Information Assurance, Human Factors, and Institutional Effects in Preparedness and Response.* It is important that transportation systems conduct operations in a manner that does not unnecessarily increase risk, even in normal operation. Therefore, assurance of the reliability and accuracy of electronic information received on a regular, continuous basis is critical. Research can help to define and establish "fail-safe" mechanisms for maintaining this assurance. Systems still may become unstable; however, when they do or when untoward events occur, a more complete understanding is essential, through advanced research, of human response to such conditions and how negative manifestations can be neutralized.

Research topics within each of these four areas are presented in Table D-1. The table indicates the type of research needed, and validation of the principal goals of and challenges to successful accomplishment of the research, targeted infrastructure vulnerabilities, and level of importance/priority. Assigning priority creates the recommended hierarchy for allocating limited funding resources. Sections 3.1-3.4 provide more detailed descriptions of each topic within the research categories.

3.1 Identification and Measurement of and Awareness Training for System Vulnerabilities

3.1.1 Vulnerability Analysis of Existing Systems

Description

This analysis would consist of a broadly encompassing investigation into the status of existing vulnerabilities within and between operating modes. Special emphasis is given to situations in which communications architectures are generally open, and a distributed/decentralized command and control system is not a management philosophy. Pilot studies of actual operations would be performed (with concurrence of management); buy-in and adoption (with peer review); development (with validation); and application of appropriate simulation, gaming, and optimization measures.

A representative panel, consisting of elected and appointed technical decision-makers, would serve as an ongoing advisory committee for project oversight and guidance. The objective is to weigh the susceptibilities and instabilities possibly inherent in existing systems against the potentially greater operating costs and reaction times of closed architectures and/or distributed control. A model or set of models may need to be tailored specifically for application to three to five prototypical structures in transport operations. The U.S. Department of Defense (DoD) and Federal Emergency Management Agency Consequences Assessment Tool Set can provide a workable departure for developing and applying a consolidated tool.

Goals and Challenges

The objective of applied research is to identify (for up to five typical organization types across transportation modal operations) significant vulnerabilities that can exist as a function of the communications architecture and/or control system in place. Should such vulnerabilities be identified, it still could be difficult to get operating entities to consider a serious restructuring instead of an alternative, less vulnerable, but possibly more stable (and costly) architecture or control structure. Several research teams would need to work from three to five years to identify and build the appropriate tools, even with all stakeholders participating in the process.

Table D.1 Summary of Research Topics by Category

Research Topic					
No.	Title (Type[a])	Product	Goals and Challenges	Threats and Vulnerabilities	Priority Category[b]
	Indentification and Measurement of and Awareness Training for System Vulnerabilities				
1	Vulnerability Analysis of Existing Systems (A)	Information, policy guidance	Conduct pilot studies to get to the root of the issue and to obtain "buy-in" from private operators	Complexity	Most important
2	Simulation Tool Development: (B, A, ATD)	Software and training packages for "what if" situations.	Identify and capture relevant contingencies to include in each system simulation structure; generate appropriate and comprehensive input data for conducting analyses impartially; automate decision support; maximize productivity of infrastructure investment; assure continuity; understand trade-offs.	Physical, cyber, interdependencies	Very important
3	Determination of Risk Perception of Transport System Managers (B, A)	Information and training	Identify key characteristics at all appropriate decision levels; quantify important parameters.	Physical, cyber, interdependencies	Very important
4	Communication and Inculcation of Sound Risk Management Principles (ATD, POP)	Information and training	Develop comprehensible language and terms for transmitting useful knowledge; use effective communication methods.	Complexity, cyber, interdependencies	Very important

Research Topic					
No.	Title (Type[a])	Product	Goals and Challenges	Threats and Vulnerabilities	Priority Category[b]
5	Capacity Margin Analysis (A)	Information, policy guidance	Quantify avoided contingency losses in net benefit calculations.	Complexity, interdependencies	Important
6	Emergency Communications (A)	Information, policy guidance	Acknowledge that practices and systems differ across modes and infrastructures.	Interdependencies	Very important
Development/Adaptation of Monitoring, Detection, Mitigation, and Incident Response Hardware					
7	Real-time Hazarrd Threat and Detection Monitoring (B,A, ATD, POP)	Instruments, algorithms, diagnostics	Increase or adapt capability to detect/classify physical/cyber threats and component failure cost-effectively and expeditiously; add new capabilities.	Complexities, physical, cyber	Most important
8	Robotics Development and Adaptation (B, A)	Hardware (robots, servo-mechanisms), instruments	Protect responders; assist victims; expedite recovery; assist in surveillance and remote detection.	Physical, cyber	Very important
9	Improvement of In-use Performance and Replacement Functionality of Transportation Structures (A, POP)	Lightweight, portable component application and replacement structures	Match advanced materials with specific structural replacement needs; develop efficient, longevity-producing features for physical infrastructure.	Physical	Very important
10	Unified Vehicle Guideway Systems (Hardening) (A)	Improved equipment, structures, materials	Link to threat identification technologies and advances in materials science.	Physical	Very important

Research Topic					
No.	Title (Type[a])	Product	Goals and Challenges	Threats and Vulnerabilities	Priority Category[b]
	Development/Adaptation of Monitoring, Detection, Mitigation, and Incident Response Software				
11	Asset Management (A, ATD)	Software for case analyses; hardware/ integrated software for flaw detection	Add reliability and utility to decision makers.	Physical	Very important
12	System Representation Improvement (ATD, POP)	Compre-hensive databases for threat management, incident prevention, and multiple system response	Maximize amount of data on relevant subjects that can be clearly collated for rapid comprehension.	Physical, cyber	Very important
13	Intrusion Detection: Adaptation and Custom Development (ATD, POP)	Software	Selectively adapt and apply NASA, DOE, USCG, and DoD tools to transportation systems.	Physical, cyber	Most important
14	Cyber Vulnerability Data Warehouse (ATD, POP)	Clearinghouse for all cyber vulnerabilities affecting transportation systems	Construct models of transportation computer systems and comprehensive configurations data center.	Cyber	Important
15	Threat/ Intelligence Database and Network (potentially under DOJ/FBI leadership) (ATD, POP)	Clearinghouse for all threats related to transportation systems; real-time intelligence for response and law enforcement	Coordinate with FBI National Infrastructure Protection Center to develop all relevant information.	Physical, cyber interdependencies	Most important

Research Topic No.	Title (Type[a])	Product	Goals and Challenges	Threats and Vulnerabilities	Priority Category[b]
	Information Assurance, Human Factors, and Institutional Effects in Preparedness and Response				
16	Information Assurance (A, ATD)	Advanced, integrated software systems with high level of AI	Apply random encryption and AI techniques to assure message continuity and integrity.	Cyber, interdependencies	Most important
17	Software Assurance (A, ATD)	Software with advanced fault checking and self-diagnosis	Assure nondegrading, reliable performance of network control software.	Interdependencies	Most important
18	Human Factors Analysis (A)	Information and training	Characterize the problem and seek a solution, not the reverse.	Complexity, physical	Most important
19	Recovery Training (A)	"Triage" education; training with optimization tools developed in vulnerability analysis of existing systems	Apply developments in dynamic traffic assignment in these situations.	Interdependencies	Important
20	Computer Emergency Response and Emergency Response and Recovery Assessment Capacity Building (B, A, POP)	Information	Maintain study resources in "standby" mode, for rapid deployment when needed.	Physical	Very important

Research Topic					
No.	Title (Type[a])	Product	Goals and Challenges	Threats and Vulnerabilities	Priority Category[b]
21	Public Infrastructure/ Private Security (POP)	Information	DOT has committed to support this objective with research on optimal deployment of capability.	Complexity, interdependencies	Most important

[a] B = basic; A = applied; ATD = advanced technology development; and POP = proof of principle and validation.

[b] The order of the R&D topics within a priority category (i.e., most important, very important, important) does not imply relative importance.

Rationale for the Research and Desired Results

This research targets awareness training, but it also can pertain to informing policy development.

Timeframe and Resource Requirements

In the near term (before 2002), researchers would conduct pilot studies of actual transportation operations. Funding required for these efforts is estimated to be $9 million. Before 2005, research activities would include developing assessment tools, completing peer review, and validating specific tools. Funding required for this effort is estimated to be $9 million. Before 2010, researchers would complete their assessments of the transportation system. The cost for this work is estimated to be $6 million.

3.1.2 Simulation Tool Development

Description

Among all of the vulnerability assessment tools that can be developed, implemented, and communicated to decision makers, none are more important than simulation and gaming. Both applied (possibly adaptational) and developmental research are needed to build and tailor software and training packages for "what if" situations, covering inter-and intrametropolitan operations for each of the major means of transportation–air, highway, rail, waterway, and intermodal combinations.

Knowledge of, and sensitivity to, control structures within all operations are required to develop sufficiently comprehensive, effective software. The transportation system must operate as a complex network, not as a set of simple point-to-point connectivities. To meet this goal, it is essential that operations personnel and decision makers accurately simulate and understand the network dynamics. Basic (to extend network theory) and applied (to apply to specific conditions) research are needed to understand the principles and guidelines that govern the construction of software and training packages for network management within and across models. Flexibility within the modeling structures should make it possible to explore the effects of new control hierarchies.

Modeling tools would be validated for each mode and applicable control structures. Thus, their development must be accompanied and shaped by real-world exercises, including compiling existing physical inventories of the total transportation infrastructure, analyzing representative sample pieces of the individual systems, evaluating intersystem connectivity nodes, and identifying all physical and cyber choke points. Pilot studies are essential during the early stages of development.

Goals and Challenges

The goals of these R&D efforts are to identify and capture all relevant contingencies to include in the simulation structure for each system, to generate appropriate and comprehensive input data for analyses, and to identify the conditions under which analyses can be conducted impartially. Selecting and correctly programming the appropriate probability constructs for reliable simulation (e.g., Monte Carlo, Bayesian/Markovian, "chaos," or hybrid methods) are a significant challenge. The goal is to develop tools that (a) assure continuity of operations, (b) contribute to automated decision support, (c) maximize the productivity of the existing infrastructure to help guide investment decisions, and (d) show clearly that unavoidable trade-offs exist among productivity, service reliability, and preparation for rare events.

Rationale for the Research and Desired Results

This research targets awareness training for threats and vulnerabilities, one of the five essential action areas identified above. It could lead to the identification and remediation of existing infrastructure vulnerabilities and to the prevention or mitigation of new threats; it also could help to optimize the overall use of transportation resources and increase preparedness of system operators. More generally, although strictly within the context of infrastructure security, it could help to assure continuity of operations, contribute to automated decision support, maximize productivity of the existing infrastructure, help to guide investment decisions, and show clearly the unavoidable trade-offs that exist among productivity, service reliability, and preparation for rare events.

Timeframe and Resource Requirements

In the near term (before 2002), researchers would identify and evaluate ways to create tools that can be used to predict and manage events. Funding required for these efforts is estimated to be $15 million. Before 2005, research activities would include developing and validating the basic tools created in the near-term research. Funding required for this effort is estimated to be $15 million. Before 2010, researchers would validate and deploy the completed set of tools. The cost for this work is estimated to be $5 million.

3.1.3 Determination of Risk Perception of Transport System Managers

Description

A systematic effort to understand and formalize awareness and perception of the risks inherent in current transport operations is necessary for building components of the simulation tools. Through basic research, analysts would characterize and quantify the elements of these structures, while through applied research, they would explore the use of this systematic characterization within each mode and control hierarchy of the transportation infrastructure.

Goals and Challenges

Researchers would identify and develop quantitative measures of the key characteristics of risk perception at all appropriate decision levels. Again, conducting one or more initial pilot studies in a real-world operational context is essential so that private-sector managers understand and accept the merits of the research objective and its value to them.

Rationale for the Research and Desired Results

This research targets awareness training for threats and vulnerabilities and intrusion and attack prevention. A basic understanding is necessary for constructing simulation tools to identify and remedy infrastructure vulnerabilities and prevent new threats.

Timeframe and Resource Requirements

In the near term (before 2002), researchers would conduct scoping activities. Funding required for these efforts is estimated to be $2 million. Before 2005, researchers would complete the analyses and have operating training in place for all functions. Funding required for this effort is estimated to be $2 million. Before 2010, researchers would identify and implement fully secure emergency response communications.

3.1.4 Communication and Inculcation of Sound Risk Management Principles

Description

Operators would have an information and training package about risk as a result of research described above (Section 3.1.3). Training, however, also is needed at all levels, not just for key decision makers, but to inculcate a "security awareness culture" across operating entities. The best means to provide this training and successfully communicate its message varies by worker task, scope of responsibility, and level of education.

Training can be conducted from remote locations via, for example, computer platforms (using CD-ROM) or the Internet. Thus, recent developments in distance learning and training should be considered. The result of applied research in this area is the development of systematic training tools appropriate for each mode and control hierarchy; actual implementation, however, would require field-testing and updating of each package. Implementation would include conducting a case study of adoption and use of formal risk management procedures by at least one operating entity for each physical distribution mode. Proof of principle would demonstrate the effectiveness of risk management principles. Training also should cover security management/acquisition for managers, network security, security administration for system administrators, forensic analysis, and security testing and certification.

Goals and Challenges

This research effort is aimed at developing language and terminologies for knowledge transmission that are useful and comprehensible at all appropriate levels. The goal is to convince officials in the transportation sector, lawmakers, and others with vested interests that vulnerability management is necessary for normal daily operation and that it has a potentially high payoff.

Rationale for the Research and Desired Results

This research targets awareness training for threats and vulnerabilities, intrusion and attack prevention, and incident management. Development of a training program should incorporate the accepted cycle of identifying requirement analyses (e.g., task, organization, person within each structure) with task-based determination of the associated knowledge, skill, and abilities (KSAs) followed by instructional objectives tailored to instill each set of KSAs. It is necessary to communicate the true magnitude and type of risk to operating authorities so that they can identify and remedy infrastructure vulnerabilities, prevent new threats, and institutionalize the results of analyses conducted under Sections 3.1.1-3.1.3.

Timeframe and Resource Requirements

In the near term (before 2002), researchers would develop a training program that would consider providing training from remote locations, such as computer platforms or the Internet. Funding required for these efforts is estimated to be $2 million. Before 2005, researchers would complete analyses and have training in place and operable. Funding required for this effort is estimated to be $2 million. Before 2010, researchers would identify and implement fully secure emergency response communications.

3.1.5 Capacity Margin Analysis

Description

Although "excess" infrastructure in the transportation system may not be an economically productive asset to owners, it may be essential to the protection of broader national interests with regard to total carrying capacity and security. In this case, the obligation to maintain a surplus capacity margin may more appropriately reside with the entire nation (i.e., taxpayers). Applied economic research at a high level of sophistication is needed to fully compute the costs and benefits of, and to guide national policy about, retaining capacity margin in (at a minimum) the rail freight, mass transit, and inland waterway systems. The effort is a logical follow-on to Section 3.1.2 and concomitant to Section 3.1.1.

Goals and Challenges

This research seeks an accurate quantification of the losses from contingencies expected to arise in the absence of surplus capacity (i.e., avoidance of these losses would be the chief net benefit).

Rationale for the Research and Desired Results

This research is targeted at incident mitigation and incident management. Because rail carriers, to cite a specific situation, are now actively eliminating "excess" capacity, waiting until well into the next century to begin this investigation could result in the loss of potentially critical links in the infrastructure.

Timeframe and Resource Requirements

In the near term (before 2002), researchers would develop a training program that would consider receiving training from remote locations, such as computer platforms or the Internet. Funding required for these efforts is estimated to be $2 million. Before 2005, researchers would complete analyses and have an operating training program in place. Funding required for this effort is estimated to be $2 million. Before 2010, researchers would identify and implement fully secure emergency response communications.

3.1.6 Emergency Communications

Description

Vulnerability can be an issue before and after an incident. Specifically, the emergency communications system that must support mitigation and management actions in the aftermath of an event can be vulnerable to sabotage or misuse. Applied research is needed to identify and develop the best means for securing communications systems channels.

Goals and Challenges

The need for security cuts across all critical infrastructures, but a "one size fits all" set of solutions may not exist. This project would identify the solutions most appropriate for responses to disruptions of transportation infrastructure to enable development and deployment of adequate systems.

Rationale for the Research and Desired Results

Research targets incident mitigation, incident management, and functional recovery, but it also can be related to protection from intrusion and attack if "fail-safe" communications systems are discovered. This project gives a needed head start to product development for fully functional and secure emergency response communications.

Timeframe and Resource Requirements

In the near term (before 2002), researchers would identify and implement a fully secure emergency response communications function. Funding required for these efforts is estimated to be $6 million. Before 2005, this technology would be commercialized. Funding required for this effort is estimated to be $2 million.

3.2 Development/Adaptation of Monitoring, Detection, Mitigation, and Incident Response Hardware

3.2.1 Real-time Hazard, Threat, and Detection Monitoring

Description

Transportation's special needs for dealing with physical and cyber threats and detection monitoring equipment are associated with the isolation and scale of much of the infrastructure, the openness of public access to potentially vulnerable spaces (e.g., transit stations, garages), the reliance of most operating systems on the accuracy of electronic data, the overall visibility of structures (i.e., high public profile), and the demonstrated willingness of physical and cyber offenders to attack. This vulnerability is especially critical in the chem/bio area and in malicious computer "hacking" threats.

Component failure or impeding failure needs to be avoided to ensure uninterrupted control of systems; however, means for detecting impending failure at remote sites are in their infancy with respect to the number and complexity of parameters monitored. High-resolution broadband applications, a possible solution to this problem, are not widely used for (or adapted to) transportation systems. Because many sites and structures need detectors across the physical and electronic dimensions of the transportation system, the cost of such detectors must decrease before an effective deployment can occur.

Goals and Challenges

Even if the unit cost of reliable detectors and monitors decreases substantially, the number required to cover the entire transportation network in fixed distributed configurations may still be prohibitively large unless a supporting logistics analysis can identify cost-effective placement strategies. Thus, both cost-reduction advancements and logistics analyses are needed.

Rationale for the Research and Desired Results

This research targets physical and cyber *intrusion detection,* attack and failure prevention, and *incident management* for scenarios that have either produced incidents or amply demonstrated feasibility. Thus, it is highly probable that this technology will not be available within the next 2-10 years.

Timeframe and Resource Requirements

In the near term (before 2002), researchers would ensure that applied R&D is under contract. Initial development of detection devices would be under way. Funding required for these efforts is estimated to be $8 million. Before 2005, researchers would complete the prototype testing of the detection devices in six to eight parallel studies. Funding required for this effort is estimated to be $12 million. Increases in system capability and flexibility would continue through public-private partnerships. Before 2010, researchers would be in a position to commercialize the public-private ventures. The cost for this work is estimated to be $12 million.

3.2.2 Robotics Development and Adaptation

Description

In the aftermath of a physical attack, especially in large, semipublic spaces (e.g., terminals, transit centers), it may be hazardous for responders to intervene directly at or near the site. Applied research and some basic research are needed to identify and develop robotic technologies and remotely controlled servo modules capable of assessing damage. which usually is done by first responders. As a first step, existing DoD technologies should be investigated to determine if they are adaptable for this purpose.

Goals and Challenges

There is a need to tailor and deploy applications that can protect responders, assist victims, and expedite recovery without significant delay. The most effective means of assuring such deployment is to conduct pilot studies early in the project (i.e., involve highly likely locations, such as mass transit stations). Test scenarios for such a pilot study should be constructed pursuant to information collected for Transit Cooperative Research Program Synthesis Report No. 27, *Emergency Preparedness for Transit Terrorism* (Transportation Research Board 1997).

Rationale for the Research and Desired Results

This research targets incident management and, to a lesser degree, functional recovery to provide a required comprehensiveness of response and real-time remediation capability not currently available for many attack scenarios.

Timeframe and Resource Requirements

In the near term (before 2002), researchers would develop and adapt robotic technology for remotely controlled modules to be used in situations in which first responders face dangerous hazards. Funding required for these efforts is estimated to be $5 million. Before 2005, researchers would complete the prototype testing of the remotely controlled modules. Funding required for this effort is estimated to be $7 million. Before 2010, researchers would be in a position to commercialize public-private ventures.

3.2.3 Improvement of In-use Performance and Replacement Functionality of Transportation Structures

Description

In the aftermath of physical attack, especially involving geographically isolated, but important, load-bearing structures (e.g., bridges, trestles, tunnels), it may be critical to bring the severed distribution link back into service in a fraction of the time normally required to provide temporary repairs. Strategic, simultaneous removal of key structures at multiple interchanges or at places where essential road and rail links are proximate could trigger a dangerous, if short-term, disruption of national commodity flow. Applied research with proof of principle is needed to understand the strength and durability of advanced, inexpensive, lightweight materials to provide modularity, portability, and performance safety for the various infrastructures. These attributes are currently not available except possibly for military application.

It is also important to understand performance safety of various infrastructures currently in place. As a first step, the adaptability of existing DoD technologies, as well as those of other agencies and organizations for which deployment of temporary structures is integral to their mission, would be investigated. In conjunction with this research, it also would be prudent to perform logistics analyses to define the optimal positions for stationing outage-response teams and materials. A broader, longer-term goal of this effort, in the context of recovery from incidents, would be to assemble a comprehensive disaster-recovery manual of practice. Such a manual also would be developed in conjunction with the computer emergency response topic discussed in Section 3.4.5.

Goals and Challenges

Advanced materials need to be matched with specific structural replacement requirements across multiple modes and missions. Reliable longevity of assets in place and their ability to withstand and mitigate physical attack are equally important objectives. In addition, structural modules would be located so as to minimize the total deployment time to locations where links are severed.

Rationale for the Research and Desired Results

The research targets functional recovery, which is clearly hampered by delays in restoring service to critical physical links. Functional durability (i.e., mitigation, recovery) is also targeted, but not all needs are known.

Timeframe and Resource Requirements

In the near term (before 2002), researchers would develop and adapt materials to maximize modularity, portability, and /or durability of the function of permanent and temporary structures within the transportation system. Funding required for these efforts is estimated to be $5 million. Before 2005, researchers would complete field testing of up to five applications. Funding required for this effort is estimated to be $7 million. Before 2010, the goal would be to commercialize these structures.

3.2.4 Unified Vehicle/Guideway Systems (Hardening)

Description

Advances in transportation technology, especially in intelligent transportation systems (ITSs), automated highway systems (AHSs), and magnetic levitation, would increase the integration of vehicles and the guideways on which they travel (the so-called "intelligent vehicle infrastructure"). Such integrated systems could become more vulnerable to both physical and cyber attack, but preservation of their structural integrity would be essential to their protection in both senses. To that end, surface transportation experts need to enhance the blast resistance of aircraft (possibly by reviewing R&D plans from the Federal Aviation Administration). They also need to conduct applied research in damage-tolerant design for fixed guideways and other fixed structures.

Goals and Challenges

The specific threats for which the need exists (the threats would differ among modes and applications) must be identified. Advances in materials technologies need to be linked to a systematic improvement in guideway system equipment and structural durability.

Rationale for the Research and Desired Results

This research targets incident mitigation with respect to transport concepts emerging as actual hardware, but for which many risks are currently unknown and need to be anticipated.

Timeframe and Resource Requirements

In the near term (before 2002), researchers would plan to complete scoping studies of materials technology needed to improve the durability and resistance to damage from physical and cyber attacks on transportation systems. Funding required for these efforts is estimated to be $2 million. Before 2005, researchers would develop prototypes to improve the durability of transport systems. Funding required for this effort is estimated to be $7 million. Before 2010, the goal would be to commercialize this technology.

3.3 Development/Adaptation of Monitoring, Detection, Mitigation, and Incident Response Software

3.3.1 Asset Management

Description

In a broader context than that of security maintenance, operating executives need to be able to manage network-configured physical and cyber assets in the most productive manner possible to maintain competitiveness and use passenger—and freight-carrying equipment in the best way possible. Understanding and instituting these principles would provide the foundation for successful security assurance structures.

Goals and Challenges

The capability for quantitatively defining and identifying the most efficient use of resources is not uniform across all transportation modes and not well demonstrated in the field. Development is continuing in flaw detection hardware and software. Appropriate decision analysis support tools also are in the development stage. This research spans all action areas.

Rationale for the Research and Desired Results

Specially tailored hardware and software needs cannot be met at the current level of operation-specific knowledge.

Timeframe and Resource Requirements

In the near term (before 2002), researchers would conduct scoping studies of how to make the most efficient use of physical and cyber resources.

Funding required for these efforts is estimated to be $1 million. Before 2005, researchers would validate and peer review prototype tools for decision analysis support. Funding required for this effort is estimated to be $2 million. Before 2010, the goal would be to commercialize this technology. Funding required for this effort is estimated to be $1 million.

3.3.2 System Representation Improvement

Description

One way or another, formatted data applications cut across all research categories in this document. Because such data are stored and processed through electronic media, database development needs are included here. Data are now available in both publicly accessible and privately controlled media, but only a fraction of the content has been systematically collated to enhance and inform emergency response. Much more data may need to be collected and usefully transcribed to an accessible visual medium—for example, geographic information systems (GISs). These data structures are critical to a more thorough understanding of physical vulnerabilities in the transportation infrastructure.

This topic is tied closely with infrastructure management because the representational capability envisioned involves the entire process, not simply the overlying (and underlying) physical phenomena. Thus, the comprehensible representation of data on system performance (e.g., capacity, speed, cost, connections, restrictions, ownership) is as important as, or equal to, that on location and configuration of public and private distribution channels and other hardware. Successful translation and adaptation of data on comprehensive system process characteristics would be the signal contribution of this undertaking.

Goals and Challenges

Researchers would maximize the amount of useful data that can be collated into clear, comprehensible formats for visual display in a manner that improves the understanding of interconnected and dependent systems and enhances the real-time, in-situ capabilities of incident responders and managers. A pilot study with direct private-sector participation and public-private interactions is essential to the ultimate acceptance of research results. Such a study would influence database development at an early stage by populating the data of series with systems data of direct relevance to the needs of ultimate end users.

Rationale for the Research and Desired Results

Technology development and proof of principle would be targeted at all action areas, but especially at awareness training, incident mitigation, and incident management. The technology and many of the capabilities exist;

the challenge is to adapt and adopt them to these action areas in the most useful and complete manner.

Timeframe and Resource Requirements

In the near term (before 2002), requirements would be defined and development contracts awarded to at least two teams by the end of 2000. Methods for managing transport system data in a clear format would be improved. Funding required for these efforts is estimated to be $20 million. Before 2005, in addition to integrating the database, researchers would complete testing and validation of a regional prototype suite of tools. Funding required for this effort is estimated to be $30 million. Before 2010, researchers would implement multiple applications, with full U.S. coverage assumed. Funding required for this effort is estimated to be $20 million.

3.3.3 Intrusion Detection

Description

On-line software (such as a real-time firewall) is needed to detect and automatically invoke countermeasures to cyber intrusions in day-to-day electronic transaction and control processes. The ability of this technology to forecast and detect such incursions, for nonmilitary applications, is generally in its infancy. Because of the significant quantity and diversity of electronic data interchanges that occur across transportation operations on a daily basis, this sector is vulnerable. Pilot studies, in particular with transportation clients, are strongly recommended.

Goals and Challenges

Researchers should adapt current capabilities in this area, including Computer Emergency Response Teams and incident response activities under development by DoD, the National Aeronautic and Space Administration, the U.S. Department of Energy, and others. Adaptation would occur first in transport operation data flow systems and then in identification and completion of knowledge and performance gaps. Direct integration with the U.S. Coast Guard's Computer Incident Response Team is a possibility.

Rationale for the Research and Desired Results

Technology development and proof of principle would target intrusion and attack prevention. It is believed that the technology and many of the capabilities exist; the challenge is to adapt and adopt them to these action areas in the most useful and complete manner.

Timeframe and Resource Requirements

In the near term (before 2002), researchers would define requirements and award contracts to customize intrusion detection systems for the transportation infrastructure. Funding required for these efforts is estimated to be $4 million. Before 2005, researchers would complete the design and testing of systems and begin to implement multiple applications. Funding required for this effort is estimated to be $6 million. Before 2010, intrusion detection for physical and cyber assets would be commercialized. Funding required for this effort is estimated to be $1 million.

3.3.4 Cyber Vulnerability Data Warehouse

Description

Because of the diversity of computer systems and networks used throughout the transportation sector, models of their functions and interdependencies need to be constructed. Moreover, a comprehensive database of known cyber vulnerabilities specific to these systems needs to be developed. Both objectives could be served by establishing a data vulnerability clearinghouse, possibly modeled after one at Carnegie-Mellon University. This clearinghouse would contain the details of hardware, software, and communication components of existing and emerging systems. Through this mechanism, owners of vulnerable data repositories and networks could be notified early of a potential cyber incursion, as well as have a real-time channel to the latest information on firewalls and other security practices.

Goals and Challenges

Development teams must craft within a single facility a combined reference and proactive response capability that meet a wide variety of computer support and security needs across all transportation operations.

Rationale for the Research and Desired Results

Proof of principle would target intrusion and attack prevention. It is believed that the technology and many of the capabilities exist; the challenge is to adopt them, while adapting them to these action areas in the most useful and complete manner.

Timeframe and Resource Requirements

In the near term (before 2002), researchers would define requirements and award contracts for an integrated facility that would provide intelligence concerning physical and cyber threats to the transportation system. Funding required for these efforts is estimated to be $1 million. Before 2005, researchers would complete a fully functional facility. Funding required for this effort is estimated to be $1 million.

3.3.5 Threat/Intelligence Database and Network

Description

The function described here would be closely integrated with that described in Section 3.3.4 (Cyber Vulnerability Data Warehouse). However, the emphasis would be on developing and disseminating intelligence in regard to specific terrorist plots for destroying physical infrastructure and malicious hacking (computer terrorism) directed at transportation functions. Activities could be modeled on, and directly coordinated with, those of the National Infrastructure Protection Center to be operated by the Federal Bureau of Investigation (FBI). This topic and the cyber vulnerability data warehouse topic could be consolidated if an interagency agreement was drafted to create a comprehensive clearinghouse under the aegis of a Transportation Infrastructure Protection Threat Analysis Center.

Goals and Challenges

Early warning information and intelligence channels exist, especially for mass transit and aircraft operations. Proof of principle requires broadening and examining the scope in depth to embrace all transportation infrastructures. An office of the U.S. Department of Justice or the FBI probably would lead the networking effort to develop data, supported by multiple public- and private-sector organizations.

Rationale for the Research and Desired Results

Proof of principle and validation target intrusion and attack prevention. It is believed that many of the necessary capabilities exist. The challenge is to adopt them, while adapting them to these action areas in the most useful and complete manner.

Timeframe and Resource Requirements

In the near term (before 2002), researchers would define requirements and award contracts for an integrated facility for providing intelligence in regard to threats. Funding required for these efforts is estimated to be $1 million. Before 2005, researchers would complete a fully functional clearinghouse. Funding required for this effort is estimated to be $2 million.

3.4 Information Assurance, Human Factors, and Institutional Effects in Preparedness and Response

3.4.1 Information Assurance

Description

Artificial-intelligence (AI)-based technologies can be used to ensure that a near-zero probability exists that electronic information and data flows that are degrading or corrupted (because of component failure or instability) would not be detected. Message encryption techniques are more sophisticated and able to thwart most hostile interception and decoding efforts. These capabilities are needed in the transportation infrastructure, but additional research could be required to define the most suitable approach for specific applications.

Goals and Challenges

Researchers would adapt information security capabilities available from DoD and other lead federal agencies to transportation data flow systems. Once these capabilities are adapted for the transportation infrastructure, researchers would identify and fill knowledge and performance gaps.

Rationale for the Research and Desired Results

Applied technology development is needed to support incident mitigation in a cyber context. Many of the capabilities exist: the challenge is to adopt these capabilities while adapting them to transportation operations in the most useful and complete manner.

Timeframe and Resource Requirements

In the near term (before 2000), requirements should be defined and utilization of existing tools well advanced. Funding required for this effort is estimated to be $2 million. Before 2005, design and testing should be completed, and tools should be ready for field implementation. Funding required for this effort is estimated to be $3 million. Before 2010, the AI-based technologies would be implemented and commercialized at an estimated cost of $1 million.

3.4.2 Software Assurance

Description

Artificial-intelligence based technologies can limit to near zero the probability that purpose-based software installed in critical day-to-day information handling systems would deteriorate without detection and remedy. Further development of on-line fault checking and self-diagnostic capability of software is needed.

Goals and Challenges

The continuous, reliable performance of network control-related software, whatever the nature of the operational command and control structure, must be ensured, and there must be no degradation without diagnosis.

Rationale for the Research and Desired Results

Applied research and technology development is needed to support cyber incident detection and mitigation. Some operational needs may not be met by existing capabilities.

Timeframe and Resource Requirements

In the near term (before 2002), researchers would define requirements and use existing tools to develop AI-based technologies to ensure, to the degree possible, the security of electronic information and data flows. Funding required for these efforts is estimated to be $2 million. Before 2005, researchers would complete the design and testing of these new tools. Funding required for this effort is estimated to be $3 million. Before 2010, AI-based technologies would be implemented and commercialized. Funding required for this effort is estimated to be $1 million.

3.4.3 Human Factors Analysis

Description

Humans always must be "in the loop" in all efforts to minimize (1) vulnerabilities, through predicting and evading dangerous physical and cyber incidents, and (2) negative consequences when such incidents occur. For the transportation infrastructure, it is important to know if experience has shown that the human role is uniformly beneficial (especially if fully automated alternatives exist). If the human role is not totally beneficial, researchers need to determine what training, education, and sensitivity conditioning would increase the likelihood of beneficial human intervention.

Goals and Challenges

Researchers must characterize actual problems and limitations in event prediction and response that are specifically attributable to human factors so that solutions to these shortcomings can be found. Conversely, they need to avoid bringing canned theories into play in search of human factor remediation "needs" (i.e., to discover rather than to apply).

Rationale for the Research and Desired Results

Applied research is needed to support all five action areas, but especially vulnerability assessment, incident mitigation, and incident management. A major effort is needed to develop information packages and training programs for operating authorities. A newly developed training regimen would incorporate the accepted cycle of identifying requirement analyses (e.g., task, organization, person within each structure), with task-based determination of the associated knowledge, skill, and abilities (KSAs). These steps would then be followed by instructional objectives tailored to instill each set of KSAs.

Timeframe and Resource Requirements

In the near term (before 2002), researchers would characterize problems and limitations inherent in human preparedness, prediction, and response. Funding required for this effort is estimated to be $6 million. Before 2005, researchers would fully identify and implement changes for preparedness and prediction. Funding required for this effort is estimated to be $4 million.

3.4.4 Recovery Training

Description

Understanding of "triage" decision processes and other essentials of emergency management is not normally incorporated into the training of individuals for high levels of control responsibility in transportation operations. The best techniques and principles for communicating such understanding have not been identified. The optimization tools developed under Category 1 projects should be incorporated into a training and awareness program tailored to each mode of operation and control organizational structure.

Goals and Challenges

Many recent methodological advancements, including those from dynamic traffic assignment theory, need to be used in educating key managers about the essentials of response and recovery.

Rationale for the Research and Desired Results

Applied research is needed to develop training for incident management and functional recovery. A major effort may be required to prepare information packages and training programs for all operating authorities. Development of the training regimen should incorporate the accepted cycle of identifying requirement analyses (e.g., task, organization, person within each structure), with task-based determination of the associated KSAs, followed by instructional objectives tailored to instill each set of KSAs.

Timeframe and Resource Requirements

In the near term (before 2002), researchers would implement a contract for developing a training program for recovery from an incident involving the transportation infrastructure. Funding required for this effort is estimated to be $1 million. Before 2005, researchers would fully implement the program at an estimated cost of $2 million, and before 2010, continue the training program at an estimated cost of $1 million.

3.4.5 Computer Emergency Response and Emergency Response and Recovery Assessment Capacity Building

Description

Lessons learned from real emergencies, especially those that disrupt the transportation infrastructure, are generally anecdotal and not systematically categorized. Little, if any, formalized economic impact analysis has been performed to determine the costs and benefits associated with various degrees of emergency preparedness. Trained teams are not available on a continuous or standby basis to collect and disseminate information about (1) the effects of, and mitigation strategies for, computer emergencies or (2) the human factors in responding to an actual emergency and how appropriate measures may be facilitated or hindered by them.

The establishment of a team modeled on, for example, the Computer Emergency Response Team at Carnegie-Mellon University, would provide the needed readiness for the first contingency, while multiple teams, each responsible for a specific geographic region, would deal with the second type. The latter organizations, collectively termed Emergency Response and Recovery Assessment Teams, would conduct interviews, develop chronologies, and generally identify cause and effect and *do's* and *don'ts* in unfolding emergencies. Their ultimate responsibility would be to uncover and formalize the entire body of knowledge of "best practice" in emergency response and recovery actions, especially actions pursuant to attacks on the physical and cyber infrastructure.

Goals and Challenges

Resources, motivation, and efficiency are needed for planning for persons who respond to emergencies. Trained, capable study groups must "stand by" for rapid deployment into the field if a significant emergency occurs.

Rationale for the Research and Desired Results

Applied research is needed to develop an extensive body of knowledge about the best way to accomplish—as well as how *not* to execute—incident management and functional recovery in real time. The outcome would include (1) training tools and programs for emergency responders and (2) identification of technology and coordination needs, with special emphasis on transportation incidents. Development of training must incorporate the accepted cycle of identifying requirement analyses (e.g., task, organization, person within each structure), with task-based determination of the associated KSAs, followed by instructional objectives tailored to instill each set of KSAs.

Timeframe and Resource Requirements

In the near term (before 2002), researchers would define the requirements and procedures needed for developing training materials for emergency responders. Research contracts also would be developed. Funding required for these efforts is estimated to be $3 million. Before 2005, trained teams would be deployed to stand by at strategic locations. Funding required for this effort is estimated at $5 million. Before 2010, and active information exchange would be introduced and procedures would be revised as needed. Funding required for this effort is estimated at $3 million.

3.4.6 Public/Private Infrastructure Security Responsibility

Description

This topic highlights how critical the transportation infrastructure is as a national asset. This importance transcends ownership, which, if true, means that governmental bodies in the United States, especially the federal government, must assume more direct financial and oversight responsibility to assure its security.

Most private operators maintain that they are fully and independently capable of managing their own security, that is, until some hostile incident precipitated by an outside force beyond their control disrupts functionality and, by extension, the movement of goods and people. This issue is predominantly one of policy, but it also requires analysis of jurisdictions and legal structures to clarify (1) command and decision chains for mitigating incidents and (2) management responsibilities in such situations.

Goals and Challenges

In strategic planning, the U.S. Department of Transportation is committed to meeting this objective, and the agency may support research to identify ways to deploy coordinated public and private capabilities in an optimal manner. A unique study approach *may* be required for each control and modal configuration; therefore, six to eight different teams should be involved.

Rationale for the Research and Desired Results

Formalizing of, and agreement to, a set of principles is needed. Doing so would define the foundation on which all structures for enhancing capabilities (in each of the five action areas) would be built.

Timeframe and Resource Requirements

In the near term (before 2002), scoping conferences would be conducted, requests for proposals issued, and project teams selected. Funding required for this effort is estimated to be $2 million. Before 2005, legislation would be proposed (as needed).

Section 4
R&D Topic Roadmaps

This section describes an appropriate roadmap for meeting the 21 research needs identified in Section 3 and summarized in Table D.1. It identifies chronological and complementary links among projects that need to be incorporated into any action plan.

4.1 Vulnerability Analysis of Existing Systems

The goal is to identify (and ultimately mitigate) possibly unrecognized vulnerable pathways in systems with a high degree of centralized command and control and/or open architectures for transmission of electronic information. The objective of applied research is to identify, for up to five typical organization types across transportation operations, significant vulnerabilities that can exist as a function of the communications architecture and control system in place. Research activities should begin as soon as possible after 2002. This topic is interrelated with Topics 2 through 4 and will inform Topics 5, 7, 11, and 16-19. (See figure for explanation of topic numbers, i.e., descriptions.)

4.2 Simulation Tool Development

The goal is to provide a suite of event prediction and management tools that decision makers can use in a gaming framework to (1) shape the construction of preparedness plans for physical and cyber threats, actual attacks, and optimal use of resources; (2) assure continuity of flows in the distribution system; (3) significantly improve the productivity of existing infrastructure; (4) assist in automating decision support systems; and (5) reveal trade-offs among productivity, service reliability, and preparedness for rare events.

The objective of basic and applied research and advanced technology development is to capture and accurately model within the simulation structure all relevant contingencies for each area and mode of transportation, and to enable accurate, detailed modeling of different control hierarchies and the response of system disruptions to these hierarchies. Research activities should be undertaken as soon as practicable, but no later than 2001 because these tools are needed in calendar year 2006; by that time, the United States may be experiencing a "Golden Age" of seamless, multimodal, door-to-door transportation. This topic is interrelated with Topics 1, 3–5, 11, 18, and 19.

4.3 Determination of Risk Perception of Transport System Managers

The goal is to identify and formalize quantitative measures that capture the important characteristics of risk perception at all appropriate decision levels. The objective of basic and applied research is to understand these characteristics across all modes and to inform researchers that construct simulation and training tools. Research activities should be undertaken as soon as practicable, concurrent with the development of the simulation tools to be available after 2002. This topic precedes Topic 4 and is interrelated with Topics 1, 2, 5, 11, 18, and 19.

4.4 Communication and Inculcation of Sound Risk Management Principles

The primary goal is develop an information and training package about risk, with tools systematically designed for each type and level of control hierarchy. The users are operating authorities in all modes. A second key goal is to institutionalize the principle that daily vulnerability management is a necessary part of normal operation. The objectives of applied technology development are therefore to (1) communicate the nature and magnitude of security risk to decision makers via language and technologies that maximize the transmission of useful, comprehensible information at all appropriate levels; and (2) to prove the principle of vulnerability management in day-to-day practice.

This project would bring relevant aspects of developments in distance learning and training (e.g., via the Internet) into the workplace. Advanced technology development and proof of principle inculcate a physical and cyber security awareness mindset at all levels of operation by tailoring education and training to each worker task, scope of responsibility, and level of education.

Training needs are to be defined and training programs under contract by the end of 2000. Training and support activities are to be under way by the end of 2003, subsequent to development of the simulation described in Topics 1 and 2 and concurrent with, and indirectly related to, activities in Topics 5 and 11. Adoption of principles and practices should begin no later than about 2004. This topic follows Topic 3 and is interrelated with Topics 1, 2, 11, 18, and 19.

4.5 Capacity Margin Analysis

The goal is to develop reliable quantitative estimates of the expected losses from contingencies that arise in the absence of surplus carrying capacity in each component of the transportation system. The objective is to identify an appropriate and necessary level of "surplus" capacity over which federal, state, and/or local governments assume responsibility for maintenance or direct support if they are not economic assets to the owner. Research activities should be undertaken as soon as practicable but will be influenced by the results of research from Topics 1-3; effort could be completed by the end of 2005. This topic is related to Topics 1-4, 11, 18, 19, and 21.

4.6 Emergency Communications

The goal is to identify (and ultimately implement) the secure systems solutions most appropriate for responses to disruptions of transportation infrastructure. The objective is to provide a head start for product development in the area of fully functional and secure emergency response communications. Research activities are under way, but they should be continued or expanded through 2003. This topic is related to Topics 8, 12, 15, 16, 18, and 19.

4.7 Real-time Hazard, Threat, and Detection Monitoring

The goal is to reduce both unit and deployment costs of detection devices, including those with high-resolution broadband capability. Development for transportation applications is at a relatively early stage in this area. Basic and applied research, followed by advanced technology development and proof of principle and validation, is targeted at preventing physical and cyber intrusion and attack.

Physical (and some cyber) incursions have already occurred, demonstrating the existence of willingness and capability to carry out such incursions. Research and development activities should be undertaken as soon as feasible after 1999, with six to eight parallel analyses being completed by the end of 2005, and public-private partnerships in place (and increasing in number) also by that time. This topic is related to Topics 1, 8, 10, 12-14, 16, and 17.

4.8 Robotics Development and Adaptation

The goal is to identify and develop robotic technologies and remotely controlled servo modules capable of performing the damage assessment duties of first responders without their direct physical intervention. Basic and applied research should be performed to investigate the adaptability of technologies developed and used by DoD and other lead agencies, to identify unmet needs, and to tailor development of the applications to efficient and thorough recovery operations that assist victims and protect responders. A needs assessment and concept development should begin as soon as feasible after 1999; prototype development should be completed by the end of 2005, with public-private partnerships increasing thereafter. This topic is related to Topics 6, 7, 12, 15, 19, and 20.

4.9 Improvement of In-use Performance and Replacement Functionality of Transportation Structures

The goal is to understand the strength and durability of advanced, inexpensive, lightweight materials for permanent and temporary replacement structures that will enable a modularity, portability, and/or durability of function (while meeting high performance standards) generally not available to transportation operations, except in military applications. Basic research should be performed to investigate the adaptability of DoD technologies, identify unmet needs, and apply proof of principle by matching advanced materials with specific structural replacement needs across multiple modes and missions.

Applied research would be conducted to identify and develop materials to meet functional durability needs for maximizing longevity of assets. Needs assessment and capabilities matching should begin as soon as feasible after 1999, with field tests of competing designs in up to five applications completed by the end of 2005 and commercialization of modular components in place by the end of 2007. This topic is directly related to Topics 5, 10, 19, and 20.

4.10 Unified Vehicle/Guideway Systems (Hardening)

The goal is to enhance resistance to damage from physical and cyber attacks on existing and emerging transportation infrastructures in which the vehicle and guideway constitute integrated systems. The objective of applied research is to identify needs and adapt materials technologies to the systematic improvement of durability in guideway equipment and structures.

Spin-off applications of hardening and other durability improvements to more general types of equipment and structures (e.g., bridges, buildings) are an expected ancillary benefit of this research. Scoping studies should begin in 2000, and research should be under contract to multiple entities by the end of 2001. Comprehensive threat characterization and design of prototypes should be completed by 2008, with field tests, standards definition, commercialization, and some system implementation well under way by 2010. This topic is related to Topics 7, 9, 19, and 20.

4.11 Asset Management

The goal is to define and/or identify reliable quantitative measures to enable each mode and operation to generate plans and programs to use assets that most efficiently use physical and cyber resources. Applied and advanced technology development research address such problems as flaw detection and decision analysis support. The objective is to inculcate globally optimal management principles across all modes.

Requirements should be defined in 2000 and at least two teams awarded development contracts. Database integration and validation testing of a regional/modal prototype set of management tools should be completed by the end of 2005, with direct applications increasing thereafter, at least through 2007. This topic is directly related to Topics 1-5, 9, 10, 12, 14-18, and 21.

4.12 System Representation Improvement

The goal is to maximize the amount of useful data currently available but still in need of transcription into a visual display, that is, collated into clearly comprehensible formats. The objective of advanced technology development and proof of principle and validation for this topic is to improve understanding of interconnected and dependent systems. Knowledge about the structural layouts and strategic organization of such systems is critical for preparing for, and responding to physical and cyber attack.

Requirements should be defined in 2000 and at least two teams awarded development contracts. Database integration and validation testing of a regional prototype set of visual display tools should be completed by the end of 2005, with direct applications increasing thereafter, at least through 2007. This topic is related to Topics 6-8, 13, 14, and 18-20.

4.13 Intrusion Detection

The goal is to upgrade the prevention measures for physical and cyber intrusion and attacks. Because it is believed that the technology and many of the capabilities exist, the objective of advanced technology development and proof of principle and validation for this topic is to adopt and adapt them for action areas in transportation operations, filling in knowledge and performance gaps as completely as possible.

Requirements should be defined in 2000 and development contracts awarded. Design and testing of tools should be completed by the end of 2005, with field implementation thereafter. This topic is related to Topics 7, 12, 14, 16, and 17.

4.14 Cyber Vulnerability Data Warehouse

The goal is to provide access to early warning notification of potential cyber incursion, as well as a real-time channel to the latest information on firewalls and other security practices, to the owners of vulnerable data repositories and networks in the transportation sector. Within a single facility, development teams must craft a combined reference and proactive response capability that meets a wide variety of computer support and security needs across all transportation operations.

Requirements should be defined and development contracts awarded by the end of 2000. The database should be completed and the protocols for access and use of the warehouse should be in place by the end of 2005. This topic is related to Topics 11-13, 15-17, and 19.

4.15 Threat/Intelligence Database and Network

The goal is to craft an efficient, fully integrated facility to develop and disseminate intelligence in regard to specific terrorist plots for destroying physical infrastructure or maliciously "hacking" into transportation functions (computer terrorism). Activities could be modeled on, and directly coordinated with, those of the FBI's National Infrastructure Protection Center. This topic and Topic 14 (discussed above) could be consolidated if an interagency agreement was in place to create a comprehensive clearinghouse under the aegis of a Transportation Infrastructure Protection Threat Analysis Center. Proof of principle and validation require a broadening and deepening of the scope of existing intelligence networks to embrace all transportation infrastructures.

Requirements should be defined and data development contracts awarded by the end of 2000. The clearinghouse should be fully functional by the end of 2005. This topic is related to Topics 6, 8, 11, and 14.

4.16 Information Assurance

The goal is to identify and implement the most appropriate AI-based technologies for preventing acceptance of unintentionally corrupted or maliciously erroneous electronic information in the various transportation operations. Because the technology and many of the capabilities exist, the objective of applied technology development for this topic is to adopt these capabilities while adapting them to specific needs for message continuity and integrity in transport operations, thereby filling knowledge and performance gaps.

Requirements should be defined and use of existing tools well advanced by the end of 2000. Design and testing should be completed, and tools should be ready for field implementation by the end of 2005, with deployment increasing thereafter. This topic is related to Topics 1, 6, 7, 11, 13, 14, and 17.

4.17 Software Assurance

The goal is to identify and implement the most appropriate AI-based technologies for on-line fault checking and self-diagnosis in critical day-to-day information-handling systems for transportation. Applied technology development is needed to support cyber-incident mitigation.

Requirements should be defined and teams under contract by the end of 2000. Design and testing of customized tools should be completed, and tools should be ready for field implementation by the end of 2005. This topic is related to Topics 1, 6, 7, 11, 13, 14, and 16.

4.18 Human Factors Analysis

The goal is to characterize the problems and limitations in event preparedness, prediction, and response that are specifically attributable to the human role in the operation and maintenance of transportation systems. In particular, applied research is needed to identify and quantify these problems and limitations in vulnerability assessment, incident mitigation, and incident management. The objective is to develop information packages and training programs applicable to a wide range of operations and authorities.

Requirements should be defined and teams under contract by the end of 2000. New and modified procedures, tools, and control systems should be in the demonstration and training phases by the end of 2005. This topic is related to Topics 1-5, 11, 12, 19, and 20.

4.19 Recovery Training

The goal is to bring many methodological advancements, including those from dynamic traffic assignment theory, to educate key managers at all relevant levels about the essential components of response and recovery as appropriate to their respective and collective operations. The goal of applied research into training needs for incident management and functional recovery training would be to develop packages that would maximize communication to, and endorsement by, all operating authorities.

Training needs should be defined and training programs should be under contract by the end of 2000. Training should take place across all operations no later than 2005. This topic is related to Topics 1-6, 8-10, 12, 14, 18, and 20.

4.20 Computer Emergency Response and Emergency Response and Recovery Assessment Capacity Building

The goal is to develop and formalize an extensive body of knowledge about the best way to accomplish—and, conversely, how *not* to execute—incident management and functional recovery in real time. The recommended applied research method involves maintaining trained, capable study groups in "stand-by" mode for rapid deployment into the field if a significant emergency occurs. This practice would enable systematic recording and documentation of specific actions and events or dissemination of necessary information. The objective of the research is to develop training programs for emergency responders, with special emphasis on transportation infrastructures and incidents.

Data needs and collection procedures should be defined and training programs should be under contract by the end of 2000. Sets of trained teams would then be deployed in stand by mode for two to four years thereafter, with information and training dispersal occurring widely across all operations no later than 2008. This topic is related to Topics 8-10 and 12-14.

4.21 Public/Private Infrastructure Security Responsibility

The goal is to formalize an agreed-upon set of principles that define the foundation and governing of the mechanisms for enhancing capabilities to protect physical and cyber components of the transportation infrastructure. The objective is to analyze jurisdictions and legal structures to clarify command and decision chains for incident mitigation and situation management. Proof of principle and validation would focus on optimal deployment of public and private capabilities for mutual reinforcement across all relevant control structures and modal operations.

Scoping conferences should be conducted, and six to eight research teams should be selected in 2000, with research recommendations submitted in 2002 and any necessary legislation proposed no later than 2005. This topic is related directly to Topics 5 and 11, but it crosscuts all action areas and therefore is indirectly related to all topics.

4.22 Crosswalks and Milestones

Figure D.1 classifies the topics by action area and interrelationships. Each R&D topic is assigned a row and/or column. By reading across each row or down each column, it is possible to see how that a specific topic area is related to other topic areas in one or more of the five action areas (Section 2). For example, R&D Topic 1, Vulnerability Analysis of Existing Systems (column 1), is related to Simulation Tool Development, Determination of Risk Perception of Transport System Managers, and Communication and Inculcation of Sound Risk Management Principles through the Awareness Training action area.

Further, Topic 1 is related to Capacity Margin Analysis through the Incident Mitigation and Incident Management areas; to Real-Time Hazards, Threat, and Detection Monitoring, Information Assurance, and Software Assurance through Intrusion and Attack Prevention and Incident Management; to Human Factors Analysis through Awareness, Mitigation, and Management (three areas); and to Recovery Training through Incident Management and Functional Recovery. This topics relationships to Asset Management and Public/Private Responsibility cut across all action areas.

Table D.2 shows the milestones that the study team agreed on as being achievable for each R&D topic up to 2010.

	1	2	3	4	5	6	7	8	9	10	11	12	13	14	15	16	17	18	19	20	21
2	A																				
3	A	A																			
4	A	A	A																		
5	Mi,Ma	Mi,Ma	Mi,Ma	Mi,Ma																	
6																					
7	P, Ma																				
8						Ma, R	P														
9					P, Ma																
10							P, Mi		Mi, R												
11	X	X	X	X	X	X	X	X	X	X											
12						Mi,Ma	P, Mi,Ma	Ma			X										
13							P				X	P, Mi									
14											X	P, Mi	P, Mi								
15						P, Mi,Ma		Ma, R			X			P, Mi							
16	P, Ma					Mi	P, Mi				X		P, Mi	P, Mi							
17	P, Ma					P, Mi	P, Mi				X		P, Mi	P, Mi		P, Mi					
18	A,Mi, Ma	A,Mi, Ma	A,Mi, Ma	A,Mi, Ma	A,Mi, Ma	A,Mi, Ma					X	A,Mi, Ma									
19	Ma, R	Ma, R	Ma, R	Ma, R	Mi,Ma R	Ma, R		Ma, R	Ma, R	Ma, R	X	Ma, R		Ma, R				Ma, R			
20								Ma, R	Ma, R	Ma, R	X	Ma, R						Ma, R	Ma, R		
21	X	X	X	X	X : Mi,Ma	X	X	X	X	X	X	X	X	X	X	X	X	X	X	X	

A = Awareness training
P = Intrusion and attack prevention
Mi = Incident mitigation
Ma = Incident management
R = Functional recovery
X = Crosses all action areas

Figure D.1 Topical Interrelationships by Action Area[a]

[a]Numbering Key for Figure D.1

No.	Description of R&D Topic
1	Vulnerability Analysis of Existing Systems
2	Simulation Tool Development
3	Determination of Risk Perception of Transport System Managers
4	Communication and Inculcation of Sound Risk Management Principles
5	Capacity Margin Analysis
6	Emergency Communications
7	Real-time Hazard, Threat, and Adaptation
8	Robotics Development and Adaptation
9	Improvement of In-use Performance and Replacement Functionality of Transportation Structures
10	Unified Vehicle/Guideway Systems (Hardening)
11	Asset Management
12	System Representation Improvement
13	Intrusion Detection
14	Cyber Vulnerability Data Warehouse
15	Threat/Intelligence Database and Network
16	Information Assurance
17	Software Assurance
18	Human Factors Analysis
19	Recovery Training
20	Computer Emergency Response and Emergency Response and Recovery Assessment Capacity Building
21	Public/Private Infrastructure Security Responsibility

Table D.2 Summary of Transportation R&D Roadmap

R&D Topic				
No.	Title	Near Term (Resource Estimate[a])	Achieved by ~2005 (Resource Estimate[a])	Achieved by ~2010 (Resource Estimate[a])
1	Vulnerability Analysis of Existing Systems	Conduct pilot studies of actual operations. ($9 million)	Develop assessment tools. ($9 million)	Complete assessments of transportation systems. ($6 million)
2	Simulation Tool Development	Identify and evaluate ways to create tools that can be used in event prediction and management ($15 million)	Develop and validate basic tools. ($15 million)	Validate and deploy completed model suite. ($5 million)
3	Determination of Risk Perception of Transport System Managers	Conduct scoping. ($2 million)	Complete analyses. ($1 million)	Update as required.
4	Communication and Inculcation of Sound Risk Management Principles	Develop training program. ($2 million)	Complete analyses and have training actively occurring in all operating functions. ($2 million)	Identify and implement fully secure emergency response communications.
5	Capacity Margin Analysis	Sign contract for analytical team(s). ($1 million)	Complete analytical effort. ($1 million)	
6	Emergency Communications	Identify and implement fully secure emergency response communications. ($6 million)	Commercialize high-reliability, secure emergency response communications. ($2 million)	
7	Real-time Hazard, Threat, and Detection Monitoring	Ensure applied R&D is under contract. Develop detection devices. ($8 million)	Complete prototype testing. ($12 million)	Commercialize public-private ventures. ($12 million)
8	Robotics Development and Adaptation	Develop and adapt robotic, remotely controlled modules. ($5 million)	Complete prototype testing. ($7 million)	Commercialize public/private ventures.

R&D Topic				
No.	Title	Near Term (Resource Estimate[a])	Achieved by ~2005 (Resource Estimate[a])	Achieved by ~2010 (Resource Estimate[a])
9	Improvement of In-use Performance and Replacement Functionality of Transportation Structures	Develop and adapt materials to maximize modularity, portability, and/or durability. ($5 million)	Complete field testing in up to five applications. ($7 million)	Commercialize structures.
10	Unified Vehicle/Guideway Systems Hardening	Complete scoping studies of materials technologies. ($2 million)	Develop prototypes to improve durability of transport systems. ($2 million)	Perform field testing, and define and implement standards. ($2 million)
11	Asset Management	Conduct scoping. ($1 million)	Validate and peer-review prototype tools. ($2 million)	Commercialize tools. ($1 million)
12	System Representation Improvement	Develop contracts with at least two teams. Improve methods to manage transport system data in a clear format. ($20 million)	Integrate database. Complete prototype tools. ($30 million)	Implement multiple applications. ($20 million) (full U.S. coverage assumed)
13	Intrusion Detection	Define requirements and award contracts to customize intrusion detection systems. ($4 million)	Complete design and testing of systems. Begin to implement multiple applications. ($6 million)	Commercialize intrusion detection for physical and cyber assets. ($1 million)
14	Cyber Vulnerability Data Warehouse	Define requirements and award contracts. ($1 million)	Complete and verify database. Warehouse access protocol. ($2 million)	
15	Threat/Intelligence Database and Network	Define requirements and award contracts for an integrated facility for providing intelligence concerning threats. ($1 million)	Complete a fully functional facility. ($2 million)	

R&D Topic No.	Title	Near Term (Resource Estimate[a])	Achieved by ~2005 (Resource Estimate[a])	Achieved by ~2010 (Resource Estimate[a])
16	Information Assurance	Define requirements and use existing tools to develop AI-based technologies. ($2 million)	Complete design and testing of new tools. ($3 million)	Implement and commercialize AI-based technologies. ($1 million)
17	Software Assurance	Identify requirements for on-line fault checking in information systems. ($4 million)	Complete design and testing of new tools in critical information systems. ($6 million)	Complete field implementation and commercialization. ($1 million)
18	Human Factors Analysis	Characterize problems and limitations inherent in preparedness, prediction, and response. Award contract. ($6 million)	Fully identify and implement changes for preparedness/ prediction. ($4 million)	
19	Recovery Training	Contract for training program development. ($1 million)	Implement training program. ($2 million)	Continue training program. ($1 million)
20	Computer Emergency Response and Emergency Response and Recovery Assessment Capacity Building	Define needs and procedures. Develop research contracts. ($3 million)	Deploy trained teams to standby mode at strategic locations. ($5 million)	Introduce active information exchange and revise procedures as needed. ($3 million)
21	Public/Private Infrastructure Security Responsibility	Conduct scoping conferences. Issue requests for proposals. Select project teams. ($2 million)	Propose legislation (as needed).	

[a] Resource estimates reflect qualitative, order-of-magnitude judgments. They are intended to be representative of the resources needed for the R&D topics and are based on assumptions concerning the scope, the expected level of effort, and the pace of the research. Detailed cost estimates must be prepared in concert with the development of detailed R&D plans.

Note

Several areas of substantive disagreement surfaced in reviewer comments on earlier drafts of this report. These areas, and the responses by the team, are provided below.

1. **Risk management and risk evaluation in transportation operations are well-established, private-sector management practices that require no additional research.** Some reviewers expressed dissatisfaction with the roadmap's implicit premise that private-sector managers and decision makers need additional education and training in risk management for physical and cyber vulnerabilities. They expected those officials to be insulted and possibly angered by the presumption that any "expert" from outside their industry could add useful information.

There is little doubt that, without early and direct interaction with such managers through, for example, a pilot study to discover the actual extent of their information needs, the ultimate findings of any risk management research would have little value because such findings would be ignored by the very audience to which they are directed. This is why the roadmap emphasizes and reemphasizes the importance of early management involvement and "buy-in" for many of the projects described.

In general, the team confirmed, after speaking with several private-sector management representatives, that officials me looking for better information on which to base their strategic security decisions, especially in cyber vulnerability. Moreover, the recent, major, and protracted disruptions in commodity flow on the domestic rail system argue that the presumed resiliency of the line haul transportation system is not as complete as some would hold. Such critical system performance failures under *normal* operating practice do not bode well for a swift and wholly satisfactory system recovery from major physical or cyber attacks.

2. **The roadmap does not give sufficient attention to air transport security needs.** The team does not dispute that the roadmap's list of recommended projects contains few projects *specifically* targeted at air transportation, although many are as relevant to aviation as to other transportation modes. To avoid redundancy and duplication of effort, the team has deferred to (and incorporated by reference) the programs and projects outlined in the FAA's Security Research and Development Program developed pursuant to the Final Report of the White House Commission on Aviation Safety and Security.

3. **A critical path diagram is needed.** A critical path diagram implies that a functionally inseparable fixed chronology and chain of dependencies are necessary to accomplish the desired set of goals. The team uniformly agrees that such fixed dependencies do not exist for the research program outlined. Although certain activities clearly must precede others (for exam-

ple, fact-finding, documentation, and formalization of procedures before training begins), none of the actual *research* needed is contingent on the completion of other research in the roadmap. Additional discovery, updating, and refinement of results can occur in parallel or in tandem across virtually the entire project slate. In a sense, this action was deliberate on the part of the team, which individually and collectively believes that all research is equally valid and could produce useful results almost immediately. Thus, no research effort should be hindered or vitiated because it is chronologically "downstream" of other work that may not be progressing satisfactorily.

CHAPTER 7

PRELIMINARY RESEARCH AND DEVELOPMENT

ROADMAP FOR PROTECTING AND ASSURING THE VITAL HUMAN SERVICES INFRASTRUCTURE[1]

1 This document is one component of a longer report entitled *Preliminary Research and Development Roadmap for Protecting and Assuring Critical National Infrastructures* (Transition Office of the President's Commission on Critical Infrastructure Protection and the Critical Infrastructure Assurance Office. Washington, D.C. July 1998).

Contents

Section 1 Introduction

1.1 Scope of the Infrastructure

1.2 Characterization of the Infrastructure

1.3 Issues and Trends

Section 2 Threats and Vulnerabilities

2.1 Water-supply Systems

2.2 Emergency Services

2.3 Government Services

Section 3 R&D Topics and Activities

3.1 Water-supply Systems

3.1.1 Identification and Characterization of Biological and Chemical Agents

3.1.2 Biological and Chemical Agent Detectors

3.1.3 Supervisory Control and Data Acquisition Systems

3.1.4 Vulnerability Assessment of Water-supply Systems

3.1.5 Center of Excellence for Risk Assessment of Water-supply Systems

3.2 Emergency Services

3.2.1 Detectors and Detection Systems for Emergency Services

3.2.2 Integrated Emergency Management System

3.2.3 Multihazard, Real-time Simulation and Modeling

3.2.4 Behavioral/Psychological Studies of Reactions to Incidents

3.2.5 Decontamination Technologies

3.2.6 Systems Analysis of Public Health Emergency Response Systems

3.3 Government Services

3.3.1 Support Systems for Reconfiguring Government

3.4 Summary of R&D Topics

Section 4 R&D Topic Roadmap

Tables

E.1 Summary of Research Topics for Vital Human Services

E.2 Summary of Vital Human Services R&D Roadmap

Section 1
Introduction

1.1 Scope of the Infrastructure

The President's Commission on Critical Infrastructure Protection has examined the eight critical infrastructures identified in Executive Order 13010. While this work was underway, it became convenient to group some of the original critical infrastructures into a single category. This new category, called vital human services, encompasses three infrastructures: water-supply systems, emergency services, and government services.

Water-supply systems are characterized by sources of water; reservoirs and holding facilities; aqueducts and other transport systems; filtration, cleaning, and treatment systems; pipelines; cooling systems; and other delivery mechanisms that provide water for domestic and industrial applications. Also included in this infrastructure are systems for dealing with water runoff, wastewater, and fire-fighting needs.

Emergency services encompass medical, police, fire, and rescue systems, and their personnel who respond to emergencies. These services typically are provided at the local level (city, county, or metropolitan area). In addition, however, state and federal response plans define emergency support functions to assist in mitigation plans and in preparation, response, and recovery activities from various incidents.

Government services refer to the ability of federal, state, and local governments to provide essential services to the public during and after an emergency. Types of emergencies include natural disasters (e.g., floods and hurricanes), military attacks, technological emergencies, or other emergencies that seriously degrade or threaten our nation's security. Preparedness planning in this area requires identifying functions that are required during an emergency, identifying personnel to perform those functions, and developing plans and the capability to execute those plans. This critical infrastructure is closely linked with each of the other infrastructures considered by the Commission.

1.2 Characterization of the Infrastructure

The vital human services infrastructure provides services used by a large number of our nation's citizens and residents. Water-supply systems typically provide water to metropolitan areas as well as to many rural areas for uses such as irrigation. Providing wastewater treatment is also a common function of government organizations. These services are provided on an "on-demand" basis and are essential for maintaining public health.

The emergency services category includes both planning for, and responding to (during and after), emergencies. As such, any member of the general public is a potential recipient of these services. Emergency services must also be provided on an "on-demand" basis to avoid endangering the health and safety of people or their property.

Depending on the services provided, the public relies on government services with varying levels of urgency, reliability, and quantity. Maintaining or restoring government services during and after an emergency is the main research and development (R&D) objective for this part of the vital human services infrastructure.

1.3 Issues and Trends

The three components within vital human services are significantly intra- and interdependent. For example, government services may not be able to provide adequate fire-fighting services if the water-supply system is not operating. Likewise, emergency response functions can be hampered if part of the transportation infrastructure is out of order. Therefore, the vital human services critical infrastructure is inexorably linked to the other infrastructures and requires interagency coordination and cooperation.

The vital human services infrastructure typically is funded through one or more types of tax. In this era of tax cuts and shrinking government, these services frequently do not receive sufficient financial support to maintain current standards of service. This lack of support is especially relevant to new areas of emphasis that traditionally have not received significant support from available resources. Protection of the infrastructure has not been emphasized in the past; however, it is now becoming an area of great concern.

Section 2
Threats and Vulnerabilities

Because the three components of the vital human services infrastructure are intradependent as well as interdependent, they share many of the same threats and vulnerabilities. However, some threats and vulnerabilities relate primarily to one component. Each of the components of the vital human services infrastructure is discussed in detail below.

2.1 Water-supply Systems

The water supplied to U.S. communities is potentially vulnerable to terrorist attacks by insertion of biological agents, chemical agents, or toxins. The possibility of such an attack is of considerable concern, as current news headlines have highlighted. Individuals who harbor political differences with the present government are capable of conducting such attacks. Moreover, international problems, such as the current situation with Iraq, lend credibility to the notion that independent or foreign government-sponsored terrorists could initiate an attack of this kind.

Most U.S. water-supply systems are fairly safe from attacks initiated when contaminants are introduced upstream (e.g., reservoirs, lakes, rivers) because hazardous agents either do not mix well (chemical agents and toxins) or survive (biological agents) in water. Most urban water systems supply a high volume of water that effectively dilutes the toxic properties of contaminating agents and thereby provides a protective element. Unfortunately, rural water systems and distribution networks may not have this same protective element. Although highly lethal biological agents, such as anthrax and botulinum toxin, would not generally pose a threat of contamination to water-supply systems, these agents could be a threat if they were inserted at critical points in the system; theoretically, they could cause a large number of casualties. Furthermore, a recent outbreak of cryptosporidosis in Milwaukee is a good illustration of how large populations can be infected when water treatment is compromised. In this instance, the illness was associated with a fairly unique microbe, *Cryptosporidium parvum,* which is immune to normal water treatment and survives well in water.

In addition to being vulnerable to biological and chemical contamination, water-supply systems are also vulnerable to physical and cyber attacks. For example, pumping stations can be quite vulnerable to attacks that would require many months to recover. Some municipal water-supply systems are also vulnerable to attacks on industrial facilities. An attack can lead to a release of pollutants into their water outflow systems, which could, in turn, contaminate nearby intake systems for the municipal systems. Furthermore, many water-supply systems are operated by means of computer systems, which are vulnerable to cyber attacks. R&D topics in these areas are discussed later.

In general, vulnerability or risk evaluations that involve biological or chemical attacks by terrorists have not been performed for U.S. water-supply systems. However, a limited number of systems have been evaluated on behalf of the Commission. The results of these analyses indicated that most water-supply systems are vulnerable to a terrorist attack through the distribution network. Moreover, additional vulnerabilities can also be present.

Although, in general, vulnerability analyses of possible terrorist attacks have not been conducted, every system examined on behalf of the Commission had provisions in place for responding to natural disasters and system failures. These provisions ranged from system monitoring to emergency response plans. Although the industry has considered natural disasters and system failures, additional research in fault-tree analysis of low-probability events would be beneficial. Also, R&D activities are needed to assess system vulnerability and the risk from terrorist attack.

R&D directed toward reducing the effects of terrorist attacks would also be appropriate.

Training methods must be developed and implemented so that water-system employees can detect, evaluate, and respond to biological and chemical incidents. Methods of communicating and working with professional emergency response personnel regarding such incidents must be integrated into this training program.

2.2 Emergency Services

The general, potential threats to water-supply systems are also of great concern to emergency services personnel. Among the most vulnerable persons in emergency services are the first responders, typically local police, fire, and/or emergency medical personnel. The attack in Tokyo, for example, in which a chemical agent was introduced into a subway tunnel highlights the vulnerability of first responders. Fortunately in that case, terrorists used an agent that was short-lived and inefficiently distributed; otherwise, casualties would have been much higher.

In most U.S. communities, the first responders to accidents, explosions, or incidents that involve human illness are fire fighters, police officers, and emergency medical technicians (EMTs). They are specially trained to deal with a variety of materials, but not with weapons of mass destruction, such as biological or chemical warfare agents. The U.S. Department of Defense (DoD) recognizes this deficiency and has initiated a series of seminars, exercises, and tests to train and inform management and response teams about the hazards of these agents and to identify and demonstrate improved response procedures and equipment.

Despite the training and heightened awareness of biological and chemical toxicities, first responders do not have adequate detection and personal protection equipment. This equipment needs to be portable, rugged, sensitive, and quantitative; it also must be capable of providing rapid results. For example, the Chief of the Chicago Fire Department envisions a portable unit that is part of a fire-fighter's oxygen backpack and that reports readings on a heads-up display in the faceplate of the fire-fighter's mask.

2.3 Government Services

In effect, government services are subject to most of the threats and vulnerabilities faced by the other critical infrastructures. This conclusion is based on the complexity of the government services area and its interdependencies on the services provided by the other infrastructures. Within vital human services, government typically is responsible for providing water-related services and emergency response, so the relationship to threats and vulnerabilities is even stronger. Of course, government services has its own set of threats and vulnerabilities as well, in that government personnel and facilities are potential targets. Terrorists may see them as a means to make political statements and expose perceived weaknesses in local, state, or federal government.

Section 3
R&D Topics and Activities

The vital human services R&D team identified several areas in which R&D is needed. These topics were selected on the basis of the personal knowledge of the team members, discussions with other experts, and the findings of earlier work done on behalf of the Commission.

The following subsections summarize information about R&D in these areas. These topics are categorized on the basis of their respective components of the vital human services infrastructure to ease characterization of the R&D topics. The descriptions and discussions of threats and vulnerabilities show the significant intra- and interdependency among these topics. They can affect more than a single component of the vital human services infrastructure and also more than one critical infrastructure.

A general challenge in establishing an R&D program for this critical infrastructure is to integrate it with ongoing programs within DoD; the U.S. Department of Energy; other federal, state, and local agencies; and organizations in the private sector. The needs for vital human services must be factored into the goals of other research programs to minimize duplication of effort among the programs and to ensure that optimum use is made of the limited resources available.

3.1 Water-supply Systems

Potential topics and activities for R&D in water-supply systems include identifying and developing countermeasures for potential biological and chemical contaminants; developing detection equipment to identify potential contaminants of concern within a water-supply system; evaluating system vulnerability and risk to both biological and chemical agents and to physical and natural phenomena; developing information systems to promote a response that effectively minimizes adverse impacts; and developing system-specific contingency plans.

3.1.1 Identification and Characterization of Biological and Chemical Agents

Description

Many types of biological and chemical agents can be used to disable a drinking water-supply system. Of these agents, a number require basic research to determine how they would "behave" in a water-supply system. A database or registry of such biological and chemical agents would be a valuable asset. This database or registry could include the physical and chemical properties of the agents and characterize their behavior in an environment containing disinfectant agents, such as chloramine or hypochlorite. For example, it is not known how the nerve agent VX or botulinum toxin would behave in a disinfectant environment typical of post-treatment, water-distribution networks. Similarly, the solubility of trichotecene mycotoxin T-2, another chemical agent of concern, has not been measured in the laboratory. Tests of these agents could be made under actual conditions experienced in water-supply systems. For example, chlorine and chloramine levels, the pH level, and other parameters may vary within and among water-supply systems, and it is important that suspected agents and their countermeasures be tested under the appropriate conditions.

A second component of this R&D topic is additional applied research to investigate the actual risks of certain threat agents or materials. Often, insufficient data are available to give an accurate prediction of the ability of these materials to adversely affect human health or to identify appropriate treatment or antidotes if people have been exposed to them.

Some research is already being conducted in this area, and any new work would be designed to complement existing programs. Among the programs already underway are those at Aberdeen Proving Ground and those conducted on behalf of the Chemical and Biological Defense Command within DoD.

Goals and Challenges

One goal for this research is to develop solid data concerning water solubility and stability for all agents of concern. In addition, researchers need to gather information that shows the effectiveness of various countermeasures, including treating the water system, supplying antidotes, and providing other forms of medical assistance to affected parties. This information could be compiled in an electronic format and made available to the vital human services community for their use.

A major challenge in this area is the large number of potential biological and chemical agents for which information needs to be developed, compiled, and made available.

Rationale for the Research and Desired Results

Because the number of biological and chemical agents potentially available to terrorists continues to increase, basic information is needed on (1) the behavior of these agents in water-supply systems and (2) the risks they pose to the public. The research described here provides a scientific foundation upon which to base decisions regarding the threats posed by these agents.

The results of this research would lead to the development of an information database on biological and chemical agents. In addition, such a database would have potential for use in evaluating terrorist activities directed at water-supply systems.

Timeframe and Resource Requirements

This effort would be a continuing process, as researchers characterize more agents as potential terrorist weapons. In the near-term (before 2002),[2] researchers would characterize the spectrum of agents that are known or that lack sufficient data. They also would identify some agents not currently suspected. To meet near-term goals would require approximately two to three years of effort. The cost is estimated to be about $14 million. Subsequent efforts over the mid-term timeframe (2003-2005) would involve identifying currently unknown agents and characterizing their physical and chemical parameters and behavior. Researchers would identify risks and develop countermeasures, as well as develop and implement a database and information exchange mechanisms. Estimated expenditures for this research are likely to increase because of the unknown, but potentially large, number of agents. A total cost of $15 million is estimated to be required for these efforts.

New agents for use by terrorists and new risks for water-supply systems are likely to be identified for many years to come. Therefore, it is proposed that the research in identification and characterization be continued for at least five years, that is to 2010. This additional R&D would occur approximately from 2006 to 2010 and cost an estimated $25 million.

3.1.2 Biological and Chemical Agent Detectors

Description

A major deficiency in protecting our water-supply system infrastructure needs to be addressed. That deficiency is detecting contaminants. To eliminate this problem, researchers need to develop detectors that can identify potential biological and chemical agents rapidly enough to implement effective mitigation measures. For example, a sensor capable of identifying the presence of *Bacillus anthracis* spores or *Cryptosporidium parvum* oocysts in a water-supply system would be beneficial for mitigating the consequences from either a terrorist attack or a potential natural phenomenon. Many water suppliers have noted that such a sensor should be inexpensive, but highly reliable, to promote its use in the field.

Researchers need to focus immediately on detectors that sample water continuously for the agents of interest. Of course, similar devices are

---

2 All years referenced in this document are fiscal years.

needed for air sampling, but the problems are different. It is uncertain whether current antibody-based sensors have adequate sensitivity or speed. Antibody sensors also have problems with degradation over time. Current technology allows reasonable sensitivity (approximately 104 cells per milliliter) detection in about 10 minutes and some quantification. However, this technology has not yet been applied effectively to biological agents.

One example of research under this topic is the development of new technologies for rapid detection of contaminants of concern (e.g., anthrax, botulinum toxin, VX). This type of detector could routinely monitor a water-supply system or test a system suspected of being biologically or chemically contaminated. Another component of this research is tracking contaminants as they move through the water distribution system. Development of computer models for this purpose, supplemented by various measurements, is another component of this research.

Another area for study is the development of improved detection systems for monitoring the chlorine levels in water-supply systems. Such research would be based on the premise that terrorists could decide to de-chlorinate the water before introducing biological or chemical contaminants. Continuous monitoring of the chlorine level could alert water suppliers to potential terrorist activities.

Goals and Challenges

The goal of this research is to develop detectors for materials of interest, such as biological and chemical warfare agents and toxins. These detectors must be sensitive, fast, inexpensive, and quantitative. A challenge is that each of these characteristics is beyond current technology for biological agents. Current biological detectors are insensitive, slow, expensive, and generally nonquantitative. Instruments are available for detecting particles, but they are not able to differentiate between benign, suspended material and biological agents. Sensitive and quantitative systems are also available for chemical analysis; however, they are generally expensive, and detection is slower than real time.

Rationale for the Research and Desired Results

Many experts are concerned that few, if any, of the currently available detectors are capable of meeting the needs associated with biological and chemical agents. Research conducted in this area would be directed at developing a set of detectors appropriate for the various needs associated with biological or chemical agents.

Timeframe and Resource Requirements

Research for developing the instruments needed to detect biological and chemical agents in water-supply systems would occur from the present time through 2010. In the near-term (before 2002), researchers would conduct an extensive and detailed evaluation of ongoing R&D programs to determine which programs are relevant to this specific R&D topic. Their evaluation would include looking at basic science programs that have potential application in water-supply systems. R&D would also be conducted to adapt current detectors for use with biological and chemical agents of interest. These goals could be completed in two to three years. The estimated cost is approximately $30 million.

Beginning around 2003 and lasting for about three years, researchers would work to improve the sensitivity of the detectors so that they could detect agents in lower concentrations than is currently possible. Flow-through technologies in these detectors would be improved to allow real-time measurements. Researchers also would develop completely new, more sensitive detectors. Among the possible improvements in detector technologies to be examined are the use of novel excitation molecules, different sensor mechanisms, and engineering the receptor molecules to a solid-phase sensor. Funding requirements are estimated to be approximately $45 million.

From about 2006 to 2010, researchers would continue to develop new detectors to meet more stringent requirements associated with newly identified agents. Research also would be directed at those new requirements. The estimated cost for these efforts is $55 million.

3.1.3 Supervisory Control and Data Acquisition Systems

Description

Supervisory Control and Data Acquisition (SCADA) systems are used routinely to monitor and control water-supply systems. They consist of an interconnected array of instruments, monitors, control mechanisms, and panels that provide information to system operators and allow them to regulate the water flow, adjust purification systems, and generally control the quantity and quality of the water flowing into and through the system. Tens of thousands of SCADA systems are used for water-supply systems in the United States; however, they have different levels of sophistication and security.

An R&D plan for SCADA systems requires researchers to examine all components of such systems, including the individual sensors and other instruments, the data transmission and storage mechanisms, the control systems, and the security levels (or lack thereof). Once recommendations have been made for improving the security of SCADA systems, a series of pilot projects would be designed to demonstrate the effectiveness of the improved security efforts.

Goals and Challenges

The principal goal of this research is to develop protocols for designing and implementing SCADA systems that integrate measures for preventing intrusions or disruptions that could severely affect water-supply systems in the United States. Part of the R&D would focus on pilot testing or demonstrations of SCADA systems that have been developed under such protocols.

One of the major challenges for researchers in this area is the vast array of SCADA systems in the United States. These systems have a variety of designs and functions. The design and conduct of research programs must reflect these differences. Also, research must be conducted to reduce vulnerabilities in SCADA systems in the most effective way.

Another challenge is to account for the numerous interfaces among different SCADA systems throughout the water-supply network. A gallon of water is potentially monitored and controlled by many such systems as it flows from its source to the end user. Such systems can include those used for extraction, piping, treatment, storage, distribution, and other processes. The degree of coordination and correlation at these interfaces undoubtedly varies greatly, and the challenge is to design and conduct a research program that not only addresses security issues at these interfaces but also accounts for their differences.

In some cases, water-supply systems are integrally connected with other critical infrastructures. For example, many water sources are associated with the generation of hydroelectric power. Water-based transportation could also be affected by operations of the water-supply infrastructure. For those cases in which two or more SCADA systems are involved, or in which a single SCADA system monitors and regulates the operations associated with more than one infrastructure (e.g., hydroelectric power and water supply from a dam and reservoir), the challenge is to conduct a research program that integrates all the interconnected needs of such systems.

Rationale for the Research and Desired Results

The large number of SCADA systems in the water-supply system creates various vulnerabilities for cyber intrusions. The rationale for conducting research in this area is to develop methods that reduce opportunities to disrupt the water-supply system through attacks on SCADA systems. The research program for water-supply SCADA systems would provide:

- A means to identify vulnerabilities in SCADA systems;

- A means to identify vulnerabilities caused by interfacing of the various SCADA systems along the water-supply pathway;
- Techniques for rectifying identified vulnerabilities; and
- A set of protocols for developing SCADA systems that are more secure, both within themselves and at the interfaces of different systems.

Timeframe and Resource Requirements

Near-term (before 2002) work on this R&D topic entails the development of vulnerability assessment criteria and techniques for SCADA security and systems. These activities could be completed in approximately three years at a total cost of $15 million. From 2003 to 2005, researchers would focus on developing (1) techniques to rectify security problems and (2) preliminary protocols for the design and operation of secure systems. These efforts would cost about $15 million. Initial pilot testing of more secure SCADA systems also would be done. Finally, from approximately 2006 to 2010, researchers would conduct additional pilot tests and demonstrations. Lessons learned would be integrated into a final set of design and operational protocols. The cost for this research is estimated to be $25 million.

3.1.4 Vulnerability Assessment of Water-supply Systems

Description

Another area for R&D is development of methods for finding and evaluating cost-effective options to reduce vulnerabilities of water-supply systems. This R&D effort would include establishing vulnerability criteria, developing information on possible ways to reduce these vulnerabilities to physical and cyber attacks, and developing tools to assist in determining which of the potential options are most cost effective. A series of pilot tests would also be conducted as part of this research effort. Some level of training would be required to allow water-system operators to conduct these evaluations.

Goals and Challenges

This research would produce cost-effective methods, information, and tools that could be used to reduce the vulnerability of water-supply systems to physical and cyber threats. Challenges include the significant number of water-supply systems in the United States, the diversity of these systems with regard to their capacity, location (e.g., municipal, rural, mountainous terrain), physical design characteristics, age, and other design and operating parameters. The variety of potential terrorist threats and vulnerability-reduction options also adds to the challenges of this research topic.

Rationale for the Research and Desired Results

As discussed in Section 2.2 of this report, only a limited number of U.S. water-supply systems have been examined with respect to their vulnerabilities to terrorist attacks. However, the consensus is that many systems are, to various degrees, vulnerable to physical or cyber attacks. To assist decision makers in taking steps toward reducing these vulnerabilities, it is necessary to develop an appropriate information base and standards against which to evaluate the vulnerabilities of water-supply systems as they currently exist. These same standards could then be used to evaluate the effectiveness of options for reducing any vulnerabilities. R&D on this topic would yield the appropriate information base and evaluation tools upon which to base such decisions. A key component of this research would be developing and implementing pilot projects to demonstrate the effectiveness in evaluating vulnerability-reduction options. It is significant that a representative of New York City has informally offered that their water-supply system be a part of any pilot projects dealing with this issue.

Timeframe and Resource Requirements

In the near-term (before 2002), researchers would develop criteria for evaluating vulnerability-reduction options. This activity can be accomplished at a cost of approximately $9 million. Characterizing some vulnerability-reduction process/practices also would occur. Developing evaluation methods and tools would be conducted in the next three years (2003-2005). Methods and tools would be pilot tested and validated on a number of water-supply systems. The cost is estimated to be $12 million for these efforts. Finally, from about 2006 to 2010, research would be directed toward applying lessons learned from the pilot tests, enhancing the information base and evaluation methods, and performing additional validation. The estimated funding requirement for these efforts is $16 million.

3.1.5 Center of Excellence for Risk Assessment of Water-supply Systems

Description

As the threat of terrorist activities aimed at water-supply systems increases, responsibilities of municipalities and other operators of these systems must expand to include greater involvement and investment in security. This change will create additional demands on these owners/operators—far beyond what they have traditionally faced. To assist in conducting vulnerability assessments, selecting protection or mitigation measures, and understanding the operational and risk impacts of various contaminants, a Center of Excellence for Risk Assessment of Water-supply Systems should be established as an R&D topical area. This center would call on experts in vulnerability assessment, toxicology, risk assessment, computer security, and other areas. They would conduct appropriate research, develop methods and models, characterize data on biological and chemical agents, and conduct other analyses and support services to help protect our water-supply systems. A "hot line" to the center would be established to respond to inquiries concerning the protection of water-supply systems. It may be possible to leverage DoD's existing chemical/biological help and hot lines.

The center would perform city-specific vulnerability and risk analyses for a number of "pilot" water-supply systems to establish standard methods for evaluating those systems,. Initially, numerical models would be used to assess system vulnerability, to identify optimal monitoring locations, and to define operational procedures to be followed if a water-supply system is degraded by naturally occurring or human-initiated events. With additional experience and time, subscale testing of important processes should be performed; finally, real systems should be tested when incidents occur.

The center would serve as a repository for data collected by means of geographical information systems (GISs). These data would be used to characterize and analyze water-supply systems, as well as biological and chemical agents, and to evaluate system vulnerabilities and risks. The center would communicate with water purveyors if a system failed or was attacked by terrorists. Experts in water quality, mitigation, and other areas would be available for consultation with local staff at a water-supply facility to minimize adverse effects.

Once the center and some of its capabilities have been established, a series of pilot tests would be conducted to demonstrate the effectiveness of the center in responding to potential emergencies in water-supply systems. Lessons learned during these pilot tests would be beneficial in refining the center's capabilities and any associated models and information developed to support its activities.

Goals and Challenges

The basic goals of this research are as follows:

- Establish a core of "networked" experts to develop and apply analytical models and methods for protecting water-supply systems.
- Develop and provide information on various biological and chemical agents that can be retrieved by operators of any water-supply system in the United States.
- Provide a means for communicating information on threats, mitigation options, and other areas of interest in the security of water-supply systems.
- Develop plans for responding to natural disasters, system failures, terrorist attacks, or any other threat that places the water system or the people it serves at risk.

An important goal of this R&D program is to develop a working relationship between the center and the water industry. Organizations, such as the American Water Works Association, could help to facilitate such relationships. Among the benefits of a mutually respected and trusted relationship is the advancement of the concept that threats to water-supply systems are real and that financial investments to address them are of merit. Industry support would help to move the R&D beyond merely academic interest and into real-world applications. Another benefit of such a relationship is the establishment of standards for the release of research results that might also be of value to potential terrorists.

Challenges include addressing the many types and sizes of water-supply systems and providing a means for real-time communication of system conditions so that appropriate actions can be identified and communicated to operators of the affected water-supply system. Routine testing to ensure proper and timely operation is also a challenge in the development and operation of the center.

Rationale for Research and Desired Results

If a natural disaster, system failure, or terrorist attack occurred, contingency plans must be in place to minimize adverse impacts. Coordinating various agencies, such as police, fire, and medical, is crucial to successful mitigation. Although many cities have established contingency plans for natural disasters and system failure, few cities have response plans for terrorist activities; however, in many cases, plans currently available could be used (or adapted) for use in such incidents. Assessment methods and tools need to be established, and basic information on the characteristics of potential biological and chemical agents needs to be developed. Means for communicating information to appropriate parties must also be established. Standards for vulnerability assessments, mitigation effectiveness, and other metrics of importance must be developed. These standards would assist individuals who have assumed security responsibilities in addition to their responsibilities of ownership and operation of systems.

A Center for Risk Excellence would help to provide information efficiently to water-supply system operators regarding risks they face and appropriate responses to those risks. Information would be developed and placed in a format and medium appropriate for on-line use by water-system operators. Methods and tools would also be developed, tested, applied, and distributed through the center.

Timeframe and Resource Requirements

The Center for Risk Excellence could be established within approximately six months and produce initial results shortly thereafter. The start-up and operating costs for the near-term (before 2002) are estimated to be $8 million. From 2003 to 2005, the center would collect, assess, and distribute information; develop, verify, and apply models; develop response plans; and perform other activities. Funding for these efforts is estimated to be $9 million. Finally, researchers would re-examine the role of the center and define its long-term objectives and the most effective methods for accomplishing them. Funding needed for these activities (2006–2010) is estimated to be approximately $11 million.

3.2 Emergency Services

Research and development activity in emergency services has not kept pace with the growing number of contaminants that this infrastructure will potentially encounter. First responders have expressed a need for real-time detection systems, for personal protective equipment, and for ways to manage emergency situations that arise from biological or chemical contaminants. In-depth and continuous training in dealing with practical situations must be provided for all emergency response personnel, including supervisors. Treatment methods and techniques for providing appropriate antidotes are also insufficient.

Several specific research projects have been identified and discussed in earlier work done of behalf of the Commission. Examples of these projects include Modernization of Emergency Services Training and Exercises, Safe and Resilient Communities, Improved Evacuation Modeling, and Vulnerability of the U.S. Economy to a Catastrophic Disaster. Other R&D projects include those conducted at Natrick Laboratories through the Defense Advanced Research Project Agency and the U.S. Army Soldiers Systems Command. The Commonwealth of Massachusetts and the City of Boston are establishing Cooperative Research and Development Agreements with Natrick Laboratories to address the issue of inadequate personal protection equipment for local first responders.

The Vital Human Services R&D Roadmapping Team has agreed that some of these projects could help significantly to improve the protection of this critical infrastructure. However, these projects are more specific than the R&D topical areas being developed in this effort. The Roadmapping Team therefore elected to consider the following R&D topical areas.

3.2.1 Detectors and Detection Systems for Emergency Services

Description

As noted earlier, the need for detectors and associated systems for addressing biological and chemical agents is increasing. Emergency services require improved detection on several fronts: detecting an initial incident; protecting responders; treating injured or ill individuals; and decontaminating the affected areas or individuals. In each area, detection requirements must be established and instrumentation developed. Existing programs, such as the Chemical Warfare Response Improvement Program established under the Nunn-Lugar-Domenici Domestic Preparedness Program, need to be leveraged.

The activities in this area involve both basic and applied research. Basic research includes developing detectors for additional biological and chemical agents and developing means to improve the response time of existing detectors. Research into the development and/or adoption of robotic technologies also would be a major component of this program. Applied research includes the adaptation of existing detectors and detection systems to the requirements of the emergency services infrastructure.

Goals and Challenges

The goal of this research is to develop a set of detectors that can be used in response to biological and chemical incidents. These detectors must be sensitive, fast, fairly inexpensive, rugged, and quantitative. In addition, they must be insensitive to heat, cold, smoke, dust, and water.

Numerous challenges must be overcome to develop an appropriate detector for first responders. Such challenges include identifying the targets that the detector should recognize. This list of targets should include, but not be limited to, blistering and nerve agents, biological toxins, and biowarfare agents (including bacteria and viruses). Because of the large disparity among these materials, developing a common analytical system would be challenging. The elimination of false positive responses is a significant challenge and goal of this research.

Some researchers believe that a time-of-flight mass spectrometer used for detecting chemical warfare agents could be applicable in detecting biological agents. However, this large, complicated instrument requires considerable expertise to run. Data analysis is also extremely complex. The first R&D hurdle is to overcome these limitations. The second is to miniaturize the detector and strengthen it to withstand the rigors of the environment and handling commonly encountered by fire fighters, police officers, and EMTs.

Another goal of this research is to provide local first responders with adequate personal protective equipment. For example, there is no known U.S.-developed personal protective equipment that is a combination first responder bomb suit that is also encapsulated to standards appropriate for biological or chemical protection. Current research to achieve both types of protection have produced cumbersome and ineffective equipment. A challenge in this research is to integrate various types of detection into personal protective equipment rather than having separate systems for detection and protection.

Rationale for Research and Desired Results

Detection equipment at the present time (1998) is inadequate and in very short supply. Enhanced detection systems must provide information and protect emergency services personnel (e.g., provide fast response information to fire protection personnel before they enter a location suspected of being contaminated with biological or chemical agents). Thus, research areas are (1) development of a joint biological/chemical detector, (2) miniaturization of the unit, and (3) association with a heads-up display unit. Development and adaptation of robotic technologies to emergency services applications also are required to conduct emergency response activities effectively while protecting first responders to the fullest extent feasible. R&D in this area should produce a set of detectors appropriate for a range of emergency response applications and a set of robotic technologies that are useful in the emergency service infrastructure.

Timeframe and Resource Requirements

Developing a set of detectors that covers a range of emergency services needs is likely to be an ongoing process. As new contaminants are discovered (or invented), it will be necessary to have corresponding detection capabilities. For preliminary roadmapping, requirements for the known contaminants probably could be developed in the near-term (before 2002). Preliminary investigations into the expanded use of robotic technologies in the emergency services infrastructure would also be conducted during this period, as well as some basic research into new detectors. The estimated cost for this near-term effort is approximately $30 million. Research in both the basic and applied areas would continue from approximately 2003 through 2005. Funding needs are estimated to total $45 million, as a new slate of requirements and detectors would be investigated. Finally, from 2006 to 2010, most of the research would focus on applications. The estimated cost for these efforts is approximately $55 million.

3.2.2 Integrated Emergency Management System

Description

Research in this area would focus on developing an integrated emergency management support system consisting of a set of analytical tools for defining prototype systems. These prototypes could:

- Create a systematic organizational protocol and standard operating procedure for intergovernmental and interagency coordination and cooperation that involves all levels of government at the federal, state, and local jurisdictional lines of authority.
- Anticipate, indicate, and warn (in specific cases) the proper authorities of the time and location of events that could trigger emergencies;

- Create templates for use by data collectors;
- Identify members of crisis management teams and establish an "Incident Command System";
- Determine the importance of economic, social, climatological, military, and political data; develop tools to analyze these data to provide predictive capability;
- Develop a categorization scheme to describe the type of crisis; and
- Identify diplomatic, informational, economic, and military responses to crises and their potential for mitigating these crises.

This research would include examining and evaluating existing support systems used in the military and private sector to determine their applicability to a more comprehensive integrated emergency management system. It would also include the development of educational programs to inform the general public of the appropriate response(s) to potential biological or chemical incidents.

Goals and Challenges

A set of tools should be developed that characterizes and defines appropriate responses to a crisis. These tools could include statistical analysis packages, image analysis capability, and artificial intelligence-based expert systems. They could be interfaced with network functions through templates that guide data collection. Moreover, they could be linked to a series of output generators that would classify crises, generate scenarios, and assemble crisis teams. The R&D effort should also include stakeholder/user identification and involvement, characterization, classification, and analysis. Workshops, pilot studies, and multiagency training are needed to ensure support from stakeholders. As emergency situations arise, the appropriate components of this system could be pilot tested, and lessons learned would be used to improve the system. These pilot tests would also provide opportunities to illustrate the value of such a system to emergency responders, decision makers, and stakeholders.

It would be a challenge to develop systems appropriate for the full scope of possible incidents and for the range of localities potentially impacted. Smaller cities and towns would be likely to look to larger cities for assistance, and this probability should be integrated into developing these management support systems.

Rationale for the Research and Desired Results

Currently, no tool can perform all the functions required of such a system. This system would be useful in planning, training, mitigating potential incidents, and responding to incidents more expeditiously and in a coordinated manner. A critical need is to develop an interoperable and integrated telecommunications infrastructure for intergovernmental and interagency coordination. This need arises because many first responders to an incident cannot communicate with each other via radio. Likewise, many adjoining local jurisdictions and the various levels of government cannot communicate with each other in a single secure interoperable telecommunications system.

Results of this R&D topic are expected to include the establishment of protocols for creating and evaluating response options during a given set of emergencies (e.g., natural disasters, technological failures, or man-made crises). These options would consider the response policies of various agencies, their practices, and the application of new technologies to help in mitigating consequences or in performing recovery operations. Development and evaluation of recovery options would also be considered in this research topic. Results from this research would help decision makers determine how to respond to, or recover from, such incidents. For example, results could assist decision makers in responding to a release of agents in subterranean public transport systems (e.g., deciding whether the system should be vented or closed or whether a new containment mechanism is needed). Another result of this research would be a means of identifying areas of greatest impact so that mitigation measures can be taken before an incident occurs. For example, certain antitoxins could be stored near, rather than at, facilities that could be highly vulnerable to attack.

Timeframe and Resource Requirements

Initially, in the near-term (before 2002), requirements would be specified, and the development of tools would be initiated. Existing support systems would be evaluated and the appropriate capabilities adapted for application to the more comprehensive system being developed. Funding required for these efforts is estimated to be about $13 million. In the following efforts (from about 2003 to 2005), pilot tests would be conducted, lessons learned would be incorporated, and a final set of tools would be developed. Funding required for these efforts is estimated to be about $15 million. It is possible that only one or two years would be required to complete these tasks. Finally, the cost for any necessary additional research is estimated to be $5 million.

3.2.3 Multihazard, Real-time Simulation and Modeling

Description

Research would be conducted to develop methods to upgrade models that simulate hazards and protective actions to incorporate real-time data on hazard and response conditions. Techniques for presenting the results of these models in ways that are meaningful and useful to emergency managers and decision makers would be researched.

Goals and Challenges

Existing simulation models for emergency response often are useful only in the pre-and post-event phases of emergency management. Models of hazards (e.g., radio-logical or chemical dispersion) and of protective actions (e.g., evacuation) are best suited for pre-planning emergency responses, for creating plausible exercise scenarios, and for reconstructing and analyzing events. Their usefulness in real-time emergency response is limited, and research would focus on each of these limitations:

- *Real-time data are not available.* Technologies exist for collecting some real-time data (e.g., meteorological data, sensors for traffic volume) and transmitting those data to centralized locations. For example, meteorological data at chemical stockpile storage sites are used to update the Army's atmospheric dispersion model every 15 minutes. In Los Angeles, traffic sensors on freeways constantly feed real-time data to a centralized monitoring point. However, the availability of such technologies nationwide is far from complete, primarily because of cost and incompatible systems.
- *Manual data entry is time consuming.* Some background data needed by these models (e.g., highway network configuration, terrain, and topography) are not available from automatic sensors. Some efforts have been made to generate these data from GIS, using, for example, the Census Bureau's TIGER/Line files and U.S. Geological Survey's digital topography data. However, such efforts to date have required extensive manual editing to clean up or reformat the data.
- *The presentation of model results frequently fails to meet the needs of emergency managers and decision makers.* In general, existing technologies are adequate for displaying the results of models graphically (e.g., a plume overlaid on a local area map or "Thermometer bars" along roadways on a map to indicate traffic volume). However, the meaning of the results often is unclear to emergency managers and decision makers. For example, they might need to know the underlying assumptions that led to a set of results or what might happen if the assumptions changed. They usually need to know the implications of the results for the actions they take.
- *Data need to be accessible and secure.* Accessibility and security of data collection, distribution, and use is critical.

To ensure a high level of confidence in the use of such models for real-time response, the R&D efforts must include extensive validation and training. Furthermore, emergency managers and decision makers must be able to use these models in planning and training. As with several other R&D topics, true emergency situations provide opportunities for pilot tests. A significant challenge would be to develop simulation models that meet the above criteria but that are not cost prohibitive in terms of initial purchase price, the collection of data needed to conduct the simulation, or in the training of people to conduct the analyses.

Rationale for the Research and Desired Results

Reducing the cost of technologies for real-time data collection increases their availability for real-time simulation modeling. Automating the translation of data from sources into input streams needed by simulation models would make using such models feasible and allow a shorter turnaround time. Meaningful presentation and display of model results would make these models more practically useful in real-time emergency response, increasing and enhancing the real-time information available to decision makers.

Timeframe and Resource Requirements

Initially (before 2002), system requirements would be defined, and development of a prototype system would be initiated. Emergency response personnel and decision makers would be consulted to identify their needs. Existing analytical tools would be evaluated for their application to this system. Funding required for these efforts is estimated to be $17 million. From about 2003 to 2005, the prototype systems developed earlier would be pilot tested under actual emergency conditions. Results from these pilot tests would be factored into model revisions. Funding for these efforts is estimated to be $21 million. Finally, from approximately 2006 to 2010, additional pilot tests would be conducted, and a final set of models developed. These models would be distributed to appropriate organizations and agencies within the emergency services infrastructure. Funding required for these efforts is estimated to be $23 million.

3.2.4 Behavioral/Psychological Studies of Reactions to Incidents

Description

Behavioral/psychological studies to determine public and emergency responder reactions to nuclear, chemical, and biological incidents would be performed. Research would address the following questions:

- Would hospitals be overwhelmed by public demand for care following an incident? For instance, would the public view common symptoms to be related to exposure to biological or chemical agents?
- Would monitoring and decontamination facilities be overwhelmed by public demand?
- Would large "shadow" effects of the public occur outside affected areas; that is, would people take protective actions, such as evacuation, on their own, thereby hindering response actions in affected areas?

- Would the public comply with protective actions recommended by authorities? For instance, would the public follow their instinct to "flee" (that is, evacuate) rather than to shelter in place, which might be the safer action?
- If evacuation is ordered, would the public drive in a cooperative manner, which has been documented during other hazards (e.g., hurricanes), or more erratically (e.g., driven by fear)?
- Would first responders stay or abandon their jobs to care for themselves or their loved ones?
- What would be the implications of these behaviors in such areas as crowd control, resource planning, and communication of emergency information and instructions?

Goals and Challenges

Because there is not a base of experience from actual events, research of this type is necessarily hypothetical. Subjects may be asked, "What would you do if an incident were to happen?" But their responses to hypothetical questions may differ from their behavior during an actual incident. A basic goal of this research is to enhance the probability that emergency services personnel would perform their duties as planned and with the expected level of efficiency and effectiveness. Integrating the results of this research into appropriate training modules and decision making is both a goal and a challenge of this research.

A significant challenge for this research is dealing with the wide spectrum of potential events (e.g., natural disasters, technological failures, terrorist actions). This diversity is complicated by the range of possible consequences (e.g., release of different quantities of biological contaminants) and the time available for appropriate response (ranging from little or none for some types of emergencies to days or weeks for others). Another challenge is to meet the needs of the wide range of training and experience of first responders and other emergency services personnel. Some are full-time professionals, whereas other are part-time volunteers.

Another challenge would be to integrate additional training for first responders into existing training requirements and practices. For example, first responders are being taught through the DoD Domestic Preparedness courses under the Nunn-Lugar-Domenici Act of 1996 and the Department of Justice Bureau of Justice Assistance Program courses under the Death Penalty Act of 1996. Such training courses must be recognized when developing additional means of training for first responders.

Rationale for the Research and Desired Results

Some work is underway to train public authorities in identifying the risks from biological and chemical incidents and to communicate those risks to the public. Questions about public and emergency worker reactions have been studied extensively for more common hazards, such as hurricanes and "ordinary" hazardous materials incidents. However, it is unknown to what extent the findings from those studies carry over to biological and chemical incidents, which involve less familiar hazards and a higher "fear factor." It is anticipated that this research would result in methods to anticipate public and emergency worker reactions. This knowledge would enable public authorities to improve their emergency response plans and to better communicate information and instructions to the public.

Timeframe and Resource Requirements

In the near-term (before 2002), researchers would develop a baseline of anticipated and required responses through a series of subject interviews, surveys, and evaluations of historical events. Funding required for these efforts is estimated to be $6 million. From approximately 2003 to 2005, researchers would develop and conduct a set of training courses to help assure that emergency services personnel would respond appropriately and efficiently to emergencies. Techniques for improved response through enhanced communications both before and during an emergency would be developed and pilot tested. Funding required for these efforts is estimated to be $6 million. An additional year or more could be required to complete this research. The cost for this extra research is estimated to be $2 million per year.

3.2.5 Decontamination Technologies

Description

Under this R&D topic, technologies used for decontaminating structures and equipment (contaminated with biological or chemical agents) would be identified and characterized. As needed, the R&D would include developing new, more effective technologies. Protocols also would be established to help select the most appropriate technology for any situation.

Goals and Challenges

The basic goals of this research are to identify and characterize decontamination technologies that can remove biological or chemical contamination effectively and to develop a set of decision criteria to be used in selecting the most appropriate technology for a situation. Another goal is to develop such technologies for use in situations where decontamination technologies are not effective. It is probable that some of the technologies identified or developed under this research would be appropriate for other critical infrastructures. Pilot testing of decontamination technologies is a significant component of this R&D topic.

This research offers many challenges, including the wide spectrum of biological and chemical agents, the large variations in the physical design and construction materials used in the affected infrastructures, and public perceptions regarding contaminated materials and the level of decontamination required before a system could be returned to service.

Rationale for Research and Desired Results

Following an event in which any part of an infrastructure has been contaminated, it is necessary to develop and evaluate decontamination options that provide for either dismantling and disposal of the infrastructure or for its return to service. Some situations, particularly those involving biological or chemical contamination, currently have few or no established protocols or cleanup criteria needed to make decontamination decisions. This research would be designed and conducted to provide a foundation upon which to base decisions regarding decontamination options, the level of decontamination that is appropriate for resumption of services, and dismantlement and disposal requirements.

The results of this research should include a list of current and emerging decontamination technologies; a characterization of these technologies, including their costs and effectiveness against various types of biological and chemical contamination; a set of protocols or procedures for conducting the decontamination technologies; a set of recommendations for dealing with the selection of a particular technology; and explanations concerning implementation and field testing of the technology.

Timeframe and Resource Requirements

In the near term (before 2002), R&D would focus on identifying and characterizing technologies that currently exist or are nearly fully developed. A preliminary set of decontamination needs also would be developed, as well as some basic requirements in regard to the decision processes. Construction and operation of necessary research facilities would be initiated. Funding required for these efforts is estimated to be $55 million. Efforts up to 2005 would focus on developing new decontamination technologies. Some new technologies should be available for demonstration by the end of this term. A final set of protocols for selecting technologies would be completed. The estimated cost for these efforts is $75 million. Before 2010, additional technologies would be developed and readied for general use. It is also anticipated that requirements for new technologies (e.g., to address an expanded set of biological and chemical agents) would be developed, and R&D on a new set of technologies would begin. Estimated costs for these efforts are $105 million.

3.2.6 Systems Analysis of Public Health Emergency Response Systems

Description

Research under this topic would identify (1) critical elements and nodes, (2) linkages (i.e., critical paths) between these elements, and (3) vulnerabilities or failure points that place the world's populations at risk to natural (i.e., pandemic) or man-made (e.g., biological weapons of mass destruction) emergencies. This research would help to link the existing worldwide surveillance of contagious diseases to quick responses to contain, treat, and eradicate these diseases and prevent the rapid proliferation of epidemics. The systems analysis would begin with a detailed component analysis to identify all of the elements of concern. The following concerns, however, would be among the first to be examined:

- *Threat assessment.* The research would examine the ways by which patients are diagnosed with contagion and how biological agents are identified.
- *Information linkages.* How do professionals in the medical community communicate and link information resources?
- *Manufacture of vaccines and antidotes.* Many suppliers involved in the manufacture of medical supplies and vaccines are foreign or multinational companies; hence, the United States may not have the authority to direct the manufacture and distribution of their products.
- *Stockpiling of vaccines and antidotes.* Prerequisites and limitations to the production of vaccines and antidotes require that they be stockpiled for use in an emergency.

The systems analysis effort would seek to bring together federal, state, and local public health emergency response R&D needs. To accomplish this goal, it is necessary to categorize the roles and missions of agencies that support public health epidemiological decision making. This work would identify the political interests and technical concerns at various levels of decision making.

A second component of this research would examine alternative medical treatment methods and systems that could be implemented if existing medical systems and practices became overwhelmed by natural epidemics or terrorist biological and chemical assaults. For example, the need for respiratory ventilators would far exceed hospital supplies if an episode such as the sarin nerve agent attack in the Tokyo subway were to occur in a U.S. city. Another example would be the need to decontaminate large numbers of victims exposed to biological or chemical agents as the result of such an incident. What alternative methods, equipment, or resources could be used to extend the capacity of the medical response under such emergency conditions? The following lists potential areas of concern where normal channels of emergency response and patient treatment could be overwhelmed and workable alternatives may be needed to cope with a large-scale emergency:

- Patient isolation,
- Respiratory therapies,
- Decontamination,
- Emergency worker protection, and
- Multiple hazard (e.g., biological and chemical) response.

These and other areas would be examined, and alternative response methods would be developed. Researchers would investigate, characterize, catalog, and inventory in a database, alternative treatments that could be used in an emergency to treat large numbers of victims. It is not possible to predict with any degree of specificity, the types of alternative treatment strategies that would be needed in an emergency. Therefore, as a first step, it would be necessary to conduct a needs assessment. Emergency medical professionals would be interviewed and consulted to determine what equipment most likely would be in short supply and which workable medical alternatives would be needed in a national public health emergency.

Goals and Challenges

The basic goals of this research are to develop tools to assist in identifying threats and vulnerabilities to the public health emergency response systems and to develop and evaluate alternative means of meeting the needs of the public health system under extreme emergency conditions. These tools would assist in planning for terrorist or natural incidents that could otherwise overwhelm the existing systems.

Challenges include the number and diversity of emergency response and medical treatment organizations that respond to emergencies of the type considered in this research. The variety of potential emergencies and response requirements also creates a significant challenge. Potential lack of uniformity in existing equipment at medical treatment facilities also presents a challenge in identifying and developing alternative treatment options that could be used under the extreme conditions hypothesized here. As with other research topics, the challenge would be to integrate this topic with ongoing programs (e.g., a New York City program to identify the number of respirators, isolation units, etc., at the various medical care facilities throughout the city).

Rationale for the Research and Desired Results

A comprehensive systems analysis has been performed for the public health emergency response and decision-making system. This analysis is a vital first step in identifying gaps that need to be bridged to respond efficiently to natural or man-made public health emergencies. In addition, no systematic analysis and compilation of alternative methods, equipment, or resources can be used to extend medical response capacity under severe emergency conditions. Such a compilation of alternative treatment strategies would provide an important source of information for assisting the nation to respond to a pandemic or terrorist catastrophe.

Results of this research would include a set of analytical tools and procedures to be applied to medical treatment systems to identify vulnerabilities and potential solutions for extreme conditions. Also, a set of alternative treatment methods and practices to be used under such conditions would result from this research.

Timeframe and Resource Requirements

Near-term (before 2002) research would require $13 million to complete. Surveys of existing medical treatment capabilities would be conducted and work on developing systems analysis tools would be initiated. From 2003 to 2005, prototypes of analysis tools would be completed and pilot tested at various medical facilities. Lessons learned from these pilot tests would be factored in to improve analytical capabilities. A preliminary set of alternative treatment practices to be used in extreme conditions would be developed as would recommendations regarding the type of equipment needed to implement these alternatives. Preparedness exercises would be conducted to evaluate the ability of public health systems to adapt to the extreme conditions considered in this research. Funding required for these efforts is estimated to be $15 million. Research conducted during the 2006-2010 timeframe would finalize system analysis tools, databases, and other information needed for a comprehensive analysis of public health emergency response systems. Additional information on alternative treatment practices would be developed and distributed, and additional preparedness exercises would be conducted. Funding required for these efforts is estimated to be $17 million.

3.3 Government Services

Government services are strongly linked to the other critical infrastructures (e.g., water supply and pressure for fire fighting, roads and bridges for emergency response vehicles, and telephone service for communications between the public and appropriate government agencies and personnel). Thus, many of the R&D topics described in Section 3.2 (emergency services), most of the topics identified in Section 3.1 (water-supply systems), and many of the topics noted elsewhere for other critical infrastructures also apply to government services. Reasons for these overlapping research needs include:

- The large degree of interdependence of government services with other critical infrastructures; and
- The complexity of government services (e.g., the multitude of services provided by governments and the numbers and locations of people receiving these services).

The Vital Human Services R&D Roadmapping Team did, however, identify one R&D topic that would focus almost exclusively on government services. This topic is presented below.

3.3.1 Support Systems for Reconfiguring Government

Description

During and following an emergency that involves full or partial loss of government services, it is vital to re-establish these services as expeditiously as possible. Research would focus on designing and implementing a support system to prioritize reconfiguration options, to examine vulnerabilities in the reconfiguration process, and in general expedite the recovery process. A series of pilot tests would be conducted to validate and improve the models and information comprising this support system. The research would complement activities directed toward issues such as succession planning, reconstitution of services, and other military and civilian efforts focusing on government services.

Such a support system (or perhaps a family of systems) would be based on a pre-determined set of priorities for various government services. The system would contain information on the responsibilities and capabilities of all levels of government (local, county, state, and federal) so that if some or all of these services are disrupted, a plan for re-establishing services could be developed and implemented quickly. A major focus of this research would be to establish priorities for reconfiguring government functions. These priorities would depend on the type and degree of services lost, the nature of the emergency causing the loss of services (e.g., natural or man-made), and other parameters to be evaluated in the support systems.

Goals and Challenges

The goals of this research include developing and testing a set of systems designed to assist in reconfiguring government services following emergencies. As actual disasters or drills occur, a set of pilot tests could be developed to validate the models and decision methods that are built into the support systems. Another goal (and a challenge) of this research would be to integrate a reconfigured government with the recovering business and industrial sectors. It may be desirable to obtain public and private-sector concurrence on a timetable for reconfiguring essential services so that the highest priority needs of each sector are met.

One of the major challenges of this R&D effort would be to establish a knowledge base appropriate for recovering government services. Most experience-based information comes from normal conditions or from partial, typically localized, disruptions. Another challenge would be to recognize and characterize the multitude of services provided by various government entities. It is likely that differing priorities among the various levels of government would surface regarding the re-establishment of the various types of service. One of the challenges would be to develop a set of protocols to follow within a support system.

It would be a challenge, in developing a support system of this type, to integrate each of the other infrastructures and their changing status into the government reconfiguration process. Another challenge would be to develop a support system that acknowledges the spectrum of potential disasters; that is, a system that applies to disasters that are geographically limited, such as those from hurricanes; from a targeted attack on certain components of government throughout the United States; and from a more general attack in which not only government services, but also other critical, interrelated infrastructures are affected.

Rationale for the Research and Desired Results

The rationale for conducting this research is to assist in reconfiguring government services efficiently and appropriately. Restoring government services would give the public confidence that the nation could recover from any disaster. Furthermore, it would help to restore selected government services (e.g., military protection, national guard, police and fire protection, and medical services) that are required for responding to an ongoing emergency.

Researchers would develop a support system (or set of systems) to aid in recovery operations. Data and other information needed to facilitate such a recovery also would result from this research. Experience gained during pilot testing of the support system would be another valuable result.

Timeframe and Resource Requirements

The timeframe and resource requirements for this R&D topic have been estimated for three timeframes. In the near term (before 2002), basic requirements for this system would be defined and a limited prototype system developed. The funding required for this phase is estimated to be $10 million. From 2003 to 2005, a more robust prototype with additional components would be developed and pilot tested. The cost for these efforts is estimated to be $12 million. Finally, a full system would be developed and tested. The cost requirement for these efforts is estimated to be approximately $16 million.

3.4 Summary of R&D Topics

The R&D topics identified by the Vital Human Services R&D Roadmapping Team are summarized in Table E.1. These topics provide a foundation for research to enhance protection of the water-supply systems, emergency services, and government services in the United States against threats posed through physical or cyber actions or through the inherent complexities and interdependencies of the infrastructures themselves.

Table E.1 Summary of Research Topics for Vital Human Services[a]

Research Topic					
No.	Title (Type[b])	Product	Goals and Challenges	Threats and Vulnerabilities	Priority Category
		Water-supply Systems			
1	Identification and Characterization of Biological and Chemical Agents (B, A)	Data, information	Quantify risks and impacts; large number of agents.	Physical, complexities	Most important
2	Biological and Chemical Agent Detectors (B, A)	Detectors	Develop inexpensive, sensitive, fast, quantitative detectors.	Physical	Most important
3	Supervisory Control and Data Acquisition Systems (A)	Design protocols	Multiple systems; interdependencies.	Physical, cyber, complexities, interdependencies	Most important
4	Vulnerability Assessment of Water-supply Systems (A)	Information, methods, tools	Number and diversity of systems; range of options; buy-in by owners/ operators; validation.	Physical, cyber, complexities, interdependencies	Most important
5	Center of Excellence for Risk Assessment of Water-supply Systems (B, A)	Methods, information	Establish point of contact for information on threats and vulnerabilities; identify diversity in needs of water-supply systems.	Physical, cyber, complexities, interdependencies	Most important

Research Topic					
No.	Title (Type[b])	Product	Goals and Challenges	Threats and Vulnerabilities	Priority Category
			Emergency Services		
6	Detectors and Detection Systems for Emergency Services (B, A)	Detectors, robotics	Develop inexpensive, sensitive, fast, quantitative detectors.	Physical	Most important
7	Integrated Emergency Management System (A)	Software, information	Validation; stakeholder buy-in.	Physical, cyber, complexities	Very important
8	Multihazard, Real-time Simulation and Modeling (A)	Software system	Validation; response time; effectiveness.	Physical, cyber, complexities, interdependencies	Most important
9	Behavioral/Psychological Studies of Reactions to Incidents (A)	Information	Validation.	Physical	Important
10	Decontamination Technologies (A)	Technologie, information	Develop technologies, many facilities, many contaminants.	Physical, complexities, interdependencies	Most important
11	Systems Analysis of Public Health Emergency Response Systems (A)	Information; protocols for coordination	Assemble public health emergency response needs; different roles of agencies, many kinds of threats.	Physical, complexities, interdependencies	Most important
			Government Services		
12	Support Systems for Reconfiguring Government (A)	Models, data	Expedite reconfiguration of government following emergencies.	Physical, cyber, complexities, interdependencies	Very important

[a] The order of the R&D topics within apriority category (i.e., most important, very important, important) does not imply relative importance.

[b] B = basic; A = applied; ATD = advanced technology development; and POP = proof of principle and validation.

Section 4
R&D Topic Roadmap

The suggested roadmap for each of the R&D topics identified and presented by the Vital Human Services R&D Roadmapping Team is summarized in Table E.2. The accomplishments during the research timeframes (near term, before 2005, and before 2010) are summarized. More detailed information can be found in the individual topic descriptions provided in Section 3.

Table E.2 Summary of Vital Human Services R&D Roadmap

Research Topic				
No.	Title	Near Term (Resource Estimate[a])	Achieved by ~2005 (Resource Estimate[a])	Achieved by ~2010 (Resource Estimate[a])
1	Identification and Characterization of Biological and Chemical Agents	Characterize known agents. ($14 million)	Identify unknown agents and characterize their physical and chemical parameters and behavior in different environments. Develop and implement database and information exchange mechanisms. ($15 million)	Continue to identify and characterize unknown agents. ($25 million)
2	Biological and Chemical Agent Detectors	Adapt current slate of detectors for applications to the water-supply system. ($30 million)	Improve sensitivity of current detectors, enhance capability for real-time measurements, and extend detector capabilities to other agents. ($45 million)	Develop new generation of detectors to meet more stringent requirements associated with additional, newer agents. ($55 million)
3	Supervisory Control and Data Acquisition (SCADA) Systems	Develop vulnerability assessment criteria and techniques for SCADA systems. ($15 million)	Develop techniques to rectify security problems and preliminary protocols for design and operation of secure systems. Conduct pilot tests of improved systems. ($15 million)	Conduct additional pilot tests and develop a final set of design and operational protocols. ($25 million)

Research Topic				
No.	Title	Near Term (Resource Estimate[a])	Achieved by ~2005 (Resource Estimate[a])	Achieved by ~2010 (Resource Estimate[a])
4	Vulnerability Assessment of Water-supply Systems	Develop criteria for evaluating vulnerability-reduction options. Characterize options. ($9 million)	Develop and pilot test evaluation methods and tools. ($12 million)	Apply lessons learned to methods and tools, enhance information base, improve methods and tools, and perform additional validations. ($16 million)
5	Center of Excellence for Risk Assessment of Water-supply Systems	Establish requirements for development and operation of center. Start up center. ($8 million)	Develop/test tools, models, and communication methods. ($9 million)	Continue research activities from earlier phases. Reevaluate the role of the center and adjust accordingly. ($11 million)
		Emergency Services		
6	Detectors and Detection Systems for Emergency Services	Identify requirements for known contaminants. Adapt robotic technologies for this use. Initiate basic research into the science of new detectors. ($30 million)	Produce detectors with first generation requirements. Continue basic and applied research into new detectors and robotics. ($45 million)	Develop/test a new slate of detectors and robotics for emergency services. ($55 million)
7	Integrated Emergency Management System	Specify system requirements and work on the development of a prototype system. ($13 million)	Develop and test the prototype. Develop and test a full, integrated system. ($15 million)	Complete research and deploy system. ($5 million)
8	Multihazard, Real-time Simulation and Modeling	Define requirements for such a system and initiate development. ($17 million)	Develop and pilot test a prototype system. Integrate lessons learned into next version of system. ($21 million)	Conduct additional pilot tests. Develop, test, and distribute a final set of models constituting the system. ($23 million)
9	Behavioral/ Psychological Studies of Reactions to Incidents	Establish a baseline of required and anticipated responses. ($6 million)	Develop and conduct training courses. Develop and pilot test enhanced communication techniques. ($6 million)	Distribute study results and recommendations to emergency services organizations. ($2 million)

Research Topic No.	Title	Near Term (Resource Estimate[a])	Achieved by ~2005 (Resource Estimate[a])	Achieved by ~2010 (Resource Estimate[a])
10	Decontamination Technologies	Identify and characterize appropriate existing technologies. Develop decision needs for evaluating and selecting decontamination options. ($55 million)	Focus on developing new decontamination technologies. Finalize evaluation and selection criteria for deciding what technologies are most appropriate for any given application. ($75 million)	Complete development and demonstration activities on the technologies examined in the previous timeframe. Initiate research on another set of technologies. ($105 million)
11	Systems Analysis of Public Health Emergency Response Systems	Conduct surveys on treatment capabilities and initiate development of analysis tools. ($13 million)	Develop and pilot test analytical models. Develop a preliminary set of alternative treatment practices and conduct emergency preparedness exercises. ($15 million)	Complete analysis tools. Develop/distribute information on alternative treatment practices and emergency preparedness practices. Conduct additional emergency preparedness exercises. ($17 million)
		Government Services		
12	Support Systems for Reconfiguring Government	Define basic requirements for such a system and develop a limited prototype. ($10 million)	Develop and pilot test more enhanced prototypes. ($12 million)	Complete development of the system. Test, validate, and deploy full-scale system. ($16 million)

[a] Resource estimates reflect qualitative, order-of-magnitude judgments. They are intended to be representative of the resources needed for the R&D topics and are based on assumptions concerning the scope, the expected level of effort, alnd the pace of the research. Detailed cost estimates must be prepared in concert with the development of detailed R&D plans.